Switching and Linear
Power Supply,
Power Converter Design

Switching and Linear Power Supply, Power Converter Design

ABRAHAM I. PRESSMAN

Staff Engineer
Raytheon Company

HAYDEN BOOK COMPANY, INC.
Rochelle Park, New Jersey

To
ANNE
Norman, Daniel, Eric, Dotty
Jeremy and Julie

Library of Congress Cataloging in Publication Data

Pressman, Abraham I
  Switching and linear power supply, power converter
design.

  Includes index.
  1. Electronic apparatus and appliances—Power
supply. 2. Voltage regulators. 3 Electric current
converters. I. Title.
TK7868.P6P74   621.3815'37   77-14639
ISBN 0-8104-5847-0

                              Printed in the United States of America

        2   3   4   5   6   7   8   9   PRINTING

      78 79 80 81 82 83 84 85   YEAR

Preface

It is widely experienced throughout the electronics/aerospace industry that power supplies give rise to more problems in design and reliability than the complex systems which they power. This book seeks to remedy that situation. It deals with all aspects of power supply design—from the initial block diagram systems alternatives to the detailed circuit design of all the electronics within the blocks. Written for both design engineer and undergraduate with little or no knowledge of the power supply field and the available design alternatives, this text should enable them first to make the best decision on a system block diagram concept and then to implement it with detailed circuits, magnetics, and a safe thermal design.

Switching regulators—which are in the process of revolutionizing the power supply industry because of their low internal losses, small size, and weight and costs competitive with conventional series-pass or linear power supplies—are covered fully. Half-cycle width-modulated dc/dc converters, dc/dc voltage down chopping, voltage up chopping, and transformer-coupled flyback regulators are detailed. Design equations for critical components are derived and typical designs presented. The dc/dc square-wave converters, used so frequently with switching regulators in modern power supply systems, are treated in depth.

For the present, series-pass regulators remain the major design approach in the industry; these are discussed at length along with their fields of application, advantages, capabilities, and disadvantages. Logical, step-by-step design procedures are offered, and combinations of series-pass and -switching regulators that retain the best capabilities of each type in a complex system are demonstrated. Efficiencies of various combinations are calculated.

Extensive discussion is devoted to magnetics—transformer and inductor design for high-frequency switching regulators. Design equations for transformer core selection for a given power level, frequency, and magnetic flux density are derived and typical designs shown. Design of inductors with air gaps or molypermalloy powder cores to avoid saturation in usual switching regulator usages is also presented.

Elements of thermal design and heat-sink performance are evaluated, with design equations and graphs showing temperature rise as a function of power level, area, and air flow. Feedback loop stability is treated in detail. Throughout, graphs are presented which permit gain and phase-shift calculations in the usual switching regulator elements—the LC filter and operational amplifiers with RC feedback. Tailoring the gain-phase characteristic to achieve loop stability is also discussed, along with commonly occurring problems in circuits and subtle failure modes in switching and series-pass power supplies.

The electronics industry has long had a vital need for a textbook on the reliable design of all the complex electronics in a modern society—computers, communications equipment, weapons systems and satellites, industrial control, and consumer electronic equipment. It is hoped that this book will fulfill the need for a comprehensive treatment of this significant element in our modern electronic world.

ABRAHAM I. PRESSMAN

Waban, Massachusetts

Contents

1

Basic Voltage Regulators, Power Converters

1.0   Introduction

The voltage regulators considered herein generate single or multiple output dc voltages whose magnitudes are substantially constant for any value of static or dynamic load currents or input voltage within their specified limits.

Input voltages can be dc or single- or multiple-phase ac at any of the usual power line frequencies, generally ranging between 50 and 800 Hz. Magnitudes of the dc or rms ac input voltages can be higher or lower than the desired output voltages. Output voltages must remain constant to the specified accuracy with input voltages generally varying from ±5 to ±15% around their nominal values and load currents varying from 0 to 100% of maximum at each output. Often, the supplies must cope with transient input voltage changes in excess of the ±5 to ±15% steady-state variations. Duration of such transients may range from less than one to several hundred milliseconds.

Supplies are often required to have protective features such as the ability to survive short-circuited outputs or output voltage limiting above specified values. Limits on power supply efficiency, weight, size, cost, and audio and rfi noise outputs are almost always specified.

The various ways to design power supplies to meet such specifications will be dealt with in this book. In this chapter, the basic regulating and power-converting techniques available to the designer will be presented in general terms without going into detailed circuit designs. In the following chapter, systems combinations of these individual regulating schemes will be taken up in block diagram form. Finally, subsequent chapters will go into detailed circuit designs of individual regulators and combinations of regulator types comprising whole power supply systems.

1.1   DC Voltage Regulators

1.1.1 Series-Pass Regulators

The series-pass regulator is the simplest, most frequently used but least efficient regulating technique. Until the appearance of high-current, low-forward-drop transistors, usable as high-frequency single-pole switches, it was the main

1

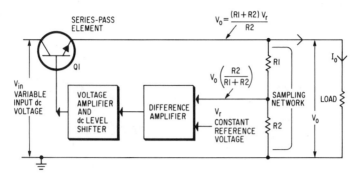

Fig. 1–1. Basic series-pass voltage regulator. Q1 is an electronically controlled variable resistance in series with the load.

and practically the only voltage-regulating technique up to power levels of 1,000 W. Techniques using constant voltage transformers and phase-controlled silicon-controlled rectifiers (SCR) have certain fields of application but are slow in response to line and load changes and will not be considered herein.

The basic series-pass regulator is shown in Fig. 1–1. It converts a variable higher voltage dc to a constant lower voltage dc. Input is dc — either from a battery source, which decreases in output as it discharges, or from a rectifier directly off an ac line source or from a rectifier following a step-up or step-down transformer.

In either of the latter cases, the rectified dc output is proportional to ac line input and will thus vary by the same ±5 to ±15% usually specified for ac line sources. Further, usual rectifier outputs will have a large-amplitude ripple voltage at some harmonic of the line frequency superimposed on the rectified dc. The series-pass regulator will eliminate both the line harmonic ripple and the slower dc variations proportional to line changes, yielding a constant output voltage. Output voltage can be made as constant as desired, limited only by the stability of the reference sources, drift in the difference amplifier, and gain in the feedback loop.

In Fig. 1–1, the output is kept constant by using the series-pass element consisting of one or a number of paralleled transistors as a variable resistance device. As the input rises or falls, the effective resistance of the series element is increased or decreased so that it, rather than the output load, absorbs the input voltage change. The series element is controlled to give a constant output voltage by the negative-feedback loop composed of the resistor sampling chain, the difference amplifier, and voltage amplifier-level shifter element.

A fraction of the output voltage, $[R2/(R1 + R2)] V_o$, is sampled and compared to a constant reference voltage, V_r. The difference amplifier yields a voltage proportional to the difference between V_r and the output sample. The amplified difference voltage is further amplified and the dc level shifted to drive the input terminal of the series element. Voltage polarities are such that a small increase or decrease in output voltage resulting from line or load changes causes the correct increase or decrease, respectively, in series element impedance to keep the output constant. The output adjusts itself so that the sampled fraction $V_o R2/(R1 + R2)$ is very closely equal to the reference voltage.

It is obvious from Fig. 1-1 that all of the output load current must flow through the series-pass element at a dc voltage drop of $V_{in} - V_o$. The minimum efficiency occurs at maximum input voltage and is equal to $P_o/P_{in} = V_o I_o \div V_{in(max)} I_o = V_o/V_{in(max)}$. The larger the difference between input and output voltage, the larger the internal dissipation for a given load current. Any dc voltage can be dropped down and regulated to any lower voltage, but the series-pass element must be capable of absorbing the maximum dissipation at its maximum voltage drop.

Thus, the series-pass regulator of Fig. 1-1 is seen to be simple, comprised only of a series voltage dropping element, resistor voltage sampling chain, difference amplifier, and voltage amplifier-level shifting device. But the relatively high dissipation across the series element at the maximum input voltage results in low output–input power efficiency.

1.1.2 Series-Pass Regulator Efficiency

In the usual power supply, whose prime input is ac line power, efficiency calculations must consider rectifier drop, ripple, transformer regulation, and transformer losses. But here, to start with, maximum attainable efficiencies will be calculated for sources with totally ripple-free dc output voltage whose magnitude can be set at any desired value to maximize regulator efficiency.

Such efficiencies will be the highest achievable for a given output voltage. Practical efficiencies for regulators with optimum ac inputs and realistic ripple voltage at regulator input terminal will be calculated in Chap. 6.

The usual series-pass element, npn or pnp power transistor, has a knee in its I_c–V_c curve at about 2.0 V (Fig. 1-2A). Although operation below the knee is possible, gain is low and a larger fraction of input changes would be transmitted to the output if operation below the knee were permitted.

Thus, in Fig. 1-1 with output taken from the emitter, the minimum input voltage permissible at the collector when the input is at its low tolerance limit is $(V_o + 2)$ volts. For a nominal input voltage of V_n and tolerances of $\pm T$ percent, minimum and maximum input voltages are then $(1 - 0.01T)V_n$ and $(1 + 0.01T)V_n$. Since the minimum input voltage must be no less than $V_o + 2$, then

$$(1 - 0.01T)V_n = V_o + 2$$

and maximum input voltage is

$$(1 + 0.01T)V_n = \left(\frac{1 + 0.01T}{1 - 0.01T}\right)(V_o + 2)$$

And minimum efficiency, which occurs at maximum input voltage, is

$$V_o/V_{in(max)} = \frac{V_o}{\left(\dfrac{1 + 0.01T}{1 - 0.01T}\right)(V_o + 2)}$$

or   Minimum efficiency $= \left(\dfrac{1 - 0.01T}{1 + 0.01T}\right)\left(\dfrac{V_o}{V_o + 2}\right)$ (1-1)

Efficiencies calculated from Eq. 1-1 are plotted in Fig. 1-3 for input tolerances of ± 5, ± 10, and $\pm 15\%$. Such efficiencies are realizable from dc sources having no ripple and at output voltages 2 V below the minimum dc input. It will

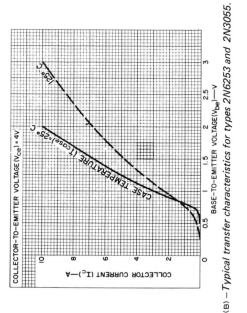

(B) – *Typical transfer characteristics for types 2N6253 and 2N3055.*

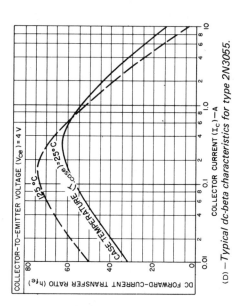

(D) – *Typical dc-beta characteristics for type 2N3055.*

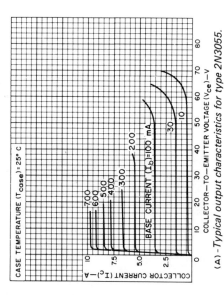

(A) – *Typical output characteristics for type 2N3055.*

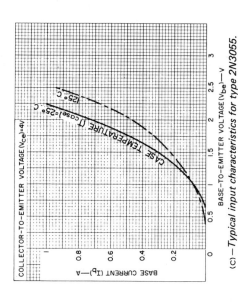

(C) – *Typical input characteristics for type 2N3055.*

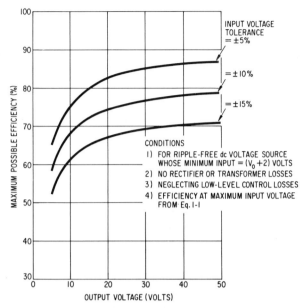

Fig. 1–3. Maximum possible efficiency versus output voltage for a series-pass voltage regulator.

be seen in Chap. 6 that when the input source is the rectified output of a transformer and when the effect of transformer losses, rectifier output ripple, and rectifier losses are considered, efficiencies considerably less than shown in Fig. 1–3 result.

1.2   Pulse-Width-Modulated Series-Switch Step-Down Converter

Figure 1–4 shows a far superior way of obtaining a lower voltage from a higher one. Instead of absorbing the difference between the input and desired output with a power-dissipating element, a low-impedance transistor switch is made to open and close periodically between input and output. If the switch S1 has zero voltage drop in its closed position, the output shown in Fig. 1–4A varies periodically between zero volts and the input voltage. The average or dc value of this waveform is $V_o = V_{in}T_c/T$, where T_c is the switch-closed time and T is the switching period. This is the voltage that would be read with a dc voltmeter at the output terminals. The ripple component has a peak-to-peak value of V_{in} volts and would, of course, not be observed by a dc voltmeter.

By adding the L1–C1 filter as shown in Fig. 1–4B, the ripple component can be reduced to any desired value, yielding a clean dc voltage of magnitude $V_o = V_{in}(T_c/T)$. By going to high switching rates permitted by transistor switches (5–50 kHz), the filter components L1 and C1 become quite small.

Fig. 1–2. Characteristics of an often-used series-pass transistor. (*Courtesy* RCA)

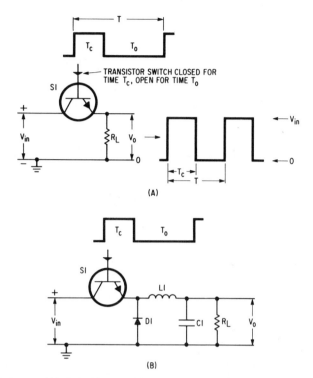

Fig. 1-4. (A) Switching voltage converter average output voltage at $V_o = V_{in}(T_c/T)$. (B) Switching voltage converter with LC filter and diode for eliminating ripple.

Any desired output voltage lower than the input can be obtained by varying the width of the "on" time T_c or the ratio T_c/T. Such a voltage stepdown is achieved at very high efficiency, since the only losses in such a stepdown are those primarily in the switch S1 when it is closed. Using a transistor switch, the voltage drop with the switch in the closed position can be as low as 1 V. During the time the switch is open, the full input voltage is absorbed, but since no current flows in it, there is no power dissipation.

During the transition between open-switch and closed-switch times or vice versa, there is a momentary overlap of high voltage and current, which does yield some losses. Even with such switching losses, efficiencies of 95% are achievable.

1.2.1 Pulse-Width-Modulated Voltage Converter Efficiency

The circuit has the interesting properties of a step-down transformer. With a relatively large inductance for L1, the current in L1 remains constant during the switch-open time. As the switch opens, there is an inductive "kick" across L1 with its input end going negative, since current in an inductor cannot change instantaneously. It goes negative until diode D1 (often referred to as a "free-wheeling" diode) latches on and starts conducting with its cathode one diode voltage drop below ground or at about -1 V. During the time the switch is open, the load current to R_L is supplied both by L1 and C1 in parallel, thus permitting a smaller C1. With L1 large enough, the current in L1 does not change appreciably between the time the switch is open and the time the switch is closed and remains equal to the average or dc output current, V_o/R_L. When the switch is closed, D1 is reverse biased, opens up, and the output current is supplied from the input source through S1.

Thus, the current taken from the input source is a series of pulses of amplitude I_o lasting for a time T_c out of every T units of time. The average value of the input current is $I_o(T_c/T)$. Input power from the source is then $V_{in}(I_oT_c/T)$. Since output voltage is $V_o = V_{in}(T_c/T)$, at an output current of I_o, output power is $[V_{in}(T_c/T)]I_o$. If for the moment, the losses in the switch and D1 can be neglected, input power must equal output power. The circuit thus acts like a step-down transformer. It takes from the input source voltage V_{in}, a current of average magnitude $I_o(T_c/T)$. It transforms this at the output to a lower voltage $V_o = V_{in}(T_c/T)$ at a stepped-up average output current I_o.

The beauty of such a step-down voltage conversion is that to be efficient the input voltage need not be close to the output. By choosing the ratio T_c/T, any input voltage can be dropped down to any lower output with internal losses of only (1) (I_o), since during the closed-switch time, S1 delivers I_o at a 1-V drop and during the open-switch time, D1 supplies the output current at about the same 1-V drop. Efficiency, considering dc losses only, is

$$E = \frac{P_o}{P_{in}} = \frac{V_oI_o}{V_oI_o + I_o(1)} = \frac{V_o}{V_o + 1} \tag{1-2}$$

The momentary overlap of high voltage and current when the switch is opening or closing can contribute losses equal to the dc losses—especially at switching frequencies of 20 kHz or higher. Thus, to a close approximation, with ac and dc losses included, efficiency is

$$E = V_o/(V_o + 2) \tag{1-2A}$$

and is independent of input voltage. In contrast, the efficiency of the series-pass regulator $E_{sp} = V_o/V_{in}$ is inversely proportional to input voltage.

Thus, a switching step-down converter for, say, 5 V output can have an efficiency of $5/(5 + 1)$ or 83% for a switching frequency below 20 kHz. A series-pass circuit whose input is a rectified ac line source may need a maximum dc input voltage of 10 V to ensure the required minimum of 2 V at the bottom of the ripple triangle at low-line tolerance. Thus, the series-pass regulator at 10 V input, 5 V output operates at 50% efficiency in contrast to the 83% possible with the switching converter. At 20 kHz or above, including ac switching losses, efficiency for the switching converter is approximately $5/(5 + 2)$ or 71%.

1.2.2 Pulse-Width-Modulated Series-Switch Step-Down Regulator

The circuit of Fig. 1–4B is only a high-to-low voltage converter. By adding a stable reference voltage source, a difference amplifier, and a dc voltage-controlled pulse-width modulator as shown in Fig. 1–5, a voltage regulator results. As the input increases or decreases, the ratio of T_c (the closed-switch time) to T (the switching period) is decreased or increased by the negative feedback circuit so as to keep the output constant.

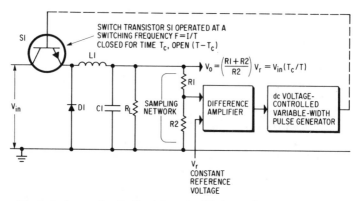

Fig. 1–5. A negative-feedback loop is added to build a switching voltage regulator.

The ratio T_c/T can be varied in a number of ways. The switching period, T, may be kept constant and the width of T_c varied or T_c may be constant and the switching period varied. A constant switching period or frequency is generally preferred, for the switching operation usually generates some noise which is easier to tolerate if it is at a fixed frequency or possibly synchronous with some fundamental system frequency such as, say, horizontal sweep rate in a CRT display system.

The switching frequency may range from about 3 to 50 kHz. Higher switching frequencies result in smaller sizes for L1 and C1 — the largest components in the system. Generally higher frequencies also result in somewhat lower efficiencies because at turnon and turnoff the momentary overlap of high voltage and current in the transistor switch S1 occurs at a higher duty cycle. Higher switching frequencies also require transistors for S1, which have faster turn-on and turn-off times. But such fast, high-frequency transistors are generally only available in lower voltage (under 100 V) ratings. Present practice, as of this writing, is to go to switching rates of about 20 kHz. For input voltages below 100 V, frequencies of 50 to as high as 100 kHz become possible with the currently available devices.

A further advantage of the switching regulator is that for ac input power, it permits substantially smaller filter capacitors than would be needed for a series-pass regulator. Since the switching regulator eliminates ripple from the output (as long as switching rate is high compared to ripple frequency), large ripple inputs can be permitted, thus allowing smaller input filter capacitors.

The large input ripple amplitude can be tolerated as long as the bottom of the ripple triangle is at least 1 V (the inherent switch drop) above the output voltage. The average or dc input can be as low as $V_{\mathrm{dc}} = (V_o + 1) + V_r/2$, where V_r is the peak-to-peak ripple amplitude. Permitting larger ripple amplitudes then means larger values of dc input voltage. This would become prohibitive for a series-pass regulator whose efficiency is $V_o/V_{in(\max)}$ but is no problem for the switching regulator whose efficiency, $V_o/(V_o + 1)$, does not degrade with high input voltages.

Since small volume is often the determining factor in a power supply system design, the switching regulator gains an advantage twice. The larger acceptable input ripple permits smaller filter capacities, and the higher efficiencies result in smaller-sized heat sinks, smaller temperature increases, and, hence, smaller cabinet cooling fans.

1.3   Pulse-Width-Modulated Step-Up Converter/Regulator

The circuit of Fig. 1–4 can only produce a voltage lower than the input voltage. A switching mode converter capable of yielding a voltage higher than the input is shown in Fig. 1–6.

An inductor L1 and switch S1 are bridged across the input voltage source V_{in}. The switch S1 is operated at a high rate, anywhere from 3 to 50 kHz, and is closed for a time T_c and open for time T_o of the period $T_c + T_o (= T)$. With the diode D1, filter capacity C_o, and load R_L placed across the switch as shown, the output voltage is stepped up to the value

$$V_o = V_{in}(T_c + T_o)/T_o = V_{in}(1 + T_c/T_o)$$
$$= V_{in}/(1 - T_c/T)$$

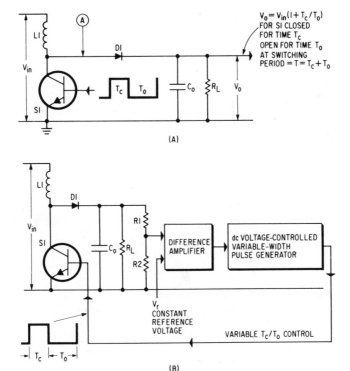

Fig. 1–6. (A) A shunt-switch voltage step-up converter. (B) Addition of a feedback loop to build a step-up switching regulator.

(as derived in Sect. 1.3.2). This circuit is often referred to as a "ringing choke" converter.

When S1 is closed, energy flows from the input source and is stored in L1. During this time, diode D1 is reverse biased, capacity C_o supplies all the output current, and its stored energy $(C_o V_o^2)/2$ is somewhat depleted. When S1 opens, since current in an inductor cannot change instantaneously, an inductive voltage step appears across L1, making the bottom end of L1 positive relative to its top end. Diode D1 becomes forward biased, and the current initially flowing through L1 and S1 now continues flowing via diode D1 into the output capacitor C_o and to the load.

The energy stored in L1 when S1 was closed, $(LI_{peak}^2)/2$, is transferred, when S1 is open, into the load and into the output capacitor to restore the energy it lost when S1 was closed and C_o alone was driving the load. The magnitude of the inductive voltage step across L1 when S1 opens is controlled by the ratio of T_c/T_o. The larger the value of T_c, the greater is the peak current and energy stored in L1; hence, the higher must be the inductive voltage impulse across L1 during the time T_o if the energy accumulated during T_c is to be transferred out during T_o.

Like the series switching converter of Fig. 1–4, this too acts like a transformer without requiring a magnetic core. Assuming lossless switching, the circuit takes an input voltage V_{in} at a dc current I_{in} and steps it up to a higher voltage $V_{in}(T_c + T_o)/T_o$ at a lower output current $I_o = I_{in}T_o/(T_c + T_o)$.

1.3.1 Pulse-Width-Modulated Step-Up Converter Efficiency

The circuit (Fig. 1–6) is not truly lossless. In practical circuits, S1 is a saturated transistor with a 1-V drop for a time T_c; D1 is a silicon diode with a 1-V drop during T_o. The average value of input current flows through S1 for T_c, then through D1 for T_o. Thus, internal losses are $I_{in}(1)$ and efficiency is

$$E = \frac{P_o}{P_{in}} = \frac{V_o I_o}{V_o I_o + I_{in}(1)}$$

Since $I_{in} = I_o(T_c + T_o)/T_o$,

$$E = \frac{V_o I_o}{V_o I_o + \dfrac{I_o(T_c + T_o)(1)}{T_o}}$$

$$= \frac{V_o}{V_o + \dfrac{(T_c + T_o)(1)}{T_o}} = \frac{V_{in}}{V_{in} + 1} \tag{1-3}$$

This is the step-up converter efficiency considering only dc losses in the switch. And as discussed in Sect. 1.2.1, when ac voltage–current overlap losses are included, efficiency is approximately

$$E = \frac{V_{in}}{V_{in} + 2} \tag{1-3A}$$

This is the maximum possible efficiency. Low-level loss of the width control circuitry will lower this somewhat, but such step-up converter efficiencies of up to 95% are easily achievable.

1.3.2 Input–Output Voltage Relationship

The relationship of the output voltage to the T_c/T_o ratio can be determined as follows. In the steady state, after a number of cycles, the output voltage stabilizes to the desired constant value V_o. Output ripple can be made as low as desired by proper choice of C_o. For a permissible ripple of ΔV_o and a dc output current of I_o, since the entire load must be supplied from C_o for a time T_c, the value selected for C_o must be $C_o = I_o T_c / \Delta V_o$.

Now when S1 is closed, there is a constant voltage V_{in} across L1, and current in it rises linearly at a rate $\Delta I / \Delta T = V_{in}/L1$. Then the increment of current in L1 when S1 is closed for a time T_c is

$$\Delta I(+) = (V_{in}/L1)T_c$$

And when S1 is open, assuming the inductive kick has driven the bottom end of L1 up to the desired output V_o, the voltage across L1 is $V_o - V_{in}$. Now with the bottom end of L1 positive, current in L1 decreases at a rate $\Delta I / \Delta T = (V_o - V_{in})/L1$. Since S1 remains open for a time T_o, the decrease in L1 current in that interval is

$$\Delta I(-) = \frac{(V_o - V_{in})T_o}{L1}$$

But in the steady state, for each cycle, the current increase in L1 during T_c must equal the decrease during T_o. Or

$$\Delta I(+) = \Delta I(-)$$
$$\frac{V_{in}T_c}{L1} = \frac{(V_o - V_{in})T_o}{L1}$$

Or
$$V_o = V_{in}\left(\frac{T_o + T_c}{T_o}\right)$$
$$= V_{in}(1 + T_c/T_o) \qquad (1\text{--}4)$$

Thus, by changing the ratio T_c/T_o, any desired step up can be obtained. Note, of course, that the switch S1, which is actually a transistor, is subjected to V_o during T_o and must have a voltage rating capable of taking that voltage with an adequate safety margin.

1.3.3 Pulse-Width-Modulated Shunt-Switch Step-Up Regulator

The step-up converter becomes a voltage regulator by the addition of a voltage sampling resistor chain, a constant voltage reference, difference amplifier, and a dc voltage-controlled variable-width pulse generator as shown in Fig. 1–6B.

As the input voltage varies, the ratio T_c/T_o is automatically adjusted to maintain a constant output voltage. An increase in V_{in} results in a decrease in T_c/T_o; a decrease in V_{in} causes an increase in T_c/T_o in accordance with Eq. 1–4.

This can be understood in a physical sense by considering an increase in V_{in} for a fixed $T_c + T_o$. Since current in the inductor rises at a rate $dI/dT = V_{in}/L$, at larger V_{in}, more energy would be stored in L1 if T_c remained fixed. Then if the increased stored energy had to be dissipated in the same T_o, output voltage would have to rise. Thus, the only way to keep the output constant is to decrease the energy stored by L1 during T_c by decreasing the duration of T_c.

The circuit can be operated in a number of ways. The frequency or period can be kept constant and the ratio T_c/T_o varied. Or often, T_c, the "on" time is kept constant and the operating frequency or period $T_c + T_o$ is adjusted to vary the ratio T_c/T_o. In either case, $V_o = V_{in}(1 + T_c/T_o)$.

Generally, a fixed frequency is preferred; as in many systems there usually is a fixed clock frequency, and it is desired to keep any noise voltages caused by such high-power switching locked in phase to the clock frequency. Yet, the circuit is often used in a constant T_c, variable period $(T_c + T_o)$ mode because of the availability of inexpensive integrated circuit control circuitry building blocks, such as voltage-controlled oscillators and fixed-width pulse generators.

The regulator also regulates against changes in load current. Because of the output impedance, a change — say, an output current increase — would tend to lower the output voltage. This is interpreted by the voltage sampling chain exactly as a change resulting from a line input change. The negative-feedback network thus changes the ratio T_c/T_o to keep the output constant.

1.4 Pulse-Width-Modulated, Single-Ended, Transformer-Coupled Energy Storage Converter/Regulator

For low output power, a useful variation of the ringing choke converter is obtained by the addition of a transformer as shown in Fig. 1–7. It uses the same principle of storing energy in the transformer primary inductance when the switch transistor is closed and transferring this energy to the secondary when the switch is open.

Output voltage control is achieved by varying the ratio of the closed-switch (T_c) to open-switch (T_o) times. Thus, output voltage depends on both turns ratio and T_c/T_o ratio, which can be controlled electronically. The dc isolation between output and input is obtained and voltage stepup or stepdown can still be achieved by selection of the turns ratio.

Operation differs from that of a conventional transformer circuit because of the polarity at the secondary. With the dot-indicated polarity on the transformer, when S1 is closed for a time T_c, the top end of the transformer secondary goes negative, diode D1 is reverse biased, and the secondary is open circuited. Current flows from the input source and is stored in the primary inductance (actually the core itself). During the time S1 is closed, C_o supplies the total output current and is chosen large enough to supply this current for the time T_c with the maximum permissible voltage droop ΔV_o. Thus, for an output current I_o, the capacitor is chosen as $C_o = I_o T_c/\Delta V_o$.

Now when S1 is open, there is an inductive voltage step across the primary and secondary driving the bottom end of the primary and top end of the secondary positive. Diode D1 becomes forward biased. In the steady state, if the voltage across C_o is to be V_o, the secondary voltage can go no higher than one diode drop above V_o — say, V_o for simplicity. Now the primary is open circuited, the secondary voltage is clamped to V_o, and, hence, the voltage across the primary is $(N_p/N_s)V_o$. The energy that had been stored in the primary when S1 was closed, absorbing current from the input source, is now delivered via the secondary into the load and into capacitor C_o to replenish the charge it lost when S1 was closed and C_o was furnishing load current by itself.

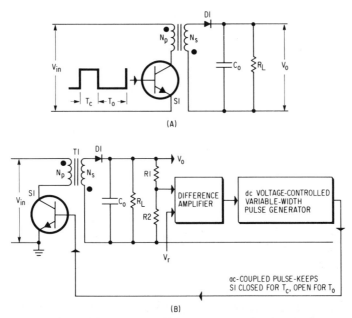

Fig. 1–7. (A) Transformer-coupled energy-storage voltage converter with S1 closed for time T_c, open for T_o; $V_o = V_{in}(N_s/N_p)(T_c/T_o)$. (B) Addition of a negative-feedback loop to build a single-ended, transformer-coupled switching regulator. $V_o = [(R1 + R2)/R2]V_r = V_{in}(N_s/N_p)(T_c/T_o)$.

Design details on the open-circuited primary inductance, transformer turns ratio, and design of the transformer with an air gap to avoid saturation because of the unidirectional current it draws will be taken up in Chap. 9.

1.4.1 Input–Output Voltage Relationship

Output voltage in the converter of Fig. 1–7 can be calculated as follows: Consider that S1 is closed for time T_c and open for time T_o. When S1 is closed, the transformer flux builds up an amount $\Delta\phi(+) = V_{in}T_c/N_p$. Now when S1 is open, the voltage across the windings reverses and causes $\Delta\phi/\Delta T$ to reverse. If the desired output voltage across N_s is V_o, then the transformer flux decreases an amount $\Delta\phi(-) = V_oT_o/N_s$. But in the steady state, the increase in flux $\Delta\phi(+)$ when S1 is closed must equal the decrease in flux when S1 is open, for, otherwise, there would be a net flux change per cycle, and the flux would continue building up to saturation. Hence, $\Delta\phi(+) = \Delta\phi(-)$ and $V_{in}T_c/N_p = V_oT_o/N_s$ or

$$V_o = V_{in}\left(\frac{N_s}{N_p}\right)\left(\frac{T_c}{T_o}\right) \tag{1–5}$$

Care must be taken that the voltage across switch transistor S1 when it is turned off does not exceed its maximum rating. The maximum voltage S1 is subjected to is the dc input plus the voltage coupled back from the secondary into the primary by the transformer turns ratio. This maximum voltage is

$$V_{S1(max)} = V_{in} + V_o(N_p/N_s)$$
$$= V_{in} + V_{in}(N_s/N_p)(T_c/T_o)(N_p/N_s)$$
$$= V_{in}(1 + T_c/T_o) \tag{1-6}$$

1.4.2 Single-Ended Transformer-Coupled Regulator

Figure 1-7B shows the usual voltage regulator obtained by the addition of a constant voltage reference, difference amplifier, and dc voltage-controlled, variable-width pulse generator in a negative-feedback loop. If the input and output grounds are not common, the width control signal to S1 must be ac coupled or coupled by a dc-isolating optoelectronic coupler.

This circuit, as the others, can be operated at a constant frequency — keeping $T_c + T_o$ constant and varying their ratio or keeping, say, T_c constant and varying the frequency or the sum of $T_c + T_o$.

In general, this single-ended converter/regulator is most frequently used for low-power, high-voltage step-up applications, for, since current flows through the transformer primary in one direction only, the core would become saturated unless an air gap is used. The addition of the air gap on the transformer makes it bulky and not too attractive at high-power levels over about 150 W.

For higher output powers, two transistors can be used, each with its own energy-storing transformer. The transistors turn on, storing energy in their transformer primary on alternate half cycles. The transistors turn off on alternate half cycles, and the energy stored in their transformer primaries is dumped out of the secondaries into the common output via individual "oring" diodes.

This "interleaved flyback" scheme uses a considerably smaller energy storage capacitor, since either one or the other transformer secondary is always supplying load current. There is actually an overlap of transformer secondary currents, since transistor "off" times are generally made longer than "on" times. Thus, despite the two power transistors and two transformers, a better ratio of output power/volume is achievable with the interleaved rather than the single-sided flyback scheme.[1]

Additional output voltages can be obtained and established at any dc output voltage level by simply adding additional secondaries with the appropriate number of secondary turns as indicated in Fig. 1-8. These outputs are also regulated against line input voltage changes as the feedback loop adjusts the T_c/T_o ratios to keep the master voltage V_{o1} constant as line input changes. Thus,

$$V_{o1} = V_{in}\left(\frac{N_{s1}}{N_p}\right)\left(\frac{T_c}{T_o}\right) = \left(\frac{R1 + R2}{R2}\right)V_r$$

$$V_{o2} = V_{in}\left(\frac{N_{s2}}{N_p}\right)\left(\frac{T_c}{T_o}\right) = \left(\frac{N_{s2}}{N_{s1}}\right)V_{o1}$$

$$V_{o3} = V_{in}\left(\frac{N_{s3}}{N_p}\right)\left(\frac{T_c}{T_o}\right) = \left(\frac{N_{s3}}{N_{s1}}\right)V_{o1}$$

These slaved output voltages will change with changes in their load currents. However, with output capacitors chosen as above to supply the load

---

[1] D. N. Cox, J. N. McIntire, A. R. Bemis, and E. T. Moore (Wilmore Engineering Co. Durham, N.C.): "Power Conditioning for Pulsed Load Applications." *IEEE Transactions on Aerospace and Electronic Systems*, November 1967.

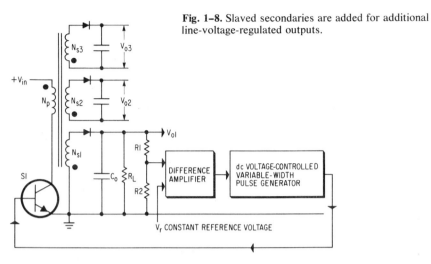

Fig. 1–8. Slaved secondaries are added for additional line-voltage-regulated outputs.

currents with minimum ripple during the off time, output impedances are low and load-caused output changes are low.

1.5 Zener Diode Regulators

Such "regulators" are not regulators in the ordinary sense in that they have no negative feedback loop to keep their output constant. They are simply low-output impedance devices operated in shunt with their loads, and, thus, output voltages are relatively independent of input voltages. They are not very "modern" or novel, but, since their design is basic to the design of the more sophisticated regulator types, they will be considered here for the sake of completeness of coverage.

1.5.1 Zener Voltage–Current Characteristics

The usefulness of zener diodes in maintaining constant output voltage lies in their low-output impedance at unique output voltages, referred to as "zener breakdown" voltages. This can be seen in the volt–ampere characteristics of some typical 400-mW zener diodes in Fig. 1–9.

It is seen in Fig. 1–9 that if the dc current bias is kept centered between zero and maximum current, then over a relatively large current range, the output impedance – the slope $\Delta V/\Delta I$ of the V–I curves – remains low. If the diode is operated in shunt with its load as shown in Fig. 1–9, the Thevenin equivalent output impedance seen looking back into the zener from the load is that of the zener diode itself – the slope of its V–I curve. Thus, relatively large load changes can be drawn from the node A with quite small output voltage changes.

However, Fig. 1–9 shows that the slope of the V–I curves tends to decrease at lower currents for the lower-voltage zener diodes. Thus, if low output changes are essential, the dc operating point in current in the zener must not be permitted to drop to this "soft-knee" region of low currents.

Zener diodes are available at a large number of discrete "zener" voltages —generally in 5% steps. They are available in various wattage ratings: 250-, 450-, and 750-mW and 1-, 5-, 10-, and 50-W power types. The milliwatt types are

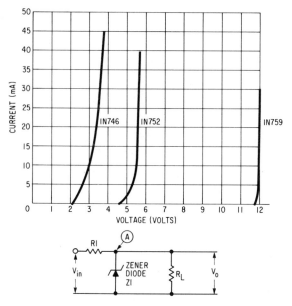

Fig. 1–9. Low-output impedance of a zener diode permits its use as a shunt regulator.

most often used as constant voltage reference sources for feedback regulators. Occasionally, they are used as simple inexpensive shunt regulators in which the load-current changes are restricted to range from the start of the "soft knee" in the $V-I$ curve to the maximum current permitted by the wattage rating. Power zeners of 1 W or greater have lower output impedance and can operate over a much larger current range.

1.5.2 Zener Diode Output Impedance

The linear plots of the $V-I$ curve mask the rather significant variation of zener output impedance with dc operating point on the $V-I$ curve. This is seen more clearly in the semilog plots of Fig. 1–10 for some typical 400-mW types. The increasing slope or soft knee at low currents and the sharper knee at low currents for the higher voltage types are seen more quantitatively in Figs. 1–10A to 1–10D.

The slope of the $V-I$ curve for small ac (60 Hz) current variations of 1 mA is referred to as the zener "dynamic impedance." A very useful curve showing at a glance the slope at various dc current levels for zeners of different discrete output voltages is shown in Fig. 1–10E. It shows that, of these 400-mW devices, the lowest output impedance types are those with zener voltages in the range of 6–8 V. It shows how strongly the output impedance is a function of dc operating current level. Thus, a 3.5-V zener has an output impedance of 70 ohms at 5 mA of dc; this can be brought down to about 11 ohms at a dc current level of 40 mA, still within the 400-mW power-dissipating capability of the device.

For small load changes of about 1 mA, the concept of dynamic impedance or Z_z is useful. It immediately gives the output voltage change for

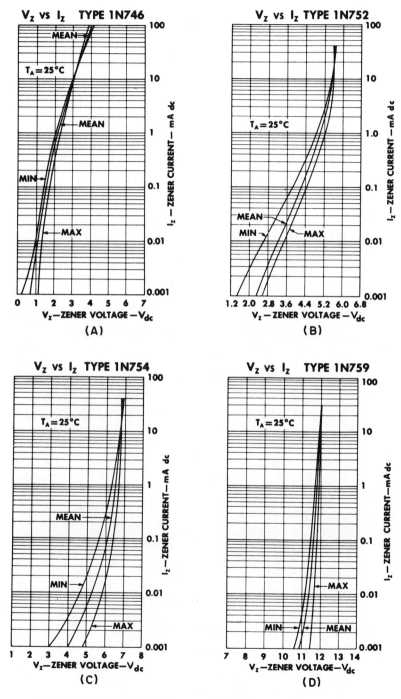

Fig. 1–10. Typical 400-mW zener diode characteristics. (*Courtesy* Texas Instruments)

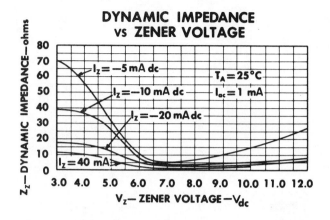

Dynamic zener impedance is measured at -20 mA dc, $I_{ac} = 1$ mA, 60 cps. (See Z_z on page one, electrical specifications). Typical distributions of dynamic zener impedance measured at -5, -10, and -40 mA dc are indicated on curve above.

(E)

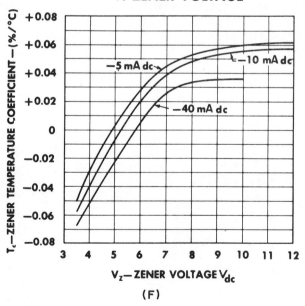

(F)

Fig. 1–10. (*Cont'd.*) Typical 400-mW zener diode characteristics. (*Courtesy* Texas Instruments)

MAXIMUM POWER DISSIPATION

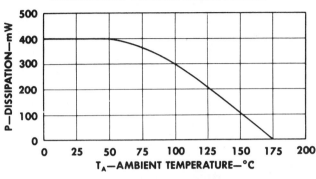

400 mW DISSIPATION

More power dissipation now allows flexibility in circuit design. 400 mw at room temperature, and 100 mw at 150°C assure you of the power needed for stable, reliable operation at elevated temperatures.

NOTE: Total power is the sum of forward and reverse dissipation when the device is required to carry forward current.

(G)

Fig. 1–10. (*Cont'd.*) Typical 400-mW zener diode characteristics. (*Courtesy* Texas Instruments)

known load changes as $\Delta V = Z_z \Delta I$. But for larger load changes, and for input (V_{in} of Fig. 1–9) voltage changing effect on output voltage, the actual $V-I$ curve must be referred to in order to determine the output voltage.

1.5.3 Zener Diode Temperature Coefficients

The zener output voltage is usually quoted at 25°C at 20 mA dc current level. Where very small voltage changes are required, such as in reference voltage sources, it is important to know the temperature coefficient of the zener voltage and its variation with dc operating current.

The curve of Fig. 1–10F shows this useful information at a glance. It shows that the zener temperature coefficient (percent change in output voltage per °C change in temperature) can be positive or negative and is a function of the zener voltage type used and its operating current level.

Thus, Fig. 1–10F shows that zero temperature coefficients can be obtained only in zener types ranging from 4.9 to about 5.8 V. But they must be operated at the indicated current level: 6 mA for a 5.1-V zener type IN751 or about 30 mA for a 5.6-V type IN752.

Obviously, if small or predictable output voltage changes are essential over a large temperature range, the dc operating current level must be held constant at close to the zero temperature coefficient point. This requires (in Fig. 1–9) that not only R_L and R1 must be held constant, but also V_{in}. Thus, V_{in} must come from a preregulated source or V_{in} must be large compared to the zener voltage. For since $I_{R1} = (V_{in} - V_z)/R1$, then

$$\frac{\Delta I_{R1}}{I_{R1}} = \frac{\Delta V_{in}/V_{in}}{1 - V_z/V_{in}}$$

Fig. 1–11. A higher-voltage zener is used to preregulate input current to a lower-voltage device.

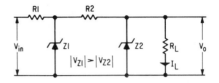

Thus, if V_{in} is only 50% greater than V_z, then from the relationship above a given percentage change in V_{in} will result in a current change in R1 (and, hence, in the zener if R_L is constant), which is three times as large as the percentage change in V_{in}.

A simple scheme often used to preregulate the input current to a zener diode is shown in Fig. 1–11. It uses a higher-voltage zener diode (Z1) as the source supply to the resistor-driven output zener. The current changes in Z2 are now only a function of load-current changes and are quite independent of V_{in} variations.

Figures 1–12A to 1–12C show temperature coefficients and other significant characteristics of some of the available 400-mW and 1- and 10-W zener diodes. Information regarding case sizes and useful applications is available from the device vendors.[2]

1.5.4 Operating Point Selection for Zener Diode Regulators

It has been seen that the zener diode output voltage and source impedance depends on its dc operating current level. This in turn depends on the input current from R1 and load current drawn by R_L.

Referring to Fig. 1–9, it is seen that since the zener voltage remains relatively constant, the current flow into the zener diode is the difference between I_{R1} and I_{R_L} or

$$I_z = \frac{V_{in} - V_z}{R1} - I_{R_L} = \frac{V_{in} - V_z}{R1} - \frac{V_z}{R_L} \qquad (1-7)$$

Thus, as R_L increases, decreasing the load current, since the total R1 current remains fixed, the current in the zener diode from R_L must increase by exactly the same amount as the load current decreased. As V_{in} increases, for a fixed R_L, the added current from R1 must be absorbed by the zener diode. Finally, as R_L, R1, or V_{in} changes, the operating point on the zeners diode $V–I$ curves (Fig. 1–9) slides up and down so as to absorb the difference between I_{R1} and I_{R_L}.

Generally, V_{in} and its tolerances are fixed and known; the maximum and minimum load currents ($R_{L(max)}$ or $R_{L(min)}$) are known. The only choice to be made then is R1. The value of R1 is chosen such that when current in the zener is at its minimum, it goes no lower than a point selected on the $V–I$ curve, which is the start of the "soft knee" in the curve, where the dynamic impedance becomes large.

With a value of R1 selected, it must then be verified that, under the component tolerance and load conditions resulting in maximum zener current,

---

[2] Motorola Zener Diode Handbook; Texas Instrument Preferred Semiconductors; and International Rectifier Corp. Engineering Handbook.

*electrical characteristics at 25°C free-air temperature (unless otherwise noted)

PARAMETER	V_Z Zener Breakdown Voltage					α_Z Temperature Coefficient of Breakdown Voltage	Z_Z Small-Signal Breakdown Impedance	I_R Static Reverse Current	
TEST CONDITIONS	I_{ZT} = 20 mA					I_{ZT} = 20 mA	I_{ZT} = 20 mA, I_{zt} = 1 mA	V_R = 1 v	V_R = 1 v, T_A = 150°C
LIMIT →	NOM	1N746-1N759 MIN	MAX	1N746A-1N759A MIN	MAX	TYP	MAX	MAX	MAX
UNIT →	v	v	v	v	v	% / °C	Ω	μΩ	μΩ
1N746	3.3	2.97	3.63	3.135	3.465	−0.062	28	10	30
1N747	3.6	3.24	3.96	3.420	3.780	−0.055	24	10	30
1N748	3.9	3.51	4.29	3.705	4.095	−0.049	23	10	30
1N749	4.3	3.87	4.73	4.085	4.515	−0.036	22	2	30
1N750	4.7	4.23	5.17	4.465	4.935	−0.018	19	2	30
1N751	5.1	4.59	5.61	4.845	5.355	−0.008	17	1	20
1N752	5.6	5.04	6.16	5.320	5.880	+0.006	11	1	20
1N753	6.2	5.58	6.82	5.890	6.510	+0.022	7	0.1	20
1N754	6.8	6.12	7.48	6.460	7.140	+0.035	5	0.1	20
1N755	7.5	6.75	8.25	7.125	7.875	+0.045	6	0.1	20
1N756	8.2	7.38	9.02	7.790	8.610	+0.052	8	0.1	20
1N757	9.1	8.19	10.01	8.645	9.555	+0.056	10	0.1	20
1N758	10.0	9.00	11.00	9.500	10.500	+0.060	17	0.1	20
1N759	12.0	10.80	13.20	11.400	12.000	+0.060	30	0.1	20

Fig. 1–12A. Temperature coefficients and output impedances of some typical 400-mW zener diodes. (*Courtesy* Texas Instruments)

ELECTRICAL CHARACTERISTICS (T_A = 25°C unless otherwise noted) *V_F = 1.5 V_{max}, I_F = 200 mA for all types

JEDEC Type No. (Note 1)	Motorola Type No. (Note 2)	*Nominal Zener Voltage V_Z @ I_{ZT} Volts (Note 2 & 3)	*Test Current I_{ZT} mA	*Max Zener Impedance (Note 4) Z_{ZT} @ I_{ZT} Ohms	Z_{ZK} @ I_{ZK} Ohms	I_{ZK} mA	*Leakage Current I_R μA Max @ Volts	V_R @ Volts	*Surge Current @ T_A = 25°C i_r − mA (Note 5)
1N4728	1M3.3ZS10	3.3	76	10	400	1.0	100	1.0	1380
1N4729	1M3.6ZS10	3.6	69	10	400	1.0	100	1.0	1260
1N4730	1M3.9ZS10	3.9	64	9.0	400	1.0	50	1.0	1190
1N4731	1M4.3ZS10	4.3	58	9.0	400	1.0	10	1.0	1070
1N4732	1M4.7ZS10	4.7	53	8.0	500	1.0	10	1.0	970
1N4733	1M5.1ZS10	5.1	49	7.0	550	1.0	10	1.0	890
1N4734	1M5.6ZS10	5.6	45	5.0	600	1.0	10	2.0	810
1N4735	1M6.2ZS10	6.2	41	2.0	700	1.0	10	3.0	730
1N4736	1M6.8ZS10	6.8	37	3.5	700	1.0	10	4.0	660
1N4737	1M7.5ZS10	7.5	34	4.0	700	0.5	10	5.0	605
1N4738	1M8.2ZS10	8.2	31	4.5	700	0.5	10	6.0	550
1N4739	1M9.1ZS10	9.1	28	5.0	700	0.5	10	7.0	500
1N4740	1M10ZS10	10	25	7.0	700	0.25	10	7.6	454
1N4741	1M11ZS10	11	23	8.0	700	0.25	5.0	8.4	414
1N4742	1M12ZS10	12	21	9.0	700	0.25	5.0	9.1	380
1N4743	1M13ZS10	13	19	10	700	0.25	5.0	9.9	344
1N4744	1M15ZS10	15	17	14	700	0.25	5.0	11.4	304
1N4745	1M16ZS10	16	15.5	16	700	0.25	5.0	12.2	285
1N4746	1M18ZS10	18	14	20	750	0.25	5.0	13.7	250
1N4747	1M20ZS10	20	12.5	22	750	0.25	5.0	15.2	225
1N4748	1M22ZS10	22	11.5	23	750	0.25	5.0	16.7	205
1N4749	1M24ZS10	24	10.5	25	750	0.25	5.0	18.2	190
1N4750	1M27ZS10	27	9.5	35	750	0.25	5.0	20.6	170
1N4751	1M30ZS10	30	8.5	40	1000	0.25	5.0	22.8	150
1N4752	1M33ZS10	33	7.5	45	1000	0.25	5.0	25.1	135
1N4753	1M36ZS10	36	7.0	50	1000	0.25	5.0	27.4	125
1N4754	1M39ZS10	39	6.5	60	1000	0.25	5.0	29.7	115
1N4755	1M43ZS10	43	6.0	70	1500	0.25	5.0	32.7	110
1N4756	1M47ZS10	47	5.5	80	1500	0.25	5.0	35.8	95
1N4757	1M51ZS10	51	5.0	95	1500	0.25	5.0	38.8	90
1N4758	1M56ZS10	56	4.5	110	2000	0.25	5.0	42.6	80
1N4759	1M62ZS10	62	4.0	125	2000	0.25	5.0	47.1	70
1N4760	1M68ZS10	68	3.7	150	2000	0.25	5.0	51.7	65
1N4761	1M75ZS10	75	3.3	175	2000	0.25	5.0	56.0	60
1N4762	1M82ZS10	82	3.0	200	3000	0.25	5.0	62.2	55
1N4763	1M91ZS10	91	2.8	250	3000	0.25	5.0	69.2	50
1N4764	1M100ZS10	100	2.5	350	3000	0.25	5.0	76.0	45
—	1M110ZS10	110	2.3	450	4000	0.25	5.0	83.6	—
—	1M120ZS10	120	2.0	550	4500	0.25	5.0	91.2	—
—	1M130ZS10	130	1.9	700	5000	0.25	5.0	98.8	—
—	1M150ZS10	150	1.7	1000	6000	0.25	5.0	114.0	—
—	1M160ZS10	160	1.6	1100	6500	0.25	5.0	121.6	—
—	1M180ZS10	180	1.4	1200	7000	0.25	5.0	136.8	—
—	1M200ZS10	200	1.2	1500	8000	0.25	5.0	152.0	—

Fig. 1–12B. Some typical 1-W zener diodes. (*Courtesy* Motorola, Inc.)

ELECTRICAL CHARACTERISTICS

(T_C = 25°C unless otherwise noted) $V_F = 1.5\,V_{max}$ @ $I_F = 2$ amp on all types.

Type No.	Nominal Zener Voltage V_z @ I_{zt} Volts	Test Current I_{zt} mA	Max Zener Impedance			Max DC Zener Current I_{zm} mA	Max Reverse Current *		
			Z_{zt} @ I_{zt} Ohms	Z_{zk} @ I_{zk} Ohms	I_{zk} mA		$I_{r\,max}$ (µA)	V_{R1}	V_{R2}
1N2970	6.8	370	1.2	500	1.0	1,320	150	5.2	4.9
1N2971	7.5	335	1.3	250	1.0	1,180	75	5.7	5.4
1N2972	8.2	305	1.5	250	1.0	1,040	50	6.2	5.9
1N2973	9.1	275	2.0	250	1.0	960	25	6.9	6.6
1N2974	10	250	3	250	1.0	860	10	7.6	7.2
1N2975	11	230	3	250	1.0	780	5	8.4	8.0
1N2976	12	210	3	250	1.0	720	5	9.1	8.6
1N2977	13	190	3	250	1.0	660	5	9.9	9.4
1N2978	14	180	3	250	1.0	600	5	10.6	10.1
1N2979	15	170	3	250	1.0	560	5	11.4	10.8
1N2980	16	155	4	250	1.0	530	5	12.2	11.5
1N2982	18	140	4	250	1.0	460	5	13.7	13.0
1N2983	19	130	4	250	1.0	440	5	14.4	13.7
1N2984	20	125	4	250	1.0	420	5	15.2	14.4
1N2985	22	115	5	250	1.0	380	5	16.7	15.8
1N2986	24	105	5	250	1.0	350	5	18.2	17.3
1N2988	27	95	7	250	1.0	300	5	20.6	19.4
1N2989	30	85	8	300	1.0	280	5	22.8	21.6
1N2990	33	75	9	300	1.0	260	5	25.1	23.8
1N2991	36	70	10	300	1.0	230	5	27.4	25.9
1N2992	39	65	11	300	1.0	210	5	29.7	28.1
1N2993	43	60	12	400	1.0	195	5	32.7	31.0
1N2995	47	55	14	400	1.0	175	5	35.8	33.8
1N2996	50	50	15	500	1.0	165	5	38.0	36.0
1N2997	51	50	15	500	1.0	163	5	38.8	36.7
1N2998	52	50	15	500	1.0	160	5	39.5	37.4
1N2999	56	45	16	500	1.0	150	5	42.6	40.3
1N3000	62	40	17	600	1.0	130	5	47.1	44.6
1N3001	68	37	18	600	1.0	120	5	51.7	49.0
1N3002	75	33	22	600	1.0	110	5	56.0	54.0
1N3003	82	30	25	700	1.0	100	5	62.2	59.0
1N3004	91	28	35	800	1.0	85	5	69.2	65.5
1N3005	100	25	40	900	1.0	80	5	76.0	72.0
1N3006	105	25	45	1,000	1.0	75	5	79.8	75.6
1N3007	110	23	55	1,100	1.0	72	5	83.6	79.2
1N3008	120	20	75	1,200	1.0	67	5	91.2	86.4
1N3009	130	19	100	1,300	1.0	62	5	98.8	93.6
1N3010	140	18	125	1,400	1.0	58	5	106.4	100.8
1N3011	150	17	175	1,500	1.0	54	5	114.0	108.0
1N3012	160	16	200	1,600	1.0	50	5	121.6	115.2
1N3014	180	14	260	1,850	1.0	45	5	136.8	129.6
1N3015	200	12	300	2,000	1.0	40	5	152.0	144.0

Fig. 1–12C. Some typical 10-W zener diode characteristics. (*Courtesy* Motorola, Inc.)

its dissipation limits are not exceeded. Thus, from Eq. 1–7, minimum zener current occurs when the current available from R1 is a minimum and that drawn by the load is a maximum. If under these conditions, the zener current is to be no lower than $I_{z(min)}$, then from Eq. 1–7,

$$I_{z(min)} = \frac{(V_{in} - V_z)_{min}}{R1_{max}} - \frac{V_{z(max)}}{R_{L(min)}}$$

If t_r is the percentage tolerance in R1 and t_z is the percentage tolerance in the zener,

$$R1_{max} = \frac{(V_{in} - V_z)_{min}}{I_{z(min)} + I_{R_L(max)}}$$

$$= \frac{(V_{in} - V_z)_{(min)}}{I_{z(min)} + \dfrac{V_{z(max)}}{R_{L(min)}}} \tag{1-8}$$

or $$R1_{max} = (1 + 0.01\,t_r)R1_{nom}$$

$$= \frac{V_{in(min)} - (1 + 0.01\,t_z)(V_{z(nom)})}{I_{z(min)} + \dfrac{(1 + 0.01\,t_z)(V_{z(nom)})}{(1 - 0.01\,t_r)(R_{L(nom)})}} \tag{1-8A}$$

Now with the nominal value of R1 chosen from Eq. 1–8A, the maximum zener current is calculated. This occurs from Eq. 1–7, when the input current available from R1 is a maximum and load current drawn by R_L is a minimum, or

$$I_{z(max)} = \frac{(V_{in} - V_z)_{(max)}}{R1_{min}} - \frac{V_{z(min)}}{R_{L(max)}} \tag{1-9}$$

$$= \frac{V_{in(max)} - (1 - 0.01\,t_z)V_z}{(1 - 0.01\,t_r)R1} - \frac{(1 - 0.01\,t_z)V_z}{(1 + 0.01\,t_r)R_L} \tag{1-9A}$$

From this, maximum zener power dissipation is calculated as $I_{z(max)} \times V_{z(min)}$. Minimum value of V_z is assumed, of course, because in Eq. 1–9 that value resulted in maximum zener currents.

Design Example of Zener Regulator Calculation

To illustrate the above calculations, consider the following example. Assume in Fig. 1–9, V_{in} is +20 V with a ±10% tolerance. A stabilized voltage centered about 5.6 V is desired. Assume a 1N752 (Fig. 1–9) ±5% zener diode and a load R_L that can take a minimum of 10 and a maximum of 20 mA. The load need not be a fixed resistor—it may be a transistor load that can be drawing either high or low current. Assume the minimum permissible current in the zener is to be 10 mA to keep it above the soft knee of the V–I curve of Fig. 1–9. Then, from Eq. 1–8,

$$R1_{max} = \frac{(0.09)(20) - (1.05)(5.6)}{0.01 + 0.02} = \frac{18 - 5.88}{0.030}$$
$$= 404 \text{ ohms}$$

And for ±5% tolerance in R1,

$$R1_{nom} = 404/1.05 = 385 \text{ ohms}$$

And from Eq. 1–9,

$$I_{z(max)} = \frac{(1.1)(20) - (0.90)(5.6)}{(0.95)(385)} - 0.01$$
$$= \frac{22 - 5.3}{365} - 0.01$$
$$= 35.8 \text{ mA}$$

Then the zener dissipation at 5.6 V is $(5.6)(0.0358) = 200$ mW—safely within the 400-mW maximum rating.

From Fig. 1–10E the dynamic impedance of a 5.6-V zener in the region of 10–20 mA is roughly 10 ohms. Then a typical zener with a current change from 10 to 33 mA will exhibit a voltage change of $(0.023)(10) = 230$ mV.

With ±5% zeners, the output at any fixed current can, of course, be $5.6 ± (0.05)(5.6) = 5.60 ± 0.28$ V. This normally is of no consequence, for in most zener applications the output change with current level alone is significant. The absolute voltage level for any particular diode is compensated for by an initial potentiometer setting.

Zener dissipation must be watched carefully, since overdissipation is the most frequent cause of failure. If V_{in} (Fig. 1–9) is too close to V_z, overdissipation can easily result from small variations in V_{in} or V_z. This can be seen from the term

$(V_{in} - V_z)/R1$ in Eq. 1–9. If $V_{in} - V_z$ is a small number, small percentage variations in either V_{in} or V_z result in much larger percentage variations in their difference. Generally, unless V_{in} is stabilized as in Fig. 1–11, V_{in} should be no less than three times V_z to achieve a relatively constant I_z.

1.5.5 Temperature-Compensated Zener Reference Elements[3]

Figure 1–10F shows the temperature coefficient of zener diodes as a function of their zener voltages and dc operating current level. It is seen that if a 5- to 6-V zener can be used and operated at its optimum current level, zero temperature coefficient can be achieved. But temperature coefficients rise quickly to greater than ±0.02%/°C outside the 5- to 6-V zener range.

Temperature coefficients lower than those available from conventional zeners are achieved with "temperature-compensated reference" types. These devices use forward-biased pn junctions having a negative temperature coefficient of 2 mV/°C to cancel the positive temperature of conventional zeners.

Such reference zeners achieve temperature coefficients down to 0.0005%/°C, but they too are only that good at a fixed current level. To realize the minimum output voltage variation, they must be operated at a constant input current (referred to as I_{zt}). Input current can be kept constant by using a pre-regulated drive as in Fig. 1–11.

Figure 1–13 shows the characteristics of a typical temperature-compensated reference family—the 1N821 series. Voltages are measured at four test temperatures: −55, 0, +50, and +100°C. Voltage variation over any other temperature range can be read from Fig. 1–13B. Output voltage also varies with current as can be seen in Fig. 1–13C. The total variation is the sum of the temperature variation (Fig. 1–13B) and the current variation of Fig. 1–13C.

Output voltage variations due to zener current variations, ΔI_o, are given by $\Delta V_o = \Delta I_o(Z_z)$. Here, Z_z is the zener impedance that can be read from Fig. 1–13D at any dc current level.

Such temperature-compensated reference types are available at a large number of discrete voltages between 6.2 and 200 V. Detailed characteristics can be found in the aforementioned reference.

The primary application of such temperature-compensated reference zeners is as the constant voltage reference source in feedback-type regulators. In such applications, load-current changes can usually be kept small, and output voltages are then a function of temperature change alone.

1.6   Zener Diode–Emitter Follower Regulator

A zener diode controlling the base of an emitter follower as in Fig. 1–14A makes a very simple, inexpensive voltage regulator capable of delivering large output currents. It can handle relatively large output current and input voltage changes with output voltage changes of only 0.1–0.2 V.

The circuit is not truly a "regulator" in that it has no negative-feedback loop to keep its output constant. But for applications in which output voltage changes of 0.1–0.2 V are acceptable, its low cost, low component count, and simplicity make it a valuable and often overlooked circuit technique.

---

[3] Motorola Zener Diode Handbook.

With the recent availability of high-current integrated-circuit voltage regulators, which offer a complete series-pass-type feedback regulator in a single-transistor can, the technique has lost some of its attractiveness. Nevertheless, in many applications, it is still the simplest way to achieve the required constant voltage.

The operation of the circuit can be seen from the transistor's "transfer" characteristic (output current versus base-emitter voltage) of Fig. 1–14B. The curve is for a rather high-current transistor—the 30-A 2N3771, still only a TO3 can-size device. The slope of this transfer characteristic $\Delta I_o / \Delta V_{be}$ is referred to as the "transconductance" or g_m.

It is seen in Fig. 1–14B that in the region of 0–2 A, the slope or g_m is 10 A/volt. Thus, if the base voltage is held fixed, and current is taken out of the emitter at a fixed collector voltage, the current can go from about 0 to 2 A with the emitter falling from only 0.5 to 0.6 V below the fixed-base potential. For any small ΔI_o, the ΔV_o or ΔV_e for a fixed-base voltage is $\Delta V_e = \Delta I_o / (\Delta I_c / \Delta V_{be})$ $= \Delta I_o / g_m$.

However, in the circuit of Fig. 1–14A, the base is not held quite constant. The impedance looking back into the zener is Z_z, the dynamic impedance of the zener itself, which as can be seen in Fig. 1–10E is small but not negligible. Thus, for a base current change of ΔI_b, the base potential moves an amount $\Delta V_b = Z_z(\Delta I_b) \cong Z_z(\Delta I_o / \beta)$, where β is the transistor current gain. Then, for a current change in the output (emitter current change), the output voltage change is

$$\Delta V_o = \Delta V_{be} + \Delta V_b = \Delta I_o / g_m + Z_z \Delta I_o / \beta = \Delta I_o (1/g_m + Z_z / \beta)$$

or the output impedance looking back into the emitter is

$$\Delta V_o / \Delta I_o = 1/g_m + Z_z / \beta \qquad (1\text{–}10)$$

1.6.1 Typical Example of Zener Diode–Emitter Follower Regulator

As an example of what can be achieved with such a regulator, consider the circuit of Fig. 1–14A with the output current centered at 1.0 A and having variations down to about 0 and up to 2 A. Assume the zener diode is a 1-W type and an output voltage of about 10 V is desired. Choose from Fig. 1–12B the 1N4741 having a nominal zener voltage of 11 V and a dynamic impedance of 8 ohms. Then from Fig. 1–14B, using the 2N3771, the average value of g_m centered about the 1-A operating point is 10 A/volt, and from Fig. 1–14C, average current gain is 50 (2.5 A output current for 50 mA of input). Thus, from Eq. 1–10,

$$\Delta V_o / \Delta I_o = 1/g_m + Z_z / \beta = 1/10 + 8/50 = 0.14 \text{ ohm}$$

Or for an output current change ΔI_o of ± 1 A, the output voltage change will be only ± 0.14 V. Output voltage will be one base-emitter drop below the zener voltage. From Fig. 1–14B, at 1 A, the base emitter drop is 0.6 V. With a nominal zener of 11.0 V, output voltage will then be centered at $11 - 0.6 = +10.4$ V. As the output current changes ± 1 A, output voltage will then move the above calculated ± 0.14 V around $+10.4$ V. This is only a 1.4% output change for a 1-A current change and in many applications is acceptable.

Since g_m increases greatly with dc operating current, a device with a maximum current rating of at least 20–30 times the expected load-current changes should be chosen for emitter follower regulators. Actual value of g_m

ELECTRICAL CHARACTERISTICS (T$_A$ = 25°C unless otherwise noted)

JEDEC Type No. (Note 1)	Maximum Voltage Change ΔV_Z (Volts) (Note 2)	Test Temperature °C	Temperature Coefficient %/°C (Note 2)	Maximum Dynamic Impedance Z_{ZT} Ohms (Note 3)
$V_Z = 6.2$ V ±5.0% * @ $I_{ZT} = 7.5$ mA				
1N821	0.096	−55, 0, +25, +75, +100	0.01	15
1N823	0.048		0.005	
1N825	0.019		0.002	
1N827	0.009		0.001	
1N829	0.005		0.0005	
1N821A	0.096		0.01	10
1N823A	0.048		0.005	
1N825A	0.019		0.002	
1N827A	0.009		0.001	
1N829A	0.005		0.0005	

(A)

MAXIMUM VOLTAGE CHANGE versus AMBIENT TEMPERATURE
(with I_{ZT} = 7.5 mA ±0.01 mA)
(See Note 4)
1N821 thru 1N829

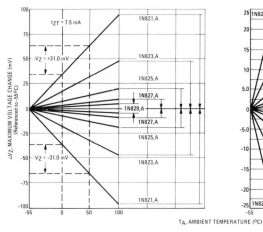
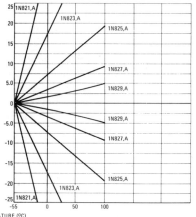

T$_A$, AMBIENT TEMPERATURE (°C)

(B)

ZENER CURRENT versus MAXIMUM VOLTAGE CHANGE
(At Specified Temperatures)
(See Note 5)
MORE THAN 95% OF THE UNITS ARE IN THE RANGES INDICATED BY THE CURVES.

1N821 SERIES   **1N821A SERIES**

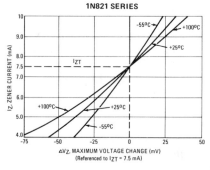
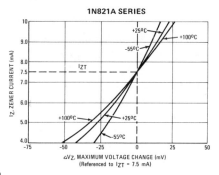

(C)

MAXIMUM ZENER IMPEDANCE versus ZENER CURRENT
(See Note 3)
MORE THAN 95% OF THE UNITS ARE IN THE RANGES INDICATED BY THE CURVES.

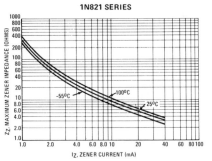

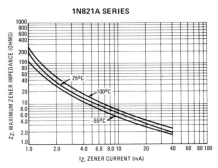

(D)

NOTE 1: Types 1N821, 1N823, 1N825, 1N827, and 1N829 are available to MIL-S-19500/159 and MEG-A-LIFE II, Levels 1, 2, and 3, specifications.

NOTE 2: Voltage Variation (ΔV_Z) and Temperature Coefficient.

All reference diodes are characterized by the "box method." This guarantees a maximum voltage variation (ΔV_Z) over the specified temperature range, at the specified test current (I_{ZT}), verified by tests at indicated temperature points within the range. V_Z is measured and recorded at each temperature specified. The ΔV_Z between the highest and lowest values must not exceed the maximum ΔV_Z given. This method of indicating voltage stability is now used for JEDEC registration as well as for military qualification. The former method of indicating voltage stability—by means of temperature coefficient—accurately reflects the voltage deviation at the temperature extremes but is not necessarily accurate within the temperature range because reference diodes have a nonlinear temperature relationship. The temperature coefficient, therefore, is given only as a reference.

NOTE 3: The dynamic zener impedance, Z_{ZT}, is derived from the 60-Hz ac voltage drop which results when an ac current with an rms value equal to 10% of the dc zener current, I_{ZT}, is superimposed on I_{ZT}. Curves showing the variation of zener impedance with zener current for each series are given in D. A cathode-ray tube curve-trace test on a sample basis is used to ensure that each zener characteristic has a sharp and stable knee region.

NOTE 4: These graphs can be used to determine the maximum voltage change of any device in the series over any specific temperature range. For example, a temperature change from 0 to +50°C will cause a voltage change no greater than +31 mV or −31 mV for 1N821 or 1N821A, as illustrated by the dashed lines in B. The boundaries given are maximum values. For greater resolution, an expanded view of the shaded area in B, left, is shown in B, right.

NOTE 5: The maximum voltage change, ΔV_Z, in C is due entirely to the impedance of the device. If both temperature and I_{ZT} are varied, then the total voltage change may be obtained by adding V_Z in C, left or right, to the ΔV_Z in B for the device under consideration. If the device is to be operated at some stable current other than the specified test current, a new set of characteristics may be plotted by superimposing the data in C, left or right, on B. For a more detailed explanation see AN-437 (Application Note).

(E)

Fig. 1–13A–E. Characteristics of typical temperature-compensated reference diodes. (*Courtesy* Motorola, Inc.)

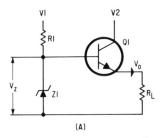

(A)

Fig. 1–14A. A base-voltage-stabilized emitter follower regulator.

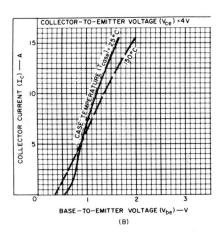

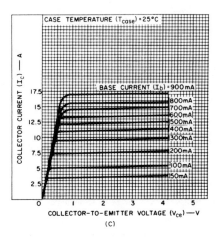

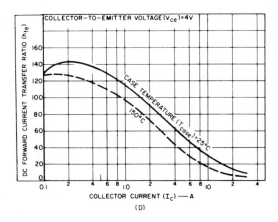

Fig. 1–14B–D. Typical transfer (B), output (C), and dc beta (D) characteristics for the type 2N3771, high-transconductance transistor. (*Courtesy* RCA)

depends strongly on the dc operating point as can be seen in Fig. 1–15 for the 2N5784 – a 3.5-A TO5 can device. Above the knee for the 2N5784, g_m averages about 4 A/volt; this would yield an output impedance of $1/g_m = 0.25$ ohm. At the center of the knee – about the 15-mA level – g_m is about 0.14 A/volt and the output impedance of $1/g_m$ is 7 ohms.

It is seen also in Fig. 1–14D that the emitter-base potential depends strongly on temperature. It varies at roughly −2 mV/°C increase in temperature. If absolute dc output voltage is important rather than low output impedance, this plus temperature coefficient of the zener diode driver must be considered.

1.6.2 Collector Leakage and Minimum Output Currents

One drawback must be considered in the use of emitter follower regulators: the effect of collector-emitter leakage current or I_{ceo}. Collector current is actually $I_c = I_{ceo} + g_m \Delta V_{be}$, where ΔV_{be} is the base-emitter voltage change beyond the point where the transfer characteristic crosses the zero current axis. Thus, even when the component $g_m \Delta V_{be}$ is zero, there will be an emitter leakage current, and the transistor base-emitter junction will lose control of the output voltage. Voltage drop across the load resistor will be $I_{ceo}R_L$ and will increase as R_L increases. Thus, if the output voltage across the load resistor is to be kept at V_o, then at its maximum value the load resistor must be able to carry away a current I_{ceo}. Or stated another way, the maximum permissible value of R_L is $R_{L(max)} = V_o/I_{ceo}$.

This effect does not often present a problem, since generally minimum load current will be restricted to above the knee in the transfer characteristic so as to give a large value of g_m.

1.6.3 Sensitivity to Collector Voltage Variations

In the discussions above, only the effect of load changes on the output voltage was considered. But the effect of voltage changes at the collector of the emitter follower cannot be ignored. There would be no problem if the collector impedance ($\Delta V_c/\Delta I_c$ of the V_c–I_c curves of Fig. 1–14) were sufficiently large. Emitter current would then depend on the emitter-base voltage alone. But the apparent flat slope of the V_c–I_c curves of Fig. 1–14 is deceptive; the impedance is quite low, especially for higher-current transistors.

Thus, for the high-current 2N3771, Fig. 1–14C, slope between V_c values of 0.5 and 4 V at I_c of 2.5 A is about $\Delta V/\Delta I = R_t = 3.5/0.25 = 14$ ohms. With so low an impedance, output emitter current is affected by collector voltage changes and may be calculated as follows.

Assume in Fig. 1–14A a collector voltage change of $\Delta V2$ and that this causes an output voltage change and an output current change ΔI_o. The finite collector impedance R_t will result in an emitter current increase of $(\Delta V2 - \Delta V_o)/R_t$. But the slight rise in V_o will tend to decrease the emitter current by an amount $g_m \Delta V_o$. Since the net current increase demanded by the load must equal that supplied from the emitter, then

$$\frac{\Delta V_o}{R_L} = \frac{\Delta V2 - \Delta V_o}{R_t} - g_m \Delta V_o$$

And
$$\Delta V_o(1/R_L + 1/R_t + g_m) = \Delta V2/R_t$$

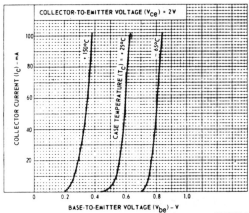

(A) *Typical transfer characteristics for types 2N5784*

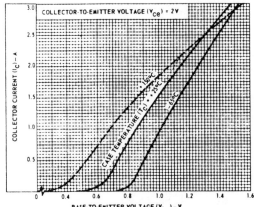

(B) *Typical transfer characteristics for types 2N5784*

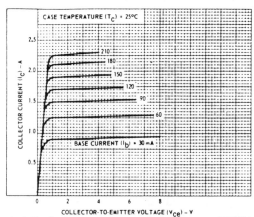

(C) *Typical output characteristics for type 2N5784*

Fig. 1-15. Typical transfer (A and B) and output (C) characteristics of a TO5 case, high-current transistor, type 2N5784.

or
$$\Delta V_o = \frac{\Delta V2}{1 + R_t/R_L + g_m R_t}$$
(1-11)

And usually $g_m R_t \gg 1$; $g_m R_t > R_t/R_L$. Then $\Delta V_o \cong \Delta V2/g_m R_t$.

And in Fig. 1-14D, for a 2N3771, $g_m = 10$ A/volt, $R_t = 14$ ohms; then

$$\Delta V_o = \Delta V2/g_m R_t = \Delta V2/(10)(14) = \Delta V2/140$$

If $V2$ were, say, a 15-V source, a 10% variation in $V2$ would result in an output variation of

$$\Delta V_o = (0.1)(15)/140 = 0.011 \text{ V}$$

Transistor types having lower g_m will generally have higher values of R_t and the attenuation factor $1/g_m R_t$ of Eq. 1-11 will still be high. Thus, for the 2N5784 (a high-current TO5 device) of Fig. 1-15, g_m is $= 4$ A/volt and R_t at 1 A is about $\Delta V/\Delta I = 7/0.05 = 140$ ohms. Then $\Delta V_o = \Delta V2/(4)(140)$, which is still an attenuation factor of 1/560.

1.6.4 Zener and Emitter Follower Power Dissipations

The selection of the source resistor R1 and maximum zener power dissipation for the zener–emitter follower regulator of Fig. 1-14A is done from Eqs. 1-8 and 1-9 just as if a resistive load were being driven. The only difference is that the variation between minimum and maximum load is large because the circuit must work safely with transistors of either minimum, nominal, or maximum current gain (β). In a safe, worst-case design, good practice is to assume the minimum β to be one-half the nominal value and the maximum twice the nominal value.

A sample calculation will illustrate the problems. Consider the circuit of Fig. 1-14A with a nominal zener diode Z1 of 11 V. Assume variations in R_L such that minimum, nominal, and maximum load currents are 0.1, 1.1, 2.1 A, respectively.

Assume in Fig. 1-14A the nominal value of $V1$ is 15 V with $\pm10\%$ tolerances, $Z1$ has $\pm5\%$ tolerances, and the source voltage $V2$ is the same as $V1$. Generally, $V2$ is a lower voltage supply than $V1$, chosen to minimize Q2 dissipation. $V1$ is a higher-voltage, lower-current, and more constant source, possibly preregulated so as to minimize zener current and, hence, voltage variations. But for the purpose of this calculation assume $V1$ and $V2$ are both the same 15-V supply with $\pm10\%$ tolerance.

Then in Eq. 1-8, maximum load current $= I_{Q1(max)}/\beta_{min}$. From Fig. 1-14D, nominal value of β at the maximum current of 2.1 A is 90. Assuming a minimum value of half that, $I_{L(max)} = 2.1/45 = 47$ mA. Assume for the zener diode, a minimum current of 5 mA will keep it safely out of the high-impedance knee at the low-current levels (this would have to be verified from the actual V–I curves for the specific zener diode). Then from Eq. 1-8, (assuming for simplicity no tolerance on R1):

$$R1 = \frac{(0.9)(15) - (1.05)(11)}{0.005 + 0.047} = 38 \text{ ohms}$$

From Eq. 1–9:

$$I_{z(\text{max})} = \frac{(1.1)(15) - (1.05)(11)}{38} - I_{L(\text{min})}$$

$$= 130 - I_{L(\text{min})}$$

And

$$I_{L(\text{min})} = \frac{I(Q1_{\text{min}})}{\beta_{\text{max}}} = \frac{0.100}{260} = 0.4 \text{ mA}$$

[assuming β_{max} equals twice the nominal value of 130 (at $I_c = 100$ mA) of Fig. 1–14D] or $I_{z(\text{max})} = 130 - I_{L(\text{min})} = 130 - 0.4 = 130$ mA.

Thus, power dissipated in the zener diode is $V_z I_{z(\text{max})} = (11)(0.13) = 1.43$ W, which would exceed the 1-W dissipation rating of the 1N4741.

Such a calculation showing that a tentative design is not workable is of great value, for it demonstrates that a design that seems easily adequate for nominal components and nominal voltages may not work at all for worst-case components and voltages. Such worst-case calculations are essential in power supply designs in which exceeding power dissipation ratings for limit values of components and voltages is the most frequent cause of failure.

In the above example, there are numerous ways to get around the problem. A 10-W zener could, of course, be used in a brute-force solution. A smaller TO5-type transistor could be used as an emitter follower or "Darlington" driver between the zener and the high-current output stage. This could probably even permit use of a smaller 400-mW zener diode. Also use of a preregulated source for $V1$ as shown in Fig. 1–11 is possible, since zener-current changes will then result only from maximum and minimum values of β.

Dissipation in the output transistor should be calculated and is $(V2_{\text{max}} - V_{z(\text{min})} - V_{be(Q1)})I_{L(\text{max})}$ watts.

PROBLEMS

1.1 In a series-pass regulator, as in Fig. 1–1 for 15-V output, with raw dc input tolerance of $\pm10\%$, what must the nominal input voltage be for safe series-pass operation at 10% low-line voltage?

With such nominal voltage what are the low, nominal, and high input voltages? What are the efficiencies at low, nominal, and high input voltages? Consider only losses across the series-pass element.

At 2 A output, what are the internal dissipations at high, nominal, and low input voltages?

1.2 What are the corresponding values for a series-pass power supply with an output voltage of 5 V and an output current of 10 A?

1.3 What are the corresponding values for a series-pass supply with an output voltage of 30 V and an output current of 6 A?

1.4 Repeat the above calculations for all three supplies for minimum voltage across the series-pass element of 3 V at 10% low-line voltage and input-voltage tolerance of $\pm10\%$.

1.5 Repeat for 4-V minimum voltage across the series-pass element at 10% low-line voltage and $\pm10\%$ line-voltage tolerances.

1.6 In a step-down switching regulator as in Fig. 1–5, for input voltages of 2, 5, and 10 V above the output, what are the efficiencies for output voltages of 5, 10, 15, and 30 V? Consider no low-level control circuit losses and consider that ac switching losses are equal to dc losses in the switch transistor and free-wheeling diode. What are internal dissipations in each case for output currents of 5 A?

1.7 In the switching regulators of Prob. 1–6, with a switching frequency of 25 kHz, what are the closed-switch and open-switch times for each supply at nominal input voltage?

1.8 In the switching regulators of Prob. 1–6, what are the dc input and output currents and powers?

1.9 In a step-up switching regulator as in Fig. 1–6, with a nominal dc input voltage of 160 V with $\pm 10\%$ tolerance, at a switching frequency of 25 kHz, what are the closed-switch and open-switch times for low, nominal, and high input voltages for an output voltage of 200 V?

What are the efficiencies, internal dissipations, and dc input currents for each input voltage at an output current of 1 A? Assume no control circuit losses.

1.10 In the single-ended switching converter of Fig. 1–7, with an input voltage of 160 V $\pm 10\%$ and an output voltage of 5 V, what is the required N_s/N_p turns ratio for $T_c = T_o$ at nominal voltage? Assume a 1-V drop in diode D1.

What are the values of T_c and T_o for a switching frequency of 25 kHz at low, nominal, and high input voltages? What is the maximum collector voltage the transistor is subjected to?

1.11 For the circuit shown in Fig. 1–7, for $T_c = 2\,T_o$ at 160 V input, 5 V output, and 25 kHz, what are the T_c, T_o, and N_s/N_p turns ratios? Assume a 1-V drop across diode D1. What are T_c and T_o at low and high input voltages and the maximum voltage stresses on the collector at each input voltage?

1.12 For the circuit shown in Fig. 1–7, at 160 V input and 5 V, 5 A output, with $T_c = T_o$ and a 1-V drop across the transistor S1 or diode D1 when each conducts, what is the internal dissipation considering no ac switching losses? Assuming ac switching losses are equal to total dc losses, what is the efficiency?

1.13 Design a zener diode regulator as in Fig. 1–9 for a nominal 5.5-V output, with maximum and minimum load currents of 30 and 5 mA, respectively. Assume an input voltage of 20 V $\pm 10\%$, resistor tolerances $\pm 1\%$, and $\pm 5\%$ zener voltage tolerance.

What is the value of R1 to maintain 5 mA minimum zener current assuming $\pm 1\%$ tolerance on R1 and $\pm 5\%$ on the zener diode? What is the maximum current into the zener and its maximum dissipation?

2

Basic Square-Wave Power Converters, Regulators

2.0   Introduction

A large variety of high-power dc/dc power converters and voltage regulators with efficiencies up to 80–90% is made possible by the availability of two major components. These are fast-switching, high-current, high-voltage transistors and transformer core materials with low losses at high frequencies and at high flux densities.

Such power converters can be operated as driven square-wave power amplifiers or self-oscillating square-wave generators. Full-wave or bridge rectifiers after the secondaries convert the square-wave power to dc. The basic circuit is either a two-transistor push–pull, four-transistor bridge, or two-transistor–two-capacitor half bridge.

This chapter discusses the basic converters themselves. In the following chapter various block diagram schemes for regulating the dc output are presented.

2.1   Driven Push–Pull Converters

2.1.1 Basic Circuit

The basic and most frequently used circuit for such power converters is shown in Fig. 2–1. It is a two-transistor push–pull power amplifier driving its load via the center-tapped primary of the transformer T1. The secondary load is coupled alternately into each half primary by alternately switching on Q1 and Q2.

The waveforms of Fig. 2–1 show some of the significant features of the circuit. It is seen that square waves of voltage or current applied alternately to the bases yield square waves of voltage and current at each collector. Thus, current flows in each transistor only on alternate half cycles when the voltage across the transistor itself is only about 1 V. Power dissipation during an "on" half cycle is thus low. During the "off" half cycle, the collector voltage is almost twice the dc supply voltage [actually $V_{dc} + (V_{dc} - 1)$]. However, the current and, hence, transistor dissipation are zero throughout the entire "off" half cycle. The following are some of the features that will demonstrate the usefulness of this circuit.

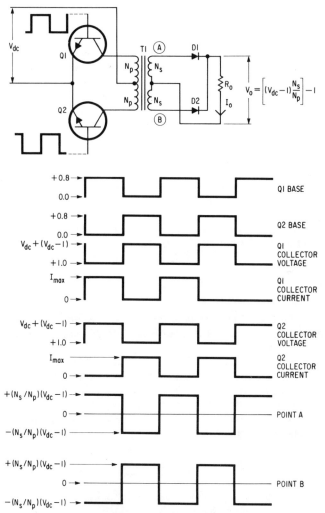

Fig. 2–1. A square-wave-driven converter.

2.1.2 Generation of Multiple-Output Voltage from a Single dc Source

The circuit converts the dc voltage from the prime dc power source to ac square-wave power at the transformer primary. One or more transformer secondaries may then be used to generate any other dc voltage higher or lower than the dc supply voltage. Secondaries, followed by rectifiers, can generate positive or negative dc output voltage of any desired magnitude.

Each dc secondary voltage thus generated is completely independent as to its absolute dc voltage level. The different voltages may have one common tie point ("output ground") and can be positive or negative with respect to that ground. The different dc output voltages may be stacked in series or may be stacked with either output terminal, above or below any other dc voltage in the system.

Thus, from one dc prime voltage source, all the necessary dc voltages for running a complex system can be generated. This can include, for example, the usual +5-V supply for driving logic circuitry, the usual ±30 V or so for magnetic-deflection cathode ray tube (CRT) sweep circuits, the normal ±15 V for operational amplifiers, and the various analog supply voltages ranging from 0 to about 30 V, positive or negative. The customary high voltages for CRT guns can also be generated: 15,000–25,000 V for acceleration and 400–4,000 V for focusing electrodes, grid bias supplies, and heater supplies.

2.1.3 Converter Efficiencies

The circuit is very efficient primarily because power is taken from V_{dc} and delivered to the transformer primary only when the transistors are on and are at their collector saturation voltage ($V_{ce(sat)}$) of 1 V or less. Thus, in each half cycle, for a primary current I_p, the power taken from V_{dc} is $V_{dc}I_p$; the power delivered to the transformer primary is $(V_{dc} - V_{ce(sat)})I_p \cong (V_{dc} - 1)I_p$. Thus, up to the transformer primary, the efficiency is

$$\frac{P_o}{P_{in}} \cong \frac{(V_{dc} - 1)I_p}{V_{dc}I_p} \cong \frac{V_{dc} - 1}{V_{dc}}$$

Since each transistor conducts only one-half of the time per cycle, its power dissipation is $1(I_p/2)$; and this is a small fraction of the generated square-wave power.

If, for the moment, transformer and transistor ac switching losses can be neglected, the efficiency from the source V_{dc} to the output at V_o (Fig. 2–1) can be calculated as follows:

To produce an output voltage, V_o, the peak flat-topped secondary voltage must be $V_o + V_d$, where V_d is the rectifier diode drop, which for a large range of current is about 1 V. Then $P_{in} = V_{dc}I_p = V_{dc}(N_s/N_p)I_o$ where

$$\frac{N_s}{N_p} = \frac{V_s}{V_p} = \frac{V_o + V_d}{V_{dc} - V_{ce(sat)}} \cong \frac{V_o + 1}{V_{dc} - 1}$$

Then
$$P_{in} = (V_{dc}I_o)\left(\frac{N_s}{N_p}\right)$$

$$\cong (V_{dc}I_o)\left(\frac{V_o + 1}{V_{dc} - 1}\right)$$

$$\cong \left(\frac{V_{dc}}{V_{dc} - 1}\right)(V_oI_o + I_o)$$

$$\cong \left(\frac{V_{dc}}{V_{dc} - 1}\right)(V_oI_o)\left(1 + \frac{1}{V_o}\right) \cong \left(\frac{V_{dc}}{V_{dc} - 1}\right)\left(\frac{V_o + 1}{V_o}\right)(V_oI_o)$$

Or
$$E = \frac{P_o}{P_{in}} = \frac{V_oI_o}{P_{in}} = \left(\frac{V_{dc} - 1}{V_{dc}}\right)\left(\frac{V_o}{V_o + 1}\right) \qquad (2\text{–}1)$$

Equation 2–1 is plotted in Fig. 2–2 at a number of commonly used output voltages for various dc supply voltages. It is seen that efficiency falls very steeply at about 5 V—a serious drawback since +5 V is often so used at high current and power levels for computer logic circuits.

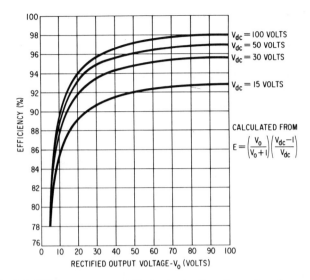

Fig. 2–2. Efficiency versus rectified output voltage for various dc supply voltages in a dc/dc converter neglecting transformer and transistor ac switching losses.

The rapid falloff in efficiency at 5 V is due, of course, to the 1-V rectifier drop needed to supply the 5-V load [the term $V_o/(V_o + 1)$ of Eq. 2–1]. By the use of newly available "Schottky" rectifier diodes, which have only about 0.5 rather than 1.0 V forward drop up to 20 A, efficiency at 5 V can be increased by about 8%. This comes about because the term $V_o/(V_o + 1)$ of Eq. 2–1 becomes $V_o/(V_o + 0.5) = 5/5.5 = 0.91$, rather than 0.83.

The efficiency calculated from Eq. 2–1 does not take into account the transformer core hysteresis losses nor resistive losses (copper) losses in the primary and secondary windings. With high-frequency transformer core materials currently available, "core" losses are generally no more than 1% up to the highest frequency in general use, about 20–50 kHz. Proper design can also keep copper loss to 2% or less. Thus, with transformer losses taken into account, efficiency will be about 3% less than that calculated from Eq. 2–1.

It is also not strictly true that current flows only when the voltage at the transistor collector has fallen to 1 V. Because of the finite rise and fall times of collector voltage and current, there is an overlap of high voltage and current at each collector voltage transition. The consequent spike of power dissipation has a duration that depends on the transistor switching speed. With currently available transistors, this spike has a width of about 0.25–2.0 μsec. The average dissipation (averaged over a full cycle) resulting from these spikes of "overlap" dissipation is

$$P_{av} = \left(\frac{t_{ol}}{T}\right)\left(\frac{1}{t_{ol}} \int_0^{t_{ol}} ei\ dt\right)$$

where T is the sum of the transistor "on" plus "off" times or switching period and t_{ol} is the duration of overlap of high voltage and current. In usual cases, the average dissipation during the overlap time may be 10 to as high as 50 times the dc dissipation of $(I_p)(1)$. But duty cycle t_{ol}/T may range from about 1/10 at the highest frequency of 50 kHz down to 1/100 at the lowermost frequency of about 5 kHz. The duration of the spikes of high dissipation is sufficiently low that only the average, not the peak, is important. As a rough rule of thumb, it can be assumed that the average overlap dissipation is equal to but, at worst, is no more than twice the dc dissipation. At 15–40 kHz, as a close approximation, if transistor ac losses are assumed equal to dc losses, efficiency due to transistor losses only is

$$E = [(V_{dc} - 1)/V_{dc}]^2 \qquad (2\text{-}1A)$$

Then, overall efficiency, including output rectifier losses, and a transformer efficiency of E_{tr} is

$$E = [(V_{dc} - 1)/V_{dc}]^2 [V_o/(V_o + 1)] \, E_{tr} \qquad (2\text{-}1B)$$

And, as discussed above, transformer losses can be kept to a maximum of 3% ($E_{tr} = 97\%$) up to frequencies of 15–40 kHz.

2.1.4 Filtering of Square-Wave Voltages

Figure 2–1 shows the transformer primary and secondary voltages have square waveforms. This is a decided advantage if the secondary voltage is to be rectified and filtered. Since the secondary waveforms are flat topped, the output beyond the rectifier diode will be flat topped and have a dc level of one diode drop or about 1 V below the peak secondary voltage of $(N_s/N_p)(V_{dc} - 1)$. This is seen in Fig. 2–3. If the collector rise and fall times were infinitely steep, as one diode ceased conducting at the end of one half cycle, the other diode would start conducting. As shown in Fig. 2–3, voltage waveforms have finite rise and fall times, and there is a voltage notch going down to zero at the cathode of the rectifier diode. For collector voltage rise and fall times of t, the width of the notch at the base is $2t$. In currently available transistors, the notch is generally under 1 μsec.

Thus, the filter capacity at the output of the rectifier diode of Fig. 2–1 can be very small, since it must supply the total output load current only for a time $2t$. Since the output voltages must not change appreciably during the time $2t$, and the load current is assumed to be constant, then the size of the filter capacitor

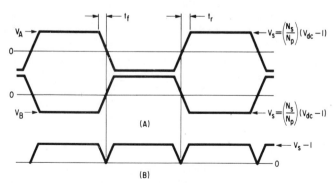

Fig. 2–3. (A) Secondary voltages for converter of Fig. 2–1. (B) Rectifier output voltage showing commutation notch.

can be calculated from $C_o = I_l(2t)/\Delta V_o$, where I_l is the load current, t is the collector rise and fall times, and ΔV_o is the permissible voltage droop during the notch. Thus, for a 5-V, 5-A output in which the permissible droop is, say, 0.1 V, the required filter capacitor for collector rise and fall times of 0.5 μsec is $C_o = (5)(1 \times 10^{-6})/0.1 = 50 \mu$F.

This is a considerably smaller capacitor than the one required for filtering sine waves, in which the filter capacitor must supply total load current for almost a full half cycle between peaks of the rectified half sine wave. For 60 Hz supply frequency, this time is 8,333 μsec.

2.1.5 Input–Output Voltage Relationship

The circuit of Fig. 2–1 is always driven hard enough at the base to saturate the collector. In saturation, most transistors used in this circuit configuration will have a collector saturation voltage under 1 V. Assuming it is 1 V and the rectifier diodes also have a 1-V drop, the rectified output voltage is

$$V_o = (V_{dc} - 1)(N_s/N_p) - 1 = V_{dc}(N_s/N_p) - (N_s/N_p) - 1$$

In general, $\quad V_{dc}(N_s/N_p) > 1 > (N_s/N_p)$

Then, $\qquad V_o \cong V_{dc}(N_s/N_p)$

Thus, a given percentage change in V_{dc} will cause the same percentage change in V_o. If V_{dc} is constant and ripple free, V_o is constant and ripple free. Any low-frequency ripple on V_{dc} will appear with the same percentage ripple (and, of course, at the same ripple frequency) at the rectified outputs.

The circuit thus has the valuable feature that, if V_{dc} is regulated and ripple free, all the multiple secondary rectified outputs are regulated against line-voltage changes to the same percentage and are also ripple free. Output voltage will then change only with load changes. But, as will be seen below, the output impedance after each rectified output is very low, and large load changes will result in small output voltage changes.

2.1.6 Output Impedance

With a constant or preregulated dc input, voltage from a converter such as in Fig. 2–1 will change somewhat with load-current changes. The output change ΔV_o for a load change ΔI_o and output impedance R_o is $\Delta V_o = \Delta I_o (R_o) = \Delta I_o(R_d + R_{ts} + R_w)$. The three components of R_o are: R_d, the diode impedance or slope of its V–I curve; R_{ts}, the impedance due to the transistor collector saturation resistance; and R_w, the impedance due to resistance in the primary and secondary windings.

R_w is the sum of the secondary winding resistance plus that of the primary reflected by the square of the turns ratio into the secondary. By proper transformer design in most cases, this is small enough to be neglected in comparison with R_d and R_{ts}.

R_{ts} is the collector saturation resistance, (slope of the transistor V_c–I_c curve below the saturation knee) reflected by the turns ratio squared into the secondary. For most transistors used in converters, R_{ts} will be in the range of 0.1–1.0 ohm. Transistors with higher values of R_{ts} will generally be high-voltage devices. These would ordinarily be selected only if the dc input voltage is large — over 100 V or so. Since such converters most often are used to produce lower voltages of -5 to $+30$ V, the step-down turns ratio is high, and the impedance reflected into the secondary is low. In most cases, collector saturation resistances reflected into secondaries can be kept down to 0.005–0.01 ohm.

The diode rectifier impedance, R_d, is a function of the diode current capacity and operating point on its V_c–I_c curve. This can be seen in the curves of Fig. 2–4 for some high-speed rectifier diodes of various current ranges. These diodes are obtainable with reverse voltage ratings from 50 to 600 V. Their impedance ranges from 0.1 ohm at the 1-A current level to 0.01 ohm at the 20- to 30-A points.

Thus, by proper choice of transistors and rectifier diodes, total output impedance $(R_d + R_{ts})$ seen looking back into a secondary can be kept in the range of 0.01–0.10 ohm. Then, in a converter such as in Fig. 2–1, operating with constant or preregulated dc input voltage, load-current changes of 5 A centered about 20 A will cause output voltage changes of only about 0.05 V.

This is often a constant enough voltage, and hence, by preregulating the dc input to a converter and choosing high-current, low-impedance rectifying diodes for each secondary, further regulation after the secondaries is unnecessary.

2.1.7 High-Frequency Operation

Almost the first decision to be made in designing a square-wave converter is the choice of operating frequency. When such converters first came into widespread use, operating frequencies of 5–10 kHz were generally chosen. But higher frequencies, up to 20–50 kHz, have distinct advantages. The two largest elements in the converter—the power transformer and output filter capacitor—become much smaller at higher frequencies. It will be shown in Chap. 8 that the maximum available load power from a given transformer is proportional to its operating frequency. Thus, for a given load power, doubling the operating frequency will roughly halve the volume of the transformer.

In Sect. 2.1.4 it was pointed out that the size of the output filter capacity depends on the rise and fall times of collector voltage waveforms. The higher-frequency transistors used with higher-frequency converters have faster output rise and fall times. Voltage notches at the secondary are thus narrower and require smaller capacitors for the same filtering.

There is a further nonelectrical advantage in going to frequencies above 10 kHz. Despite the most elaborate precautions, converters operating below 10 kHz will generate an audible hum that generally can be heard at a distance of 10–20 ft. For equipment with operators in the vicinity for long periods of time, e.g., in a computer room, this is a distracting and an absolutely prohibitive drawback. Operating frequency should be above about 18 kHz to avoid the audible hum problem.

Currently, new designs are being done at 20–50 kHz. This is now possible because of the current availability of high-current, high-voltage transistors having low turn-on, turn-off, and storage times. Thus, there are presently available transistors with a maximum current rating of 10 A and a voltage rating of

---

Fig. 2–4. Fast-switching rectifier diodes with low output impedance. (A) 1N3879 series, 6-A diodes. (B) 1N3889 series, 12-A diodes. (C) 1N3899 series, 20-A diodes. (D) 1N3909 series, 30-A diodes. (*Courtesy* Motorola, Inc.)

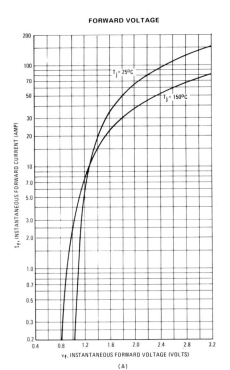

(A)

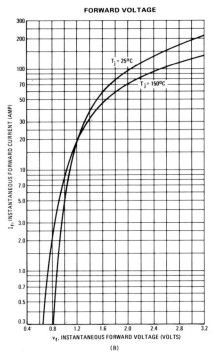

(B)

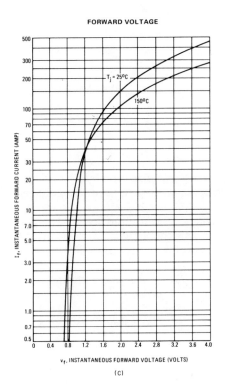

(C)

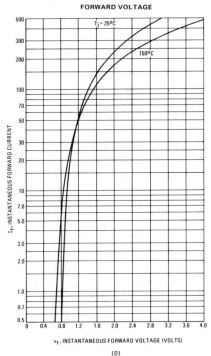

(D)

41

400 V. By operating at high forward and reverse input (forward and reverse input currents one-tenth the output current), turn-on and turn-off times can be kept down to 0.5 μsec each. Storage times can be kept down to 1 μsec by high reverse input drive by circuit tricks preventing transistor saturation.

As discussed in Sect. 2.1.3, there will be an overlap of high voltage and current during these relatively slow turn-on, turn-off, and storage times. To keep efficiency high, this "overlap" dissipation must last for as small a fraction of a half cycle as possible. Generally, the sum of rise, fall, and storage times should be permitted to be no more than 10% of the half periods. Thus, $T/2 = 10(t_r + t_f + t_s)$ or $T = 20(t_r + t_f + t_s)$. And for the abovementioned transistors, whose sum of rise, fall, and storage times is 2 μsec, the maximum frequency at which reasonably good efficiency is possible is

$$f = \frac{1}{T} = \frac{1}{20(2 \times 10^{-6})} = 25 \text{ kHz}$$

At 50 kHz, with the same high-voltage–high-current overlap, the duty cycle of the spike of "overlap" dissipation is higher, and the average internal dissipation is greater. If the thermal design is good enough, transistors whose sum of rise, fall, and storage times is 2 μsec can be used up to 50 kHz if the reduced efficiency is acceptable — but 50 kHz is about an upper limit. Higher-frequency operation is possible for low-power converters in which low efficiency is no serious drawback.

2.1.8 Transformer Core-Material Selection

The selection of transformer core-material is made mainly on the basis of minimum core dissipation, volume, and cost for a given operating frequency. Core dissipation consists of eddy current and hysteresis losses with the former dominating at higher frequencies. Eddy current losses can be reduced by going to thinner "laminations" in metallic cores or using core material with high electrical resistivity, such as ferrites. The latter have high resistivity because they are not metallic but ceramic ferromagnetic mixtures of nickel oxide and nickel, zinc, or manganese oxide.

Metal-Tape-Wound Cores

"Laminations" in the high-frequency metallic cores are not discrete flat sections stacked side by side as in lower-frequency power transformers. The "lamination" consists of a continuous thin metallic tape, oxide coated on its surface and wound in an annular segment around a toroidal bobbin. Such tape-wound cores for power-transformer applications are available in tape thicknesses of $\frac{1}{2}$, 1, 2, and 4 mils, with the thinner tape cores generally being more expensive.

Core losses increase with frequency, peak magnetic flux density, and lamination thickness. For frequencies above 5 kHz, core losses generally dictate tape thickness of 2 mils or less.

There are three major classes of metallic alloys used: 79% nickel-17% iron; 50% nickel-50% iron; and 3% silicon-97% iron. These classes are sold by various manufacturers under their own trade names. Table 2–1 shows roughly identical materials from some different suppliers.

Table 2–1. Three Major Classes of Magnetic Alloys for
Tape-Wound Cores

Material composition	Equivalent trade names
79% nickel-17% iron	Square Permalloy 80
	Square Permalloy
	4–79 Permalloy
	Square Mu 79
50% nickel-50% iron	Square Orthonol
	Deltamax
	Orthonik
	Hipernik V
3% silicon-97% iron	Magnesil
	Selectron
	Hypersil
	Microsil

The metallic alloys have higher maximum usable dc flux density than the ceramic ferrites. From the fundamental magnetic relationships, it is well known that higher-peak, magnetic-flux densities permit smaller transformer cores. It would then be thought that metal-tape cores would be a preferable choice, since they would result in smaller transformers, but core losses increase greatly with peak magnetic-flux density, and generally at frequencies above 5 kHz, to keep core losses acceptably low, operation must be limited to a peak flux density considerably below the maximum dc value.

This can be seen in Fig. 2–5, in which losses of various core materials at different frequencies for two usual peak flux densities are compared.[1] It is seen in Fig. 2–5 that at 10 kHz and 2,000 G Square Permalloy, the lowest-loss metal tape, has losses comparable to that of a typical, low-loss ferrite, Ferroxcube 3C8. Although Square Permalloy has a maximum usable dc flux density of about 6,400 G, at 4,000 G, above 10 kHz, its losses are already almost three times that of the ferrite at 2,000 G. At 6,400 G, the $\frac{1}{2}$-mil Square Permalloy has losses about seven times that of the ferrite at 2,000 G.

It can also be seen that at 5 kHz, Square Permalloy can be used at 4,000 G — twice the flux density of the ferrite — and thus would permit a smaller transformer. This would be at about twice the loss of the ferrite in watts per pound. Since the metal-tape core has about twice the density of the ferrite (8.7 g/cc as compared to 4.7 for ferrites), losses for the same power output would be four times as great as for a ferrite core.

Figure 2–5 thus shows tape-wound cores have their prime application below 5 kHz. Further useful data on tape-wound cores can be obtained from the various manufacturers.[2]

---

[1] Data courtesy of Magnetics, Inc. (Bulletin TWC-300R) and Ferroxcube Corporation (Bulletin "Linear Ferrite Materials and Components").

[2] Magnetics., Inc., Bulletin TWC-300R, "Tape Wound Cores." Arnold Engineering Co., Bulletin TC 101B, "Tape Wound Cores."

Material	Maximum practical flux density (gauss at 100°C)	Total core losses – hysteresis plus eddy current losses (watts per pound)						At operating flux density (gauss)
		100 kHz	50 kHz	20 kHz	10 kHz	5 kHz	1 kHz	
Typical low loss ferrite – Ferroxcube 3C8	3,000	40.1	20.0	6.0	2.5	1.1	0.18	2,000
½ mil Square Permalloy	6,400	41	18.0	4.7	2.0	0.80		2,000
1 mil Square Permalloy	6,400	62	22	5.7	2.0	0.70		2,000
2 mil Square Permalloy	6,400		20	5.3	1.8	0.65		2,000
¼ mil Orthonol	14,000	114	50	20	8.5	4.0		2,000
1 mil Orthonol	14,000	200	88	29	12	5.0	0.08	2,000
2 mil Orthonol	14,000		200	30	14	6.5	0.50	2,000
½ mil Square Permalloy	6,400		51	14	6.0	2.5		4,000
1 mil Square Permalloy	6,400		75	18	6.8	2.0		4,000
2 mil Square Permalloy	6,400		70	18	6.0	2.5		4,000
¼ mil Orthonol	14,000		150	45	21	10		4,000
1 mil Orthonol	14,000		250	60	26	12		4,000
2 mil Orthonol	14,000		400	62	30	14		4,000

Fig. 2-5. Total eddy current plus hysteresis losses for some typical metal-tape and ferrite core materials. (*Courtesy* Magnetics, Inc., and Ferroxcube Corp.)

Ferrite Cores

As mentioned above, ferrites are ceramic ferromagnetic mixtures of iron oxide and zinc, nickel, or manganese oxides. The raw-powdered oxides are mixed in the proper proportions, pressed into various shapes, and fired in batches in a kiln. Various shapes are possible; toroids, cup cores, U–U, U–I, E–E, and E–I are usual.[3]

In addition to their low losses at high frequencies, ferrites have the advantage that they are low in cost. Their low cost arises primarily from their batch-process manufacturing methods. Each core need not be handled and fabricated individually. Transformer assembly is also easier and less expensive than with tape-wound toroidal cores because many of the shapes—cup cores, U–U, U–I, or E–E—can have their coils prewound on bobbins that are then assembled with the core. This is less expensive than the use of the special winding machines necessary for toroidal cores. The wide variety of available shapes and sizes also offers greater latitude in core selection for optimum size, mounting, assembly means, and shape factor to fit available odd-shaped space. Ferrites generally have a lower curie temperature (temperature above which the material loses its magnetic properties). Ferrites for power transformer application generally have curie temperatures no higher than about 200°C. This contrasts with curie temperatures of about 450–700°C for the various tape-wound metal cores. But the lower curie temperatures of ferrites are rarely drawbacks for transformers with output power of 3 kW or less, for total transformer losses can be kept to a maximum of 1% of the output power. With so little internal dissipation, the transformer thermal impedance can easily be designed to have no more than a 40°C temperature rise between its interior and exterior.

Core losses in milliwatts per cubic centimeter as a function of flux density at various frequencies are shown in Fig. 2–6 for a typical low-loss ferrite (Ferroxcube 3C8). With a method for selecting a given core geometry and, hence, a volume for a desired output power, Fig. 2–6 is valuable in calculating transformer core losses. This will be taken up in detail in Chap. 8.

2.1.9 Converter Transistor Selection

The major parameters involved in selecting the transistors for the converter of Fig. 2–1 are maximum collector-emitter voltage (V_{ceo} or V_{cer}); maximum collector current; minimum current gain (β or h_{fe}) at maximum load current; switching speed (collector current rise, fall, and storage times); maximum power dissipation or junction-to-case thermal resistance; and collector voltage second-breakdown ratings.

Collector Voltage Rating

In the circuit of Fig. 2–1 it is seen that the voltage across one half primary when its transistor is on is $V_{dc} - V_{ce(sat)} \cong V_{dc} - 1 \cong V_{dc}$. During the "on" half cycle, the collector end of the winding is negative relative to the center tap. Then, assuming equal positive and negative half cycles, during the "off" half cycle the collector end of the winding must go as far above the center tap as it had been below it during the "on" half cycle.

---

[3] Ferroxcube Corp., Saugerties, N.Y., "Ferroxcube Linear Ferrites." Magnetics, Inc., Butler, Pa., "Ferrite Core Catalog FC208. Stackpole Carbon, St. Marys, Pa., Ceromag Bulletin 59. Allen Bradley, Milwaukee, Wisc., "Ferrite Cores."

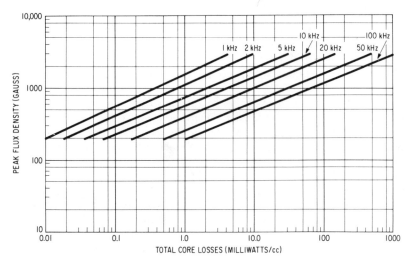

Fig. 2–6. Core losses versus frequency in Ferroxcube 3C8 material. (*Courtesy* Ferroxcube Corp.)

This comes about from the fundamental magnetic relation for a core: $e\,\Delta t = (NA\,\Delta B)\,10^{-8}$. For during the "on" half cycle when the voltage across the half winding is negative,

$$\int_{0}^{T/2} e\,dt$$

has a negative volt-second area. Then

$$\Delta B_1 = \frac{1}{NA} \int_{0}^{T/2} e\,dt$$

is a negative flux change from its starting point. During the next "off" half cycle, the flux ΔB_2 must be equal and opposite to the flux change in the "on" half cycle. For, otherwise, after a full cycle, there would be a net flux change and, after a few full cycles, the core would move into positive or negative saturation.

Thus, since the volt-second areas must be equal and opposite in alternate half cycles, the voltage at the collector end of the winding is as far above V_{dc} during the "off" time as it had been below it during the "on" time. Hence, in the two-transistor converter of Fig. 2–1, the transistor must have a collector-emitter voltage rating of at least $2V_{dc}$.

The voltage ratings must also consider tolerance on the supply voltage, which is generally $\pm 10\%$. Further, because of leakage inductance in the transformer and wiring inductance in the collector leads, there is usually an additional voltage spike at the positive-going edge of the collector voltage waveform (Fig. 8–17). A safe design should allow an additional 20% for the spike. Thus, for a nominal supply voltage of V_{dc}, the maximum voltage the transistor may be subjected to is $1.2(2)\,(1.1V_{dc}) = 2.64V_{dc}$.

For safe worst-case designs, the transistor vendor's maximum voltage rating should be derated to account for temperature effects, production spread, transients on the input voltage line, and generally unpredictable transient effects in the circuitry.

Good worst-case design practice is to assume the maximum safe voltage rating is only 50% of the vendors' specified maximum value. It is not always possible to find transistors with adequate current rating, switching speed, and a voltage rating permitting 50% derating. If derating factors must be relaxed, the most they should be relaxed to is 80% of the vendor's maximum voltage rating. Then, $2.64V_{dc} = 0.8V_{ce(max\ vendor\ spec)}$ or

$$V_{ce(max\ vendor\ rating)} = 3.3V_{dc(nom)} \qquad (2-2)$$

If the input dc is preregulated, the $\pm 10\%$ allowance for input variation is unnecessary. Then, the vendor's maximum collector voltage rating need be only $3V_{dc}$.

It can be predicted with a great degree of certainty that over a large production run, if the criteria that $V_{ce(max\ vendor\ spec)} = 3.3V_{dc(nom)}$ is not adhered to, failure rates will be high and exact failure modes will be difficult to pinpoint because of random voltage transient effects.

The collector-emitter voltage rating appropriate to the base circuit should be used in the above. When the base impedance in the "off" state is low (generally 50 ohms or less) it is the vendors' V_{cbo} rating that pertains. With "high" base impedances in the "off" state (generally above 100 ohms), the applicable rating is V_{ceo}, which may be only about 70–80% of the V_{cbo} rating. For intermediate base impedances (generally 50 ohms), the pertinent maximum collector-emitter voltage rating is V_{cer}, which if not quoted by the vendor can be assumed midway between V_{ceo} and V_{cbo}.

Maximum Collector Current Ratings

In the square-wave converter, Fig. 2–1, there may be a number of secondaries of turn ratios $N_{s1}, N_{s2}, N_{s3}, \ldots$. Each, after rectification, will supply known dc load currents of $I_{s1}, I_{s2}, I_{s3}, \ldots$. The total load current reflected into the primary is

$$I_{p(total)} = (N_{s1}/N_p)I_{s1} + (N_{s2}/N_p)I_{s2} + (N_{s3}/N_p)I_{s3} + \cdots \qquad (2-3)$$

The total current in each half primary is this total reflected load current plus some small transformer magnetizing or coercive current. Magnetizing current may be calculated from the fundamental magnetic relation:

$$H_c = \frac{4\pi N_p I_m}{10L_i}$$

Here, H_c is the peak coercive force in oersteds (about 0.6 for 3C8 ferrite, 0.1 for 17% nickel-79% iron alloys, and about 0.3 Oe for 50% nickel-50% iron alloys); N_p is the number of primary turns; L_i is the transformer magnetic path length in centimeters; and I_m is the magnetizing current in amperes. Generally, the magnetizing current will be under 2% of the load current reflected into the primary and most often can be neglected.

This total current reflected into the primary flows, of course, in each transistor only on alternate half cycles. Thus, although the average current per transistor is only half the above total, the transistor maximum current rating must be sufficiently high so that adequate gain is available at the peak current of Eq. 2–3. Transistor power dissipation is calculated, of course, on the basis of the peak current flowing at a 50% duty cycle in each transistor.

Minimum Current Gain and Input Drive

Generally, at this stage, the maximum current in the transistor is known (as calculated in the previous paragraphs) and a transistor has been selected. From its data sheets, a minimum transistor current gain (β or h_{fe}) is read. Then, the base drive current must be designed to yield at least a worst-case input current of $I_{c(max)}/\beta_{min}$. Actual input current will generally be greater than this calculated value to ensure safe transistor saturation and fast turn-on speed. Transistor turn-on speeds are usually quoted for I_c/I_{in} of 10 ($h_{fe} = 10$); hence, the base input drive circuit should be designed to yield a worst-case current $I_{c(max)}/10$.

Maximum Power Dissipation and Transistor Junction Temperatures

Each transistor carries current of the magnitude calculated in the previous section for one-half the time in each full cycle. It carries this current in saturation at a collector-to-emitter voltage drop referred to as $V_{ce(sat)}$. The magnitude of $V_{ce(sat)}$ is given in the transistor's data sheet as a function of current. $V_{ce(sat)}$ can also be read from the V_c–I_c curves, as in Fig. 2–8A. It is the collector-emitter voltage below the knee in the curves.

To ensure the collector is in saturation, the base drive for the known collector current must be equal to or greater than that shown on the V_c–I_c curve for the minimum β transistor. Generally, supplying a base current of $I_{c(max)}/10$ will ensure saturation, since h_{fe} to the knee for usable output currents is generally greater than 10. Figure 2–8A shows that $V_{ce(sat)}$ is under 1 V up to currents of 8 A. Although $V_{ce(sat)}$ is current dependent, for an initial approximation of power dissipation, it is usually taken as 1 V. Thus, for a 50% duty cycle, each transistor dissipates a power of $[I_{c(max)}(1)]/2$ watts.

But, as discussed in Sects. 2.1.3 and 2.1.7, there is a momentary overlap of high current and voltage during turnon and turnoff. The exact power wasted during switching is calculated by integrating the voltage current product during the switching time. The exact waveform during switching is generally not predictable. The overlap during current turnon is usually negligible; during turnoff it can be appreciable but will vary from transistor to transistor because of variations in storage and turn-off times.

Thus, an exact knowledge of overlap dissipation is only available from oscilloscope waveforms of the specific circuit. But for an initial estimate it can be assumed to be equal to the dc dissipation: $P_{ac} = P_{dc} = [I_{c(max)}(1)]/2$. It usually can be kept down to this value.

Thus, total dc and overlap losses per transistor are $2[(I_{c(max)}(1)]/2$ or $I_{c(max)}$ in watts for I_c in amperes. The maximum permissible power dissipation is not unique to the transistor. It depends on the transistor's thermal resistance and its heat sink design. This will be considered in detail in Chap. 4. In general, it is of greater significance to consider maximum permissible junction temperature. In the thermal design, transistor case temperature will be known. Then, the maximum junction temperature is given by

$$T_{j(max)} = T_{case(max)} + \theta_{jc} PD_{max} \tag{2-4}$$

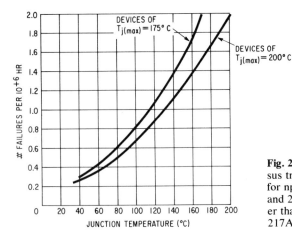

Fig. 2–7. Transistor failure rate versus transistor junction temperature for npn transistors of $T_{j(max)} = 175$ and 200°C and a power rating greater than 1 W. (From Mil Handbook 217A)

Here, $T_{case(max)}$ is the maximum case temperature in °C, θ_{jc} is the "thermal resistance" in °C per watt (between 1 and 3°C/watt for most TO3 type transistors), and PD_{max} is the maximum transistor power dissipation in watts in the specific application ($= I_c$ as above).

From this relation, once it is decided what the maximum junction temperature ($T_{j(max)}$) shall be, maximum permissible power dissipation is calculated. But the decision on $T_{j(max)}$ is based on what is considered a safe derating below what the physics of the transistor junctions can tolerate. For most silicon transistors, the absolute maximum junction temperature is either 175 or 200°C. Failure rates strongly depend on how close continuous operation is to these maximum device temperatures.

A guide to what may be gained by derating below these maximum values is obtained from the empirical failure rates quoted in Mil Handbook 217A and reproduced in Fig. 2–7. Here it is seen that for a device whose absolute maximum junction temperature is 200°C, failure rates will be two failures per million hours at 200°C. This can be reduced to one failure per million hours if operation is limited to 130°C. In general, because of the usual approximations in thermal calculations, the uncertainty in ac "overlap" losses arising from variations in transistor switching speed, maximum permissible power dissipation as calculated from Eq. 2–4 should be such as to yield a maximum transistor junction temperature of 135–150°C. Commercial equipment designs can operate closer to the maximum values of 175 or 200°C, but military or high-reliability designs should be restricted to 135 or even 105°C if feasible.

Transistor Switching Speeds

The overlap of high voltages and currents during turn-on and turn-off times was discussed in Sects. 2.1.3 and 2.1.7. The resulting high-power dissipation during this overlap time could be equal to or many times more than the dc dissipation during the "off" times, depending on the overlap duty cycle. In Sect. 2.1.7, the guideline was suggested that the sum of rise, fall, and storage times should be no more than 10% of the half cycle.

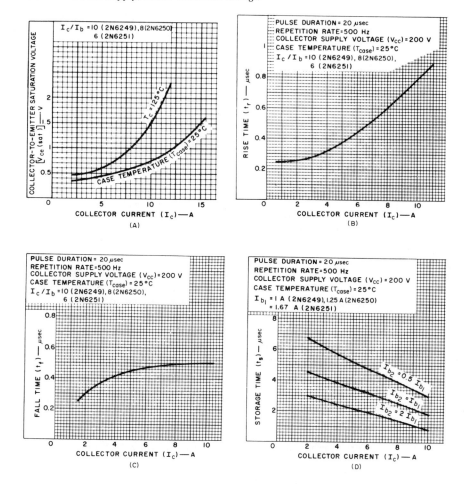

Fig. 2–8. Characteristics of a typical high-power, high-voltage fast-switching transistor: 2N6251 family. **(A)** Collector-to-emitter saturation voltage versus collector current. **(B)** Rise time characteristic. **(C)** Turn-off characteristic. **(D)** Storage time characteristic. (*Courtesy* RCA Corp.)

Rise, fall, and storage times strongly depend on forward- and reverse-base drives. This is seen dramatically in Fig. 2–8B, which shows switching times for a typical high-speed transistor family, the 2N6251. It is seen in Fig. 2–8B that the longest of the delay times is the storage time and that this can be reduced considerably by reverse-base currents (I_{b2}), which are equal to or larger than the forward-base (I_{b1}) drives. The reverse-base drives are transient—they need last only for the indicated storage times. Chapter 8 will discuss some of the circuit tricks available for achieving large reverse-base drives.

Storage time can also be reduced considerably by circuit tricks that keep the transistor out of saturation—defined as a forward-biased base-to-collector junction.

Two often-used schemes are shown in Fig. 2–9. Figure 2–9A borrows from old transistor logic technology. Diodes D1, D2, and D3 are silicon diodes. The base of any "on" transistor is two diode drops or about 1.2 V below the input node A. But the "on" collector is only one diode drop below A and, hence, is always 0.6 V positive (reverse biased and, hence, out of saturation) with respect to its base.

Assuming an 0.8-V base-emitter drop in the "on" transistor, and an 0.6-V drop in diodes D1, D2, and D3 when they are forward biased, the collector-to-emitter potential in the "on" state is $V_{be} + V_{D1} + V_{D2} - V_{D3} = 0.8 + 2(0.6) - 0.6 = 1.4$ V. This is somewhat higher than the normal saturated collector-emitter voltage and increases transistor dissipation. But the higher permissible operating frequency and decreased "overlap" losses more than offset the disadvantage of higher dc dissipation. Dissipation can be reduced somewhat by small resistors in series with D3. Diode D3 must have a reverse voltage rating of at least $2V_{cc}$.

Figure 2–9B is a Darlington connection and works in almost the same manner as Fig. 2–9A in that it prevents saturation in the high-power output transistor Q1. Transistors Q2 are lower-power, high-frequency transistors that are saturated in the "on" state. In saturation, their collectors are 0.2–0.4 V positive relative to their emitters. Since the collector-base potential of the Q1 power transistors is the same as the collector-emitter potential of the Q2 drivers,

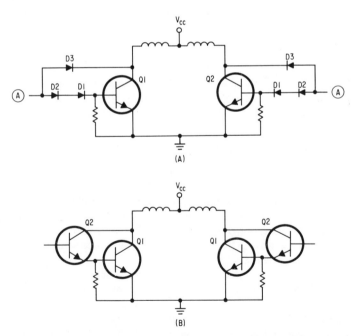

Fig. 2–9. (A) The use of diode feedback to prevent saturation and to decrease storage time is shown. (B) In a Darlington circuit, output transistors Q1 are kept from saturating by drivers Q2, which do saturate. Total storage time is still low, since Q2 transistors are faster than Q1.

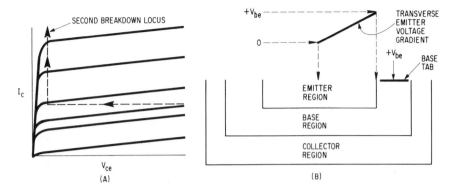

Fig. 2-10. (A) Second breakdown characterized by collector-emitter short results from high-current density at localized spots. (B) In forward-biased second breakdown, the transverse gradient causes high-current density at the periphery of the emitter.

the collector of Q2 in the "on" state is also 0.2–0.4 V positive with respect to its base, i.e., the condition for nonsaturation.

Q2 transistors do saturate and have relatively long storage times, but these are low-power transistors that generally have much higher frequency response and lower storage times than the power transistors, if they are permitted to saturate. With the circuits of Fig. 2–9, relatively low-speed power transistors can be used in dc/dc converters at frequencies in the range of 25–50 kHz.

Second-Breakdown Ratings

Second breakdown in a transistor is a sudden drop in the voltage across the collector-to-base junction as shown in Fig. 2–10A. It can commence anywhere in the I_c–V_{ce} plane and ends up with a low impedance or shorted collector-to-base junction. Current after breakdown is limited only by the source voltage and external load impedance. If the supply voltage is not removed or fused, the collector-load impedance or transistor collector-base junction generally shorts. Once the transistor has even momentarily entered second breakdown, it is permanently damaged.

Second breakdown is caused by a nonuniform current distribution across the collector-base junction. It occurs when the collector current is focused or channeled into areas much smaller than the total collector-base junction area. This gives rise to local hot spots at which the temperature is high enough to destroy the transistor.

The maximum average power dissipation rating of a transistor is based on a uniform current distribution across the collector-base junction and, hence, a uniform temperature distribution. Second breakdown can occur for high-peak power pulses with low-duty cycle and, hence, lower average dissipation than the specified maximum average dissipation if the current is focused down into a sufficiently small area.

This current focusing, which results in second breakdown, can occur under two conditions: that of forward-biased and reverse-biased base-emitter operation.

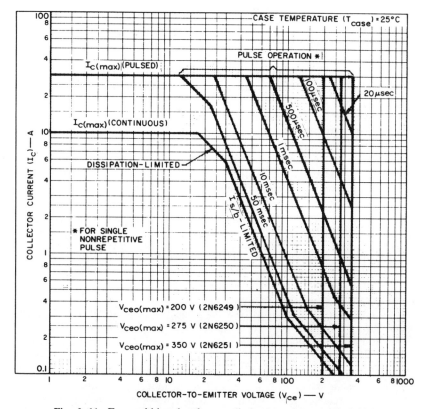

Fig. 2–11. Forward-biased safe area limit curve for a typical high-speed transistor. (*Courtesy* RCA Corp.)

Forward-Biased Second Breakdown The physical basis for current focusing can be seen in Fig. 2–10B. In an npn transistor, the positive base-emitter potential (about 0.7 V) is introduced at the base tab and causes the emitter periphery closest to the base to be more positive than its center. This comes about because of the voltage drop in the resistance of the base material.

Thus, collector current (electrons injected into the base from the n-type emitter) crossing the base-collector junction will channel down to greater concentrations opposite the more positive emitter periphery than opposite its center. At sufficiently high total current and voltage, this emitter-edge-concentrated current will result in local hot spots sufficient to destroy the transistor, even though the total power dissipation may be below the specified maximum value.

Forward-biased second breakdown can be avoided by ensuring that operation is restricted to the proper location on the vendor's "safe area" *V–I* curves such as in Fig. 2–11. The portions marked I_{sb} limited are the locations in voltage, current, and time below which operations must be restricted to ensure forward-biased second breakdown does not occur.

It is seen in Fig. 2–1 that, in the steady state, the square-wave converter passes current at a V_{ce} saturation voltage of only about 1.0 V. This would guarantee that operation is always inside the I_{sb} limit boundaries. But, in some circumstances, secondaries of square-wave converters have capacitive loads. At initial turnon, until the capacitors are charged, the transistors may not saturate down to 1 V and operation can be outside the limit curves.

A second manner in which operation may be outside the limit curves is possible even without large-load capacitance. In Fig. 2–1, it is seen that the voltage at an "off" collector stays high and no current flows until the current in the opposite transistor ceases. This high $(2V_{cc})$ voltage is ideally always coincident with zero current.

But if the off-turning transistor has storage delay and the on-turning one is driven positive at its base, simultaneous conduction can occur for 1–5 μsec of storage delay in the off-turning transistor. The "high" collector will not be able to move down until the opposite transistor comes out of storage. Thus, there can be a voltage of $2V_{cc}$ coincident with $I_{c(max)}$ for 1–5 μsec in the transistor about to turn on. This can exceed the I_{sb} limit curve in the uppermost right-hand corner of Fig. 2–11C and result in transistor failure.

Reverse-Biased Second Breakdown   Second breakdown can also occur with a reverse-biased base-emitter junction. But as can be seen in Fig. 2–12A, with a reverse-biased junction the emitter center is more positive than its periphery, since the periphery is closer to the negatively biased base.

Thus, if any current crossed the collector-base junction, it would be focused down in greater concentration opposite the emitter center, since the center is more positive than the edge. Now, with a reverse-biased base, the base ordinarily would prevent collector current from flowing. But if the collector load were inductive, energy would be stored in it during the "on" time. During the "off" time, the inductive kick would cause the collector potential to move up positive until it reached the normal V_{cbo} avalanche breakdown voltage as seen in Fig. 2–12B along the locus DEF. Now the energy stored in the inductance during the "on" time is dissipated in the transistor at a potential of V_{cbo}.

Despite the reverse-base bias, current will flow and this stored energy will focus down to the most positive point of the emitter — its center. And, since the area of the emitter center is less than its periphery, the current density at the emitter center in reverse bias is greater than at the periphery in forward bias.

Now, if sufficient energy has been stored in the inductor during the "on" time, this energy or current, focused into a very narrow central emitter area, can cause local hot spots of temperature high enough to destroy the transistor.

Vendors rate their transistors to avoid this reverse-biased second breakdown in terms of a joule rating: the energy (E_{sb}) stored in an inductive collector load that would be enough to destroy the transistor. This energy in joules is equal to the energy stored in the inductance in the collector load at the level of collector current just prior to turnoff. This stored energy is:

$$E_{sb} = \tfrac{1}{2}(L_p)(I_p^2)$$

where E_{sb} is in joules, I_p is in amperes, and L_p is in henrys. For a given collector inductance (transformer leakage inductance if the collector load is the primary of a transformer), this limits the peak collector current just prior to turnoff. If I_p is fixed, this limits the maximum permissible collector inductance.

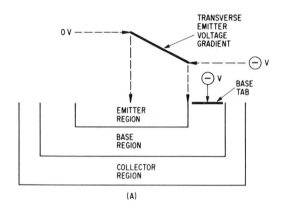

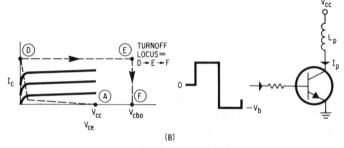

Fig. 2–12. (A) In reverse-biased second breakdown, current concentrates at the center of the emitter. (B) At turnoff with an inductive load, reverse-biased second breakdown occurs if $(1/2)(LI_p^2)$ is too large.

Since E_{sb} depends on the actual reverse bias that focuses the collector current, it is quoted in the vendor's data sheets at a standard reverse bias — usually -4 V through a 50-ohm series resistor.

2.2   Driven Bridge Converters

The two-transistor push–pull converter of Fig. 2–1 is an efficient, economical way of converting one dc prime power voltage source to a higher or lower voltage — or to a multiplicity of dc voltages.

In Sect. 2.1.9 it was pointed out that at a minimum, the transistor voltage rating must be at least twice the dc input voltage. For a safe worst-case design, if the input source has a $\pm10\%$ tolerance, the transistor voltage rating should be 3.3 times the normal input voltage.

When the dc supply voltage is in the range of the usual battery outputs of 24–30 V, there is no problem in selecting transistors of adequate switching speed, current rating, and voltage rating. Such dc/dc converters are frequently driven from the full-wave rectified 115-V ac line. The peak dc voltage at the rectifier output is about $(1.4)(115) = 161$ V (less about a 2-V silicon bridge-rectifier drop). Thus, at a minimum, the inverter voltage rating would have to be $2(160) = 320$ V; for the worst-case design, it would have to be $(3.3)(160) = 528$ V.

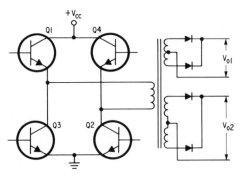

Fig. 2–13. In the bridge converter, maximum voltage stress on any transistor is V_{cc}, as contrasted to $2V_{cc}$ in the two-transistor converter of Fig. 2–1.

Currently, there are not many types available with adequate switching speed, current ratings, and voltage ratings above 450 V, and devices having the proper voltage ratings are generally expensive.

An alternative to the two-transistor push–pull circuit is the bridge converter of Fig. 2–13. Here, on alternate half cycles, diagonally opposite transistors, Q1 and Q2 or Q3 and Q4, are on simultaneously. The transformer primary moves up its hysteresis loop on one half cycle with a voltage V_{cc} across it in one polarity. In the next half cycle, it moves down its hysteresis loop with a reversed polarity of V_{cc} volts.

So the most voltage any transistor is subjected to is V_{cc} volts, rather than $2V_{cc}$ as for the two-transistor push–pull converter. The price paid for this is the cost and space of four rather than two transistors, but the added reliability more than makes up for this disadvantage, since the smaller the fraction of maximum-rated voltage the maximum voltage stress actually is, the greater the reliability is. Thus, in the two-circuit types, to operate off the same supply voltage with the same fraction of maximum voltage stress, the two-transistor converter requires devices with twice the maximum voltage rating as the four-transistor bridge. With very few transistor types with maximum voltage ratings of over 500 V available, a two-transistor converter safe worst-case design is not easy to achieve with nominal dc input voltages 160 V or more.

It should be noted that, if two transistors in series, such as Q1 and Q3 or Q2 and Q4, are on simultaneously, this presents a direct short circuit across the voltage supply and can destroy the transistors. Simultaneous conduction of Q1–Q3 or Q2–Q4 results when there is storage delay in the off-turning device. Circuit tricks to cope with this problem will be considered in Chap. 8.

2.3   Driven Half-Bridge Converters

The advantage of reducing the applied voltage across the inverter transistor from $2V_{cc}$ to V_{cc} is also offered by the half-bridge converter of Fig. 2–14. The half bridge replaces two of the inverter transistors by two capacitors

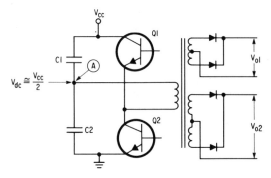

Fig. 2–14. In the half-bridge inverter, too, maximum voltage stress on either transistor is V_{cc} rather than $2V_{cc}$ as in the circuit of Fig. 2–1.

and, hence, is somewhat more economical, but with rapidly falling transistor prices, even this advantage is not always offered. Generally, the two capacitors will occupy a larger volume than the two transistors they replace, thus further reducing the half-bridge advantage.

For the case in which the transistors are expensive, the half bridge is often used, particularly in low-power inverters. The midpoint of the capacitors charges up to an average potential of $V_{cc}/2$. Peak primary voltage is thus $V_{cc}/2$ as compared to V_{cc} for the full bridge. Thus, for the same secondary output power, the primary current and, hence, inverter current are twice those in the full bridge.

The value of the bridge capacitors is calculated from the known primary current and operating frequency. Thus, for a total output power of P_o (including transformer losses) primary current is $I_p = P_o/(V_{cc}/2)$. Then for an operating frequency of f_o, the half period is $1/2f_o$. The transformer primary is fed effectively from C1 and C2 in parallel. When Q1 is on, current flows through the primary into node A, replenishing the charge lost by both capacitors in the half cycle when Q2 was on and drew current out of node A. The voltage change across the capacitors, for $C_1 = C_2 = C$, is then

$$\Delta V = \frac{I_p \Delta t}{C_{\text{total}}} = \left[\frac{P_o}{(V_{cc}/2)(C1 + C2)}\right]\left(\frac{1}{2f_o}\right) = \frac{P_o}{2V_{cc}f_oC}$$

The percentage change in dc voltage across the capacitors is the same as the percentage change in rectified output voltage. Thus, for a percentage output ripple of V_r,

$$V_r = \frac{100\Delta V}{V_{cc}/2} = \frac{100P_o/2V_{cc}f_oC}{V_{cc}/2} = \frac{100P_o}{V_{cc}^2 f_oC} \tag{2-5}$$

And the magnitude of C for output ripple percentage V_r is

$$C = \frac{100P_o}{V_{cc}^2 f_o V_r} \tag{2-5A}$$

2.4   Square-Wave Oscillator Converters

2.4.1 Relative Merits of Driven and Square-Wave Oscillator Converters

In previous sections, the power converter was discussed as an externally driven square-wave power amplifier. Transformer design is such as to keep the magnetic core well below saturation at the top of its hysteresis loop. This yields high efficiency as core losses increase greatly with magnetic flux density. Further, it is often an advantage to have the operating frequency synchronous and locked in phase to some external system frequency, such as a computer clock or horizontal line rate in a video display. Then any noise pulses generated at high-power voltage transitions of the square wave are locked at unique times and can more easily be tolerated.

In the driven converter, peak magnetic-field intensities in the core and operating frequency are fixed by the design and will not vary as circuit parameters change.

If lower efficiency and a not too well-determined and nonsynchronous frequency are acceptable, then operating the converter as a square-wave power oscillator is very economical. The earliest power converters were in fact operated as square-wave power oscillators whose transformer characteristics and supply voltages fixed the operating frequency.

In the following sections, the fundamentals of square-wave power oscillators will be considered.

2.4.2 Single-Transformer, Square-Wave Power Oscillator Converter (Often Referred to as a Royer Oscillator[4])

The basic circuit is shown in Fig. 2–15A. Its input base drive comes from a feedback winding on the main power transformer rather than from an external source. The heart of the circuit is the square magnetic hysteresis loop transformer core, which determines the operating frequency. A typical square hysteresis loop is shown in Fig. 2–15B. Core materials commonly used are the metallic cores discussed in Sect. 2.1.8. Ferrite cores whose hysteresis loops are not as square are also usable but yield slower rise and fall times, thus causing more overlap dissipation.

Circuit operation is as follows: Consider one of the transistors, say Q1, to be on and in saturation. It is initially turned on by current from V_{cc} flowing via R1 and base winding N_{b1} to its base. It is held on for the balance of the first half cycle, by the positive voltage induced in the base winding N_{b1} by transformer coupling to the primary N_{p1}. An opposite polarity voltage induced in N_{b2} during the Q1 "on" time holds Q2 off. During the Q1 "on" time, the voltage impressed on the primary N_{p1} is $V_{cc} - V_{ce(sat)} \cong V_{cc} - 1$. This voltage feeds power to the loads via secondaries N_{s1} and N_{s2} and sufficient power to the base via N_{b1} to keep the transistor on and in saturation at a current level equal to the sum of all the secondary load currents reflected into the primary.

The voltage polarity at windings N_{b1} and N_{b2} must be as indicated in Fig. 2–15A by the dot notation. The significance of the dot notation is that if in

---

[4] G. H. Royer: A Switching Transistor, AC to DC Converter. *AIEE Transactions*, July 1955.

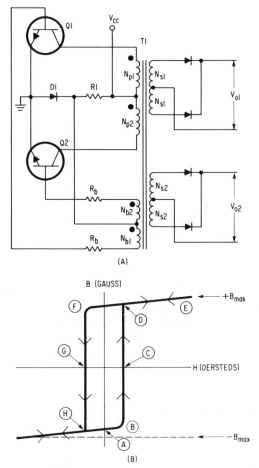

Fig. 2–15. (A) A single-transformer, square-wave oscillator converter. (B) Locus of operation on the square hysteresis loop of the T1 transformer core.

any one winding the dotted end is at any time, say, positive relative to its nondotted end, in all other windings dotted ends are simultaneously positive relative to their nondotted ends. Of course, when any one dotted end is negative relative to its nondotted end, all other dotted ends are simultaneously negative with respect to their own nondotted ends.

Thus, if Q1 is on, it is in saturation and the nondot end of N_{p1} is positive relative to its dot end. Observing the dot orientation of N_{b1}, it is seen that its Q1 base end (nondot) is positive relative to the end feeding R1–D1 and is of the correct polarity to turn Q1 on. Since Q1 is in saturation, the voltage across N_{p1} is $V_{cc} - V_{ce(sat)} \cong V_{cc} - 1$. Then the voltage induced across N_{b1} is $(N_{b1}/N_{p1})(V_{cc} - 1)$ and the base current of Q1 is

$$\frac{(N_{b1}/N_{p1})(V_{cc} - 1) - V_{be} - V_{D1}}{R_b}$$

The value of R_b is chosen small enough to saturate transistor Q1 at its minimum β and maximum load current.

Again observing the dot orientation, it is seen that the base ends of N_{b1} and N_{b2} are always of opposite polarity. Hence, as long as Q1 is driven on by the induced voltage from the primary, Q2 is held off and vice versa.

Now Q1 remains on as long as there is a voltage induced in N_{b1} by transformer coupling to the primary N_{p1}. This "on" time is fixed by the transformer and the supply voltage in a manner determined by the fundamental magnetic relationship

$$V_p = N_p A_c (dB/dt) 10^{-8} \text{ volts} \qquad (2\text{-}6)$$

Here, V_p is the instantaneous primary voltage in volts, N_p is the number of primary turns, A_c is the transformer core area in square centimeters, and dB/dt is the instantaneous rate of change of magnetic flux density in gauss per second. As long as Q1 is in saturation, there is a constant voltage $V_{ce} - V_{ce(\text{sat})}$ $\cong V_{cc} - 1$ across the primary and

$$\frac{dB}{dt} = \frac{(V_{cc} - V_{ce(\text{sat})})10^{+8}}{N_p A_c} \cong \frac{(V_{cc} - 1)10^{+8}}{N_p A_c} \qquad (2\text{-}7)$$

Since $V_{cc} - 1$ is constant, Eq. 2-6 dictates a constant dB/dt as shown in Fig. 2-16B. Thus, if the transformer core starts at, say, point B ($= -B_{\max}$) on the hysteresis loop of Fig. 2-15B, it moves linearly up in flux density along the path BCD at a rate given by Eq. 2-7. When it reaches $+B_{\max}$ at E, since there can be no further dB/dt, there can be no voltage across the primary (as indicated by Eq. 2-6) and, hence, no voltage across the secondary.

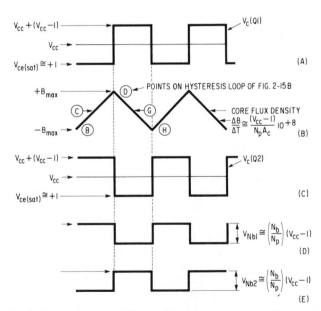

Fig. 2-16. Critical voltages and flux loci in a square-wave oscillator converter using a power transformer with a square hysteresis loop core (Fig. 2-15).

This is simply another way of stating that at E the slope of the hysteresis loop or core permeability and, hence, primary impedance have fallen to zero. The voltage across the primary thus falls to zero and the collector of Q1 is forced up toward V_{cc}. Since the voltage across N_{p1} collapses, so also does the voltage across N_{b1}.

These waveforms are shown in Fig. 2–16. Now, as the voltages across all collector and base windings collapse to zero, the current from R1, which has been diverted into the base of Q1, is partially diverted into the base of Q2, turning it partially on. Current in Q2, because of the direction of N_{p2} windings, represents negative coercive force (in the hysteresis loop of Fig. 2–15B it is the current in the left-hand plane). The core operating point moves to F and as current tends to increase in the negative coercive force direction, the core is again in a region of high permeability, and voltage can be sustained across the primary N_{p2} with the nondot end of N_{p2} negative.

With a high impedance in the Q2 collector, it starts to fall in potential as current increases. And as voltage starts to appear across N_{p2} by transformer action it appears across N_{b2} also. This provides additional drive to the base of Q2 beyond that from R1 and drives the collector Q2 negative even more rapidly. This process continues regeneratively and ends up with the collector of Q2 in saturation with $(V_{cc} - 1)$ across N_{p2}.

Since N_{p1} and N_{p2} are wound in the same direction around the transformer core, low voltage at the collector end of N_{p2} (nondot end) represents an opposite polarity voltage from the case of low voltage at the collector end of N_{p1} (dot end). Thus, in Eq. 2–7, Q1 is on when dB/dt is positive, and Q2 is on when dB/dt is negative. Hence, as Q2 turns on, core flux density starts falling linearly from $+B_{max}$ with the same dB/dt it had when Q1 was on.

Now flux moves down along the path FGH and at $-B_{max}$ the same collapse of Q2 base drive occurs as the transformer core saturates in the negative direction. The same flipover to partially turning Q1 on occurs and then a full regenerative turnon which saturates Q1 again. The core now starts moving up the hysteresis loop along BCD again.

This process continues with the transformer moving cyclically over its entire hysteresis loop — from $-B_{max}$ to $+B_{max}$ on one half cycle, then down from $+B_{max}$ to $-B_{max}$ on the next. Since dB/dt is linear, the half period can be obtained from Eq. 2–7 and is

$$\Delta T = \frac{(\Delta B N_p A_c)10^{-8}}{V_{cc} - V_{ce(sat)}} \tag{2–8}$$

and for $\Delta B = 2B_{max}$, $\Delta T = T/2$

$$\frac{T}{2} = \frac{(2B_{max}N_p A_c)10^{-8} \text{ sec}}{V_{cc} - V_{ce(sat)}} \tag{2–9}$$

The operating frequency in hertz is

$$f = \frac{1}{T} = \frac{(V_{cc} - V_{ce(sat)})10^{+8}}{4B_{max}N_p A_c} \tag{2–10}$$

Since the primary turns N_p and the core area A_c are fixed, the square-wave oscillator frequency depends only on V_{cc}, $V_{ce(sat)}$, and B_{max}, but B_{max} is a function

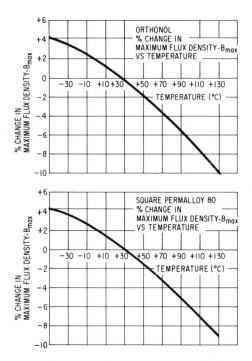

Fig. 2–17. Percent change in maximum flux density with temperature for commonly used tape-wound cores. (*Courtesy* Magnetics, Inc.)

of the transformer core material alone and is fairly independent of temperature (Figs. 2–17 and 2–18). For the usual core $V_{cc} \gg V_{ce(\text{sat})}$ and $V_{ce(\text{sat})} \cong 1.0 \pm 0.2$ for a large range of collector currents and temperatures. Then to a close approximation

$$f = \frac{(V_{cc} - 1)10^{+8}}{4B_{\max}N_p A_c} \text{ Hz}$$

And for constant V_{cc}, frequency will be constant, although not synchronous, with any system frequency.

The square-wave power oscillator is thus a simple, self-contained dc/dc power converter. It obviates the need for a separate base drive circuit, which is usually required at the input of a driven square-wave power amplifier.

2.4.3 Two-Transformer, Square-Wave Power Oscillator[5]

The idealized waveforms of Fig. 2–16 do not show a significant drawback of the single-transformer, square-wave oscillator. This drawback arises from the fact that a fundamental part of the design permits the transformer core to saturate momentarily at the end of each conducting half cycle. This fixes the end of each half period. At the instant of saturation, the transformer primary impedance

[5] J. L. Jensen: An Improved Square Wave Oscillator Circuit. *Transactions IRE,* Vol. CT4-#3, September 1957.

HYSTERSIS CURVE

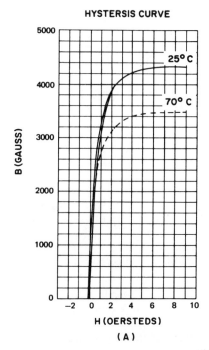

Fig. 2–18. Maximum flux density in ferrites varies more with temperature than it does in tape-wound cores. Hysteresis curves for (A) 3B7 ferrite and (B) 3C8 ferrite. (*Courtesy* Ferroxcube Corp.)

HYSTERESIS CURVE

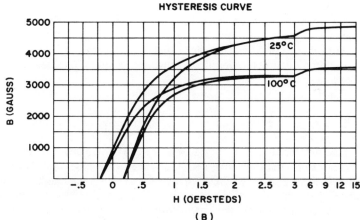

suddenly drops to zero, causing a steep rise in collector current. Although core saturation greatly reduces the collector-to-base winding coupling and removes the base drive, the "on" collector remains partly on until the stored base charge is fully swept out. There is thus a low-impedance path directly from V_{cc} to ground through the saturated primary and the collector of the "off" transistor that is turning off slowly.

This is shown in Fig. 2–19. The collector current spike at the end of each conducting half cycle can be many times the value just prior to core saturation. Although it occurs mostly at the low collector-to-emitter saturation voltage, it persists during the slowly rising collector voltage at the end of the storage time.

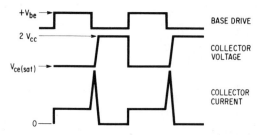

Fig. 2–19. In a single-transformer, square-wave oscillator, high collector current spikes occur at end of each conducting half cycle as the core saturates.

This results in a spike of transistor power dissipation, which can be a significant fraction of the total transistor dissipation. For sufficiently long storage and turn-off times, and a high duty cycle resulting from high frequency operation, the spike can cause transistor failure.

The two-transformer, square-wave oscillator, which has no such high current collector spike, is shown in Fig. 2–20. In this, the Jensen circuit, the high current spike is avoided by not permitting the main power transformer T2 to saturate. It is designed as a linear transformer with a core area and number of primary turns such that in a half period the total flux excursion is safely less than $2B_{max}$ (Fig. 2–15B). Since the core does not saturate, the impedance at the collector throughout each half cycle remains high – the parallel impedance of the transformer magnetizing inductance and secondary impedance as reflected to the primary.

However, transformer T1 has a square hysteresis loop core and is permitted to saturate and determine the half period in much the same way as the saturating power transformer of Fig. 2–15A.

The circuit has a number of significant advantages. First, since T2 does not saturate, there is no high current spike at the end of each conducting half cycle, efficiency is improved, and possibly destructive stresses on the power transistors are avoided.

Second, the total flux excursion in T2 can be reduced to a considerably lower value than saturation flux density. Since core losses vary roughly as $B_{max}^{1.6}$ (Figs. 2–5 and 2–6), operating T2 at a peak flux density of one-half its saturation value will reduce core losses by a factor of three. Since T1 has a much smaller core because it must supply the much lower base currents, its core losses are insignificant.

A final advantage of the two-transformer circuit is that adjustment of R_{fb} affords a simple means for varying the operating frequency. The circuit works as follows:

Positive feedback to maintain oscillations is from the output collectors via R_{fb} and the primary of T1 to the T1 secondary and back into the transistor bases. The polarity of T1 windings is as shown by the dots in Fig. 2–20. If, say, Q1 is off, Q2 on, the collector end of R_{fb} is at $2V_{cc}$, the collector end of N_{p1} is at $V_{ce(sat)}$ or about +1 V. From the dot orientation, the dot end of N_{s2} is positive and supplies enough current via R_{b2} to keep Q2 on and in saturation, as initially assumed.

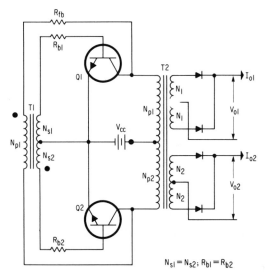

Fig. 2-20. A two-transformer, square-wave converter that avoids high-current spikes of Fig. 2-19. T2 is not permitted to saturate; frequency is determined by saturating transformer T1.

There is a unique voltage across N_{p1} that drives it between the negative and positive saturation flux densities ($-B_{max}$ and $+B_{max}$ of Fig. 2-15B). This unique voltage (V_{np1}) can be set at any desired value by choice of secondary current and turns ratio in T1 and the value of R_{fb}. With a unique voltage across N_{p1} and the primary turns and core area of T1 chosen, the half period is fixed by the fundamental magnetic relation of Eq. 2-6. The half period is given by Eq. 2-9 as

$$\frac{T}{2} = \frac{(2B_{max}N_{p1}A_{c1})10^{-8}}{V_{np1}} \text{ sec}$$

where A_{c1} is the core area of T1 and V_{np1} is the selected voltage across N_{p1}.

The circuit of Fig. 2-15 does not show one essential feature, a means to start the oscillator and swing it past "dead center," the point where one transistor has just turned off and the other must be switched on. Without such a "start" feature, the oscillations may never commence at initial application of V_{cc} at high output current or low temperature where transistor gain is low, or the circuit may hang up and stop oscillating at the end of one conducting half cycle. There are a variety of such starting circuits. Their merits and drawbacks will be discussed in detail in Chap. 8.

Design Procedures for Two-Transformer, Square-Wave Oscillators

A complete design procedure for the circuit of Fig. 2-17 must include methods of selecting specific magnetic core sizes and core materials for T1 and T2. This will be only touched on here but treated in more detail in Chap. 8. The step-by-step design choices are as follows:

Operating Frequency This must be the first decision. Higher frequencies result in smaller transformers but in lower efficiencies because of "overlap" switching losses discussed in Sects. 2.1.3, 2.1.7, and 2.1.9. A good compromise is 20–25 kHz with present-day transistors.

Output Transformer Primary Turns From Sect. 2.1.8 and Fig. 2–5, it has been determined that ferrite cores are most efficient above 10 kHz. Ferrites for low-loss power application (Ferroxcube 3C8 or Magnetics, Inc., J material) have saturation flux density at 100°C of about 2,500 G. To keep core losses down and ensure T2 does not saturate, its core is operated at a maximum flux density of 1,500 G. It can be seen from Fig. 2–6 that for Ferroxcube 3C8 core losses at 1,500 G. and 20 kHz are only 26 mW/cc.

Then, from Eq. 2–8, for operating frequency of f_o (period $= 1/f_o = T_o$),

$$N_{p2} = \frac{(V_p \Delta T)10^{+8}}{A_c \Delta B} \tag{2–11}$$

Here, ΔB is the total permitted flux excursion in gauss (from $-1,500$ to $+1,500$ G) in a ΔT of a half period with a core area of A_c in centimeters. Then for $V_p = V_{cc} - V_{ce(sat)} \cong V_{cc} - 1$,

$$\begin{aligned} N_{p2} &= \frac{(V_{cc} - 1)(T_o/2)10^{+8}}{2A_c(1,500)} \\ &= \frac{(V_{cc} - 1)(T_o)10^{+8}}{4(1,500)A_c} \text{ turns} \end{aligned} \tag{2–12}$$

Total Collector Current Generally, output voltages and maximum load currents at each output are fixed by the design requirements. Rectifier diode drops for a large range of currents will be 0.9 V. Since dc (Fig. 2–20) output voltage with square-wave drive is one rectifier diode drop below the peak secondary voltages, each secondary voltage is known, i.e., $V_{n1} = (V_{o1} + 0.9)$, $V_{n2} = (V_{o2} + 0.9)$, etc. Since $V_{np2} \cong V_{cc} - 1$, this fixes the turns ratio for each secondary, and with N_{p2} fixed by Eq. 2–12, the number of turns on each secondary is determined.

Now the total collector current due to loads alone is the sum of all the known secondary currents reflected by the turns ratio into the primary, i.e.,

$$I_{c1} = I_{o1}\left(\frac{N_1}{N_{p2}}\right) + I_{o2}\left(\frac{N_2}{N_{p2}}\right) + \cdots \tag{2–13}$$

The total collector current is the above sum of the reflected load currents plus the transformer's magnetizing current, which is given from the fundamental magnetic relation:

$$H_c = \frac{4\pi N_p I_m}{10 L_c} \tag{2–14}$$

where H_c is the coercive force in oersteds, N_p is the number of primary turns, I_m is the magnetizing current in amperes, and L_c is the mean magnetic length of path in centimeters.

Once a core is selected, L_c and H_c may be obtained from data sheets and I_m can be calculated. In most cases, I_m will be less than 5% of the total reflected load current and can be neglected. Nevertheless, total collector current is

$$I_{ct} = I_{c1} + I_m \tag{2–15}$$

Inverter Base Current   Base drive must be sufficient to saturate the transistors for the minimum transistor gain $h_{fe(min)}$ and the maximum value of collector current I_{ct}. Thus, the minimum base current could be $I_b = I_{ct}/h_{fe(min)}$. For most transistors, and collector currents in such applications, minimum values of h_{fe} as large as 30–50 are obtainable. Faster turnon is achieved by using higher base drive than given by the above relation. Transistor data sheets usually quote turn-on speed at a base drive one-tenth of the collector current. This ensures a fast turnon even with worst-case transistors and degraded h_{fe}.

Saturating Transformer Secondary Voltage/Currents   Base-to-emitter voltages for a large range of base currents sufficient to saturate the transistor will be 0.9 ± 0.2 V. If in Fig. 2–20 the voltage drop across R_{b1} is made large compared to 0.9 V, the ± 0.2 V ambiguity due to transistor and temperature variations will not change the base current significantly. Thus, at the base current of $I_{ct}/10$, V_{rb1} is chosen about $3V_{be}$ or about $3(0.9) = 2.7$ V. This makes $V_{ns1} = 2.7 + 0.9 = 3.6$ V, or rounded upward, 4.0 V.

At V_{ns1} of 4 V, V_{be} of 0.9 V, and V_{rb1} of 3.1 V, a change of 0.2 V in V_{be} would cause a change in base current of only 0.2/3.1 or 6.5%; this is adequately low.

Thus, for a nominal V_{rb1} of 3.1 V, the value of R_{b1} is

$$R_{b1} = \frac{3.1}{I_{ct}/10} = \frac{31}{I_{ct}} \text{ ohms} \qquad \text{(for } I_{ct} \text{ in amperes)} \qquad (2\text{--}16)$$

At V_{ns1} of 4 V, the reverse base voltage when a secondary half goes negative is -4 V. This is sufficiently safe, since most power transistors can take a reverse base voltage of 5–7 V.

Saturating Transformer Primary Voltage, Current, and Feedback Resistance   The design is completed with a choice of R_{fb}, N_{p1}, and a T1 core with specific area such as to cause the operating frequency to be that selected above.

The voltage across N_{p1} will be chosen first. There is considerable freedom in its choice. Once it is chosen, since V_{ns1} is 4 V, the turns ratio V_{np1}/V_{ns1} is fixed. The primary current is also fixed, since the base current selected is $I_{ct/10}$. Since V_{np1} and I_{rfb} are fixed, and the voltage across R_{fb} and N_{p1} in series is $2V_{cc} - V_{ce(sat)} \cong 2V_{cc} - 1$, R_{fb} may be determined.

The voltage across N_{p1} should not be taken as too large a fraction of $2V_{cc} - 1$. For if V_{np1} is $>> V_{R_{fb}}$, when the primary of T1 saturates, only the small value of R_{fb} will be bridged from collector to collector. Then the high-current spike we attempted to avoid will occur again.

Although there is much latitude in V_{np1}, it is usually chosen so that the total voltage across R_{fb} and N_{p1} ($= 2V_{cc} - 1$) is shared equally between these elements. Thus, the transformer turns ratio is

$$N_{p1}/N_{s1} = V_{np1}/V_{ns1} = \tfrac{1}{2}(2V_{cc} - 1)/4 \qquad (2\text{--}17)$$

Hence, the current in R_{fb} is (neglecting primary magnetizing current)

$$I_{R_{fb}} = \left(\frac{N_{s1}}{N_{p1}}\right)\left(\frac{I_{ct}}{10}\right)$$

or $$I_{R_{fb}} = \left(\frac{8}{2V_{cc} - 1}\right)\left(\frac{I_{ct}}{10}\right) = \frac{0.8 I_{ct}}{2V_{cc} - 1} \qquad (2\text{--}18)$$

And
$$R_{fb} = \frac{(2V_{cc} - 1)/2}{0.8I_{ct}/(2V_{cc} - 1)} = \frac{(2V_{cc} - 1)^2}{1.6I_{ct}}$$

$$(2-19)$$

where R_{fb} is in ohms, I_{ct} in amperes, and V_{cc} in volts.

Saturating Transformer Core Selection and Turns Calculation   The T1 primary turns can now be calculated and a core selected. From the fundamental magnetic relation of Eq. 2–6,

$$N_{p1}A_c = \left(\frac{V_{p1}\Delta T}{\Delta B}\right) 10^{+8}$$

where V_{p1} is the voltage across primary $= (2V_{cc} - 1)/2$ V, ΔT is the half period of selected frequency $(= 1/2f_o$ sec), and ΔB is twice the saturation flux density of the selected core material $(= 2B_{max}$ gauss). Then

$$N_{p1}A_c = \left(\frac{2V_{cc} - 1}{2}\right)\left(\frac{1}{2f_o}\right)\left(\frac{1}{2B_{max}}\right) 10^{+8}$$

or
$$N_{p1}A_c = \frac{(2V_{cc} - 1) 10^{+8}}{8f_o B_{max}} \text{ turns/sq cm}$$

$$(2-20)$$

for f_o in hertz, B_{max} in gauss. From Eq. 2–20, once a core has been selected with a known area A_c in square centimeters, N_{p1} may be calculated. And finally from Eq. 2–17, N_{s1} may be calculated.

2.5   Half-Cycle, Width-Modulated Converters

In the dc/dc converter of Fig. 2–1, each transistor is on for a full half cycle and the output voltage is

$$V_o = (V_{dc} - V_{ce(sat)})(N_s/N_p) - V_d$$

For
$$V_{ce(sat)} \cong V_d = 1, V_o \cong (V_{dc} - 1)(N_s/N_p) - 1$$

Thus, the average dc output voltage depends only on V_{dc} and the turns ratio. Referring to Fig. 2–3B, the output filter need only filter out the narrow notch of width $(t_r + t_f)$ between half cycles.

An extremely useful modification (Fig. 2–21) of the conventional dc/dc converter is obtained by modulating the duration of each transistor's "on" time to some fraction of a half cycle. From Fig. 2–22, it is seen that for an "on" time of T_{on}, half period of $T/2$, the output voltage after the rectifiers is a series of pulses of amplitude

$$V_o = (V_{dc} - V_{ce(sat)})(N_s/N_p) - V_{d1}$$
$$\cong (V_{dc} - 1)(N_s/N_p) - 1$$

The pulses come at half-period intervals and are of width T_{on}. The average dc voltage is then

$$V_{dc(avg)} = [T_{on}/(T/2)][(V_{dc} - 1)(N_s/N_p) - 1]$$

Thus, for a fixed V_{dc} and turns ratio, the average or dc output voltage can be set to any desired value less than $(V_{dc} - 1)(N_s/N_p) - 1$ by simply altering the ratio of $T_{on}/(T/2)$. The voltage after the rectifier will have a square notch ex-

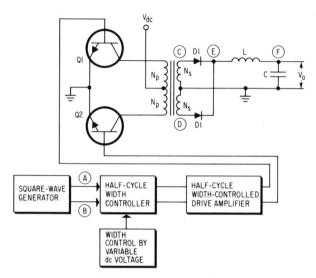

Fig. 2–21. By controlling the fraction of a half cycle that each inverter is on, average output voltage at C and D is controlled. The LC filter produces a ripple-free output at F.

tending down to zero, of width ($T/2 - T_{on}$). To smooth out this square wave of ripple, an LC filter and free-wheeling diode is added as in Fig. 1–4B and was discussed in Sect. 1.2.1. This is shown in Fig. 2–23.

As discussed in Sect. 1.2.1, the purpose of free-wheeling diode D_{fw} is to provide a path for the current in L1 to flow out to the load when neither converter transistor is on. The inductive kick at the input end of L1 drives it negative to about 1 V below ground causing diode D_{fw} to latch in. This permits the current

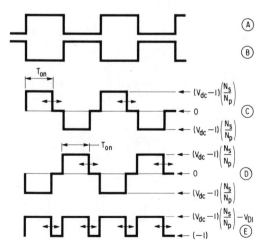

Fig. 2–22. Significant waveforms in the half-cycle, width-modulated converter of Fig. 2–21.

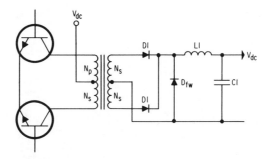

Fig. 2–23. A free-wheeling diode at the secondary output of the half-cycle, width-modulated inverter.

flowing in L1 during the "on" time to continue flowing out to the load and reduces the current drawn from C1 and hence reduces its size.

Actually, examination of Fig. 2–23 will show diode D_{fw} is not essential. If it is removed, the inductive kick at the front end of L1 will cause rectifier diodes D1 to latch in and serve the same purpose. The inductive current flows in the two half secondaries—each in series with its rectifier diode during the "off" time. Thus, diode D_{fw} can be dispensed with. If it is retained, it reduces dissipation in D1 and the secondary windings.

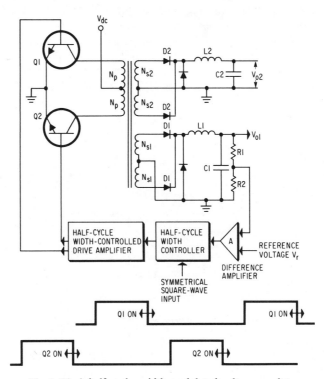

Fig. 2–24. A half-cycle, width-modulated voltage regulator.

2.5.1 Half-Cycle, Width-Modulated Converter Regulator

The addition of a negative-feedback loop to the circuit of Fig. 2–21 results in a very useful voltage regulator. This is shown in Fig. 2–24 in which the negative-feedback loop is closed around the dc output from one secondary — usually the secondary whose output must be most tightly controlled and which has the highest output current requirement.

In Fig. 2–24, a fraction of the output is sampled and compared in a differential amplifier to a reference voltage V_r. The amplified difference or dc error voltage is used to control the fraction of a half cycle during which each inverter is on. As dc input voltage decreases, or load current increases, tending to decrease output V_{o1}, the difference amplifier yields an output voltage change that increases each inverter's "on" time sufficiently to maintain a constant voltage. Similarly, a line increase or load current decrease that would tend to increase the output causes a decrease in transistor "on" time and, hence, a constant voltage. For sufficient gain (A) within the feedback loop, the output V_{o1} is

$$V_{o1} = \frac{R1 + R2}{R2} V_r = \left(\frac{T_{on}}{T/2}\right)\left[(V_{dc} - V_{ce(sat)})\left(\frac{N_{s1}}{N_p}\right) - V_{D1}\right] \quad (2\text{–}21)$$

The output V_{o1} is thus regulated against changes in V_{dc}, $V_{ce(sat)}$, or V_{D1} (load changes). Any load changes due to IR drop changes in L1 are, of course, also compensated for as the sampling resistor chain R1, R2 senses output after L1.

2.5.2 Half-Cycle, Width-Modulated Regulator Advantages

The width-controlled converter or regulator has all the advantages of the nonmodulated converter enumerated in Sect. 2.1. In brief, these advantages stem from the ability to generate multiple, independent, low-impedance output voltages from a single prime voltage source. In the conventional converter all these output voltages are proportional to the dc input voltage. To keep all output voltages independent of line input voltages, the input voltage must be preregulated in the nonwidth-modulated conventional converter.

Since all output voltages have low output impedances, this does offer a fairly satisfactory way of keeping a multiplicity of voltages constant, i.e., by simply preregulating the dc input to a conventional converter. This, however, requires handling the main power twice — once in the preregulator and once again in the nonwidth-modulated converter. With internal losses in both these elements, overall efficiency is lowered.

In the width-modulated converter regulators, the output voltage V_{o1} is regulated against line input changes. Any other dc output voltages obtained from other secondaries on the same power transformer are, hence, also regulated against line changes, since the duty cycle $T_{on}/(T/2)$ is varied to such a way as to make V_{o1} independent of V_{dc}. Thus, any other secondary output voltage such as V_{o2} is given by

$$V_{o2} = \left(\frac{T_{on}}{T/2}\right)\left[(V_{dc} - V_{ce(sat)})\left(\frac{N_{s2}}{N_p}\right) - V_d\right] \quad (2\text{–}22)$$

From Eq. 2–21

$$\frac{T_{on}}{T/2} = \frac{V_{o1}}{(V_{dc} - V_{ce(sat)})(N_{s1}/N_p) - V_{D1}}$$

and
$$V_{o2} = V_{o1} \frac{(V_{dc} - V_{ce(sat)})(N_{s2}/N_p) - V_{D1}}{(V_{dc} - V_{ce(sat)})(N_{s1}/N_p) - V_{D1}}$$

In most cases, the first term of either numerator or denominator in the above is much greater than V_{D1}. Then $V_{o2} = (N_{s2}/N_{s1})(V_{o1})$. And since V_{o1} is regulated against changes in V_{dc}, so is V_{o2}.

It should be noted that there will be a slight interaction between output voltages. Thus, in Fig. 2–24, a load current change, say, an increase in V_{o1}, will still keep V_{o1} constant because of the negative feedback. A current increase will cause a slight increase in diode (D1) drop and the IR drop in L1. This is sensed by the sampling resistors as an output voltage drop and consequently $T_{on}/(T/2)$ of Eq. 2–21 must increase to keep the output constant. Since $T_{on}/(T/2)$ increases in Eq. 2–22 also, V_{o2} will increase.

Since load current in V_{o2} has not changed, the increase in duty cycle is not accompanied as in V_{o1} by an increased drop in the diodes or the inductance. Thus, an increase or decrease in load current from V_{o1} results in increases and decreases, respectively, of the output voltage of any slaved secondaries such as V_{o2}. With low diode and inductor impedances, this effect is generally only about 0.1 or 0.2 V. Output voltages of the slaved secondaries as V_{o2} will, of course, vary with load-current changes in those secondaries, since there is no feedback around them. However, with the easily attainable low-output impedance offered by high-current rectifier diodes (Sect. 2.1.6) the effect can be kept to about 0.1–0.2 V, which is adequate for many purposes.

PROBLEMS

2.1 Considering only dc losses in the rectifier diode and inverter transistors, what is the efficiency of a converter generating 5, 10, 15, 20, 25, 30, and 100 output from the following source voltages: $+12$, $+30$, $+90$, and $+100$?

2.2 At 30-V input and 5-V output, what is a converter efficiency using Schottky rectifiers with 0.5-V forward drop? Consider only dc losses in rectifier diodes and transistors. Under the same conditions, what is efficiency at 100-V input and 5-V output?

2.3 A filter capacitor at the output of a dc/dc converter is required to filter out the commutation notch whose base width is 2 μsec. At output voltages of 5, 15, and 30 V, what is the size of required filter capacity for ripple output of 0.5 and 1% of output voltages for load currents of 1 A, 5 A, and 10 A?

2.4 Using 1N3879 rectifier diode in a dc/dc square-wave converter, assuming the primary drive voltage remained constant, what would the dc output change, at a junction temperature of 25°C, be for a load change from 0.5 to 3.0 A? From 1.0 to 5 A? What are the diode forward voltages at 0.5, 1, 3, and 5 A? What are the corresponding voltage drops at 100°C junction temperature?

What are forward voltage drops of the 1N3889 12-A type at 0.5, 1, 3, and 5 A at 150°C junction temperature?

2.5 What are total core losses for Ferroxcube cores 1F10, 144T500, 4229, 783E608 (Figs. 8–1, 8–2, and 8–6) operated at peak flux densities of 1,500, 2,000, and 2,500 G and at 10, 20, and 30 kHz using 3C8 material?

2.6 What nominal voltage rating should a transistor in the push–pull inverter circuit of Fig. 2–1 with nominal input voltage of 30 V have assuming $\pm 10\%$ steady-state input voltage tolerances, +20% turn-off spike, derating to 80% of the vendor's maximum voltage rating?

What should the nominal rating be assuming a preregulated input of 105 V constant to ±1% assuming again turn-off spike of +20%, derating to 80% of vendor's maximum value?

2.7 Assume a dc/dc converter operating from a dc input of 105 V ± 1% and generating outputs of +5 V at 5 A, ±15 V at 1 A, and ±30 V at 6 A. Assuming 1-V rectifier diode and transistor saturation voltage drops, what is the peak transistor collector current?

2.8 What is the maximum junction temperature of a transistor with 15 W dissipation, 100°C maximum case temperature, and a thermal resistance of 2°C per watt?

What is the maximum permissible transistor dissipation at 100°C case temperature if maximum junction temperature is to be 175°C?

2.9 Assume a transistor with a reverse-bias, second-breakdown stored energy rating of 2.5 mJ. With an inductive load of 50 μH in a switching mode application, what is the maximum permissible collector current just prior to turnoff?

2.10 Consider the half-bridge converter of Fig. 2–14 operating from a 300-V supply voltage at 100 W output power with a converter frequency of 25 kHz. What capacitors are required to keep a 50-kHz ripple at the output down to 2% peak to peak?

2.11 Assume a dc/dc converter as in Fig. 2–1. Under fault conditions, assume there can be a 1,000-μsec time interval during which current can flow while there is 200 V across the device. What current will cause the transistor to go into second breakdown?

2.12 Assume a single-transistor square-wave oscillator as in Fig. 2–15A. With a nominal input voltage of 160 V, a maximum flux density of 7,500 G (Square Permalloy 80 type wound core) what must be the product of (primary turns) (core area in centimeters) for an oscillator frequency of 10 kHz?

2.13 Assume a two-transformer square-wave oscillator as in Fig. 2–20. The output transformer T2 uses the 4229 ferrite-cup core of Fig. 8–2. Assume a frequency of 25 kHz ±10% and a constant supply voltage of 105 V.

    a. How many turns must there be per half primary to avoid exceeding a peak flux density of 1,500 G at the lowest frequency?

    b. At 3 V per turn, what would be the peak flux density at 25 kHz?

    c. Assuming a 1-V drop in the rectifier diode, how many turns would be required for an output of 5 V with 35 turns per half primary?

    d. With 25 A of output current at the 5-V output point, what is the peak collector current (neglecting magnetizing current)?

    e. At a base overdrive factor of 10, what is the base current in Q1 or Q2?

    f. Assuming 8 V peak to peak (end to center tap) at the secondary of T1, what is the value of base current resistor R_{b1}?

    g. Assuming half the peak collector-to-collector voltage appears across the primary of T2, what is the primary/secondary turns ratio, T1 primary current, and value of the feedback resistor R_{fb}?

    h. Assuming Square Permalloy 80 core material (saturation flux density, 7,500 G) for the T1 core, what is the product of (primary turns) (core area) for 25 kHz operating frequency?

3

Building Block Assembly of Compound Regulating Systems

3.0   Introduction

In the previous chapters, the basic building blocks of modern power supply systems were presented. The most useful of these building blocks are the series-switch step-down switching regulator (Fig. 1–5), the shunt-switch step-up regulator (Fig. 1–6B), the dc/dc square-wave converter (Figs. 2–1 and 2–13), the half-cycle, width-modulated inverter (Fig. 2–24), and the series-pass regulator (Fig. 1–1).

The usual power supply or power supply system is composed of a multiplicity of output voltages each having its own output current requirements and line and load regulation. The prime power source may be 50-, 60-, or 400-Hz ac and single- or three-phase in a delta or wye configuration. The supply may be required to work at only a single-line frequency, say, 50, 60, or 400 Hz, or it may be required to work equally well at all these frequencies with no circuit change. Further, the supply may be required to work from either a 115-, 208-, or 220-V ac line voltage with either no circuit change or a simple internal linkage change.

All these requirements can be met with different combinations and permutations of the above basic building blocks. Systems can be devised with standard electrically and mechanically configured building blocks requiring only a minimum custom circuit change to fit a large variety of applications. Or, more usually, each building block is custom designed electrically and mechanically for each different use, and the building-block concept is still useful in devising the optimum block diagram for a power supply system.

There is generally a large variety of objectives in choosing from alternative combinations of the basic building blocks. The usual objectives are to maximize efficiency and to minimize volume or weight, and, of course, cost. Ease of maintenance, repair, and fault diagnosis can be achieved by standard electrical and mechanical modularization of the basic building blocks.

In this chapter it will be shown how the basic building blocks of the previous chapters may be assembled in various combinations to achieve most of the above objectives. The treatment here will involve block diagrams only.

74

Subsequent chapters will take up detailed circuit design of the individual building blocks and their organization into complete power supply systems.

3.1 General Classes of Regulating Systems

Older types of voltage regulators whose prime input was an ac line source had a simple standard block diagram. These were composed of a 60-Hz power transformer having one or multiple secondaries, each followed by a full-wave or bridge rectifier and a series-pass regulator. The poor efficiency of the series-pass regulator (especially at low voltages as seen in Fig. 1–3), the size and weight of the input power transformer, and the size of the large filter capacitor required ahead of the series-pass regulator made this a reliable but bulky device.

Generally, such older-type voltage regulators had load power densities (output load power per cubic inch of volume) that ranged from 0.2 to 0.4 W/cubic inch. Efficiencies, taking power transformers and rectifier losses and filter ripple effects into account, were considerably lower than indicated in Fig. 1–3. They were usually in the region of 25–40% for supplies whose greatest output power was at voltages in the range of 5–25 V.

With the types of regulator systems possible with the aforementioned building blocks, load power densities of 1–2 W or sometimes up to 4 W/cubic inch are possible. Efficiencies generally range in the region of 65–80% and can achieve 95%.

The regulator systems considered herein generally contain a dc/dc voltage converter as the central element and can be grouped into six distinct classes as shown in Figs. 3–1 to 3–6.

Prime power for these supplies is the ac power line, which may be 50-, 60-, or 400-Hz and single- or three-phase. None of these six classes requires a bulky line frequency power transformer. There is thus an immediate space and weight saving. By rectifying directly off the ac power line, the supplies work equally well at 50, 60, or 400 Hz. This is an important consideration in military applications, since often the prime power source is a mobile or aircraft 400-Hz generator, but frequently the same power supplies are to be used in fixed installations or depots where only 60 Hz is available. Independence of line power frequency is important also when commercial equipment is to be sold without change either in the 60-Hz American or 50-Hz European market.

The six classes of power supply systems shown in Figs. 3–1 to 3–6 are still identifiable as having essentially the same block diagram when the prime power is dc — usually 28 V as in aircraft, submarine, missile, or spacecraft power systems. At the lower dc input, some block diagrams become preferable. These six classes of regulating systems will be discussed in the following sections.

3.1.1 Preregulator-Driven dc/ac Converter with Open-Loop Secondary Outputs

This, as seen in Fig. 3–1, is made up of a dc/ac square-wave converter fed from a dc preregulator, which is fed from a rectifier and filter directly off the ac power line. Rectifiers and filters after each of the dc/ac converter secondaries yield the desired voltages at low output impedance. There is no feedback after the input to the dc/ac converter.

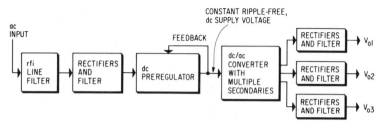

Fig. 3–1. Preregulated converter with open-loop outputs.

The preregulator may be the series-switch step-down switching regulator of Sect. 1.2, the shunt-switch step-up regulator of Sect. 1.3, the half-cycle, width-modulated inverter of Sect. 2.5, or the series-pass regulator of Sect. 1.1.

The dc preregulator produces a constant dc output voltage, independent of ac line or load variations. Since the square-wave ac output from the dc/ac converter is proportional to the dc input voltage, its output is as constant as the dc input. Because the ac output is square wave, it is easily filtered and the dc output after rectification remains only one diode drop below the peak of the ac square wave.

For sufficiently high base drive of the converter transistors, they remain in saturation and the output impedance after rectification is very low, as discussed in Sect. 2.1.6. The rectified dc output changes only slightly with load current, since the rectifier diode drops and the inverter collector saturation voltage are relatively constant with current.

With a preregulator output that can easily be kept constant to $\pm 0.1\%$ for ac line changes of $\pm 10\%$ output, dc voltages in Fig. 3–1 will change significantly only with changes in load current. Such output voltage changes can be kept to within ± 0.15 V because of the low output impedance of the rectifier diodes. This is sufficiently constant for many applications.

This system is simple, requires relatively few components, and yields many relatively constant outputs with only one feedback loop. The feedback loop has few phase-shifting components (usually a single LC or RC phase shifter) and is, hence, easy to stabilize against oscillations.

As discussed above, rectification takes place directly off the ac line input, and thus the supply works equally well at 50, 60, or 400 Hz. But since the ripple output from the line rectifier–filter combination is greatest at the lowest line frequency, the detailed circuit design of the preregulator must be able to cope with the largest amplitude ripple at the lowest line frequency.

3.1.2 Preregulator-Driven dc/ac Converter with Rectified Secondary Feedback (Fig. 3–2)

Here the building block configuration is the same as in Fig. 3–1. But the feedback to the preregulator is taken from one of the rectified outputs of the dc/ac square-wave converter. The output from which feedback is taken is the one which must be kept most constant in voltage. This usually is the 5-V logic supply in computer-type systems. With sufficient gain in the feedback loop, the output from which feedback is taken can be as constant as desired over the required line and load variations.

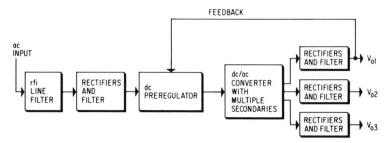

Fig. 3-2. Preregulated converter with one output feedback and slaved additional outputs.

Now the feedback operates to keep V_{o1} constant for changes in ac input voltage. In doing this, it must keep the output voltage from the preregulator constant, since the only way V_{o1} can remain constant as the line input changes is to keep the dc input to the dc/ac converter constant. And with constant dc input to the dc/ac converter, all other secondary voltages from the converter are constant for line changes alone, since they are proportional to the dc input voltage.

Thus, using only a single feedback loop, V_{o1} is kept constant at any desired voltage level for both line and load changes. And all other rectified outputs V_{o2}, V_{o3}, etc. ("slaved" outputs), are kept constant for line changes and relatively constant for load changes.

Slaved Output Absolute dc Voltage Levels

The scheme of Fig. 3-2 has the drawback that the absolute dc voltage level at the output cannot be set too accurately because the number of turns on any secondary winding in a toroidal or U–U core can be increased or decreased only in steps of one.[1] Thus, if N_{o1} and N_{on} are the secondary turns of the V_{o1} and the V_{on} outputs and V_{D1} and V_{Dn} are the rectifier diode drops for these respective outputs, then:

$$V_{on} = (N_{on}/N_{o1})(V_{o1} + V_{D1}) - V_{Dn} \tag{3-1}$$

It will be seen in Sect. 8.8.1 that in the majority of cases, for inverter square-wave frequencies of 5–30 kHz, the number of volts per turn on any windings ranges between 1 and 3. Thus, any slaved square-wave secondary voltage (before the rectifiers) can change only in increments of 1–3 V, and from Eq. 3–1 it is seen that any slaved dc output voltage depends on its own rectifier diode (V_{Dn}) drop and also on the drop in the rectifier diode (V_{D1}) inside the feedback loop.

Now the V_{o1} output voltage can be set as accurately as desired by selecting the fraction of the output voltage to be fed back to the preregulator. This sets the dc output voltage from the preregulator to give exactly the desired output at V_{o1}, and it also fixes the dc output voltage at any secondary according to Eq. 3–1. If the resulting output is not what is desired, changing the number of turns

---

[1] In E cores or cup cores, a half turn is possible with a wire linking the entire center leg and only one leg (in the E–E core) or half the periphery (in a cup core).

on any winding by 1 will change its output by the 1–3 V/turn characteristic of the transformer. The worst case, of course, is when a desired output voltage level falls exactly between voltage levels resulting from one-turn changes in the secondary. Thus, the most any slave output can be from any desired level is one-half the volts-per-turn characteristic of the transformer or usually 0.5–1.5 V. In the E–E or cup core, in which a half turn is possible, the maximum departure from a desired voltage is half this amount.

Hence, when a specific voltage level is significant (say, as 5.00 V for computer logic), this is a significant drawback for the slave outputs. But since the 5-V output can be used as the V_{o1} feedback point, it can be set exactly. In most other cases, an exact dc output level is not as important as having low output changes around a not too critical absolute level. As has been indicated above, output changes on the slaves can be kept to ±0.15 V for ±10% line changes and a large range of load changes.

Transient Response

An additional shortcoming of the scheme shown in Fig. 3–2 is that it has poorer transient response to line or load changes than the scheme shown in Fig. 3–1. This arises from the fact that the feedback loop is around more phase-shifting elements in Fig. 3–2. There is an LC phase shift (for series-switch preregulator) or an RC phase shift (for a series-pass preregulator) in the preregulator switching block.

The rectifier-filter after the dc/ac converter causes less phase shift at a given frequency than the preregulator filter. This is because the dc/ac converter output is square wave, which requires only a capacitor or an LC filter to provide adequate filtering.

Despite the low phase shift of the second filter, at any given frequency, the total phase shift is the sum of shift due to each filter alone. Thus, the frequency at which the total shift around the loop is 180° is lower in the two-filter loop of Fig. 3–2 than in the single-filter loop of Fig. 3–1. So to avoid oscillations at the frequency at which the phase shift is −180°, a phase-correcting network usually must be added within the loop. This may further reduce the frequency response before feedback.

The end result is that the frequency response after feedback is significantly lower in Fig. 3–2 than it is in Fig. 3–1. Step changes in line or load generally cause abrupt changes in output voltages with an exponential recovery to steady-state value. Because of the poorer frequency response of Fig. 3–2, its initial step change in output will be larger and its recovery time to normal will be longer than the scheme of Fig. 3–1.

Exact values of the initial step changes in output and recovery time may be calculated only after the filter characteristics are specified.

3.1.3 Unregulated dc/ac Converter with Postregulators Following Secondary Rectification (Fig. 3–3)

Here the dc/ac square-wave converter is operated directly off the line rectifier. For multiple output voltages, the dc/ac converter (Fig. 2–1 or 2–13) has multiple secondaries, each followed by its own rectifier and either series-pass (Fig. 1–1) or switching regulator (Fig. 1–5 or 1–6B). Such a scheme provides very good line and load regulation and independent absolute dc voltage setting capa-

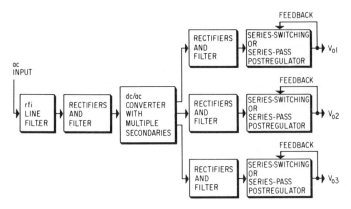

Fig. 3–3. Unregulated input converter with postregulated outputs.

bility at each output. Transient response is better than the scheme in Fig. 3–2, since the feedback loop encompasses fewer (generally over one) phase-shifting elements. The scheme is usable mainly for low output power (output current under about 0.5 A), with series-pass postregulators or for relatively few (under four) separate output voltages with switching postregulators.

Since the dc/ac converter is operated off the unregulated line rectifier, its rectified dc outputs will have the same percentage change in average dc output voltage as the ac line voltage. Thus, a $\pm 10\%$ change in ac line voltage will result in a $\pm 10\%$ change in average dc output from any rectifier. Further, the rectified dc line voltage will have a certain percentage ripple dependent on its filter capacitors and output current. The rectified dc after the dc/ac converter will have the same percentage ripple.

Thus, if the postregulators are series-pass elements, which must have no less than 1–2 V across them at all times, the average value of the dc voltage at the dc/ac rectifier outputs at nominal line voltage must be sufficiently high so that at low ac (say, -10%) line voltage and at the bottom of the ripple triangle, there are still 2 V across the series-pass element. Then, if the rectifier output voltage at nominal ac input is set sufficiently high to meet this condition, a problem arises at $+10\%$ high ac input, since now, the nominal voltage having been set high enough so that at 10% low line the dc input is not too low, at 10% high input there is considerably more than 2 V across the series-pass element. This results in very poor efficiency at high line voltage, since the efficiency is $V_o/V_{in(max)}$.

Hence, series-pass elements in the scheme of Fig. 3–3 are usable only at relatively low output currents when the poor efficiency results in still adequately low internal dissipation: $I_o(V_{in(max)} - V_o)$.

The scheme of Fig. 3–3 is more attractive when the postregulators are series-switch step-down or shunt-switch step-up regulators. Since such switching regulator efficiency is independent of the raw dc input (output of the rectifier–filter following the dc/ac converter), there is no disadvantage in permitting high dc voltages at input to the postregulator.

Further, since the switching regulator regulates against line frequency ripple at its input just as well as it does against slow variations in the average dc voltages (resulting from ac line variations within its $\pm 10\%$ tolerance), it can permit larger amplitude input ripple. This permits the use of a smaller filter capacitor at the output of the ac line rectifier than if series-pass postregulators were used. Since this line filter capacitor generally occupies a large fraction of the total-power supply space, it is desirable to minimize its size.

The main disadvantage of the scheme of Fig. 3–3 is, of course, its extravagant use of components. It uses one series-pass or switching regulator and one feedback loop for each output voltage, but up to three or four outputs this is not a significant drawback. The feedback control circuitry can in most instances be identical for each output, and, for a large range of output currents, the series-pass or switching regulator transistor and its associated circuits can be the same for each output. Thus, each output voltage can be generated with a module that is electrically and mechanically identical. The only difference is the resistor sampling network determining the exact output voltage.

Selection of dc/ac Converter Type

Use of the raw, unregulated dc to drive the dc/ac converter narrows the choice of the type of converter used. In the schemes of Figs. 3–1 and 3–2, in which a step-down preregulator is interposed between the rectified line voltage and the dc/ac converter, the dc voltage to the converter could be set at an arbitrary low value, and there is no problem of finding transistors with adequately high collector voltage ratings.

Now in Sect. 2.1.9, the maximum collector voltage rating of the two-transistor push–pull inverter was discussed. It was shown that the specification on V_{ceo} (V_{cbo} if the transistor base-emitter impedance is 100 ohms or less or if the base-emitter junction is reverse biased in the off state) should be 3.3 times the nominal dc supply voltage. This includes allowances for the off collector voltage to be twice the dc supply voltage, a tolerance of $\pm 10\%$ on the dc supply voltage, a turn-off spike of $\pm 20\%$, and derating the manufacturer's voltage rating to 80% of his maximum allowable value.

In Fig. 3–3, the filter after the line rectifier is usually a simple capacitive filter. The peak voltage at the output of the rectifier is then a 2-V drop (for a bridge rectifier) below the peak of the ac sine wave. For a nominal ac input voltage of 115 V, the peak dc output is $1.41(V_{rms}) - 2V_{diode} = (1.41)(115) - 2 = 160$ V. And if the transistor rating as discussed above is to be $3.3(V_{dc})$, then a device with a rating of $(3.3)(160)$ or 528 V is required.

The choice of transistors with a voltage rating equal to or greater than 528 V is not very large. The device must have the voltage rating and a maximum current rating corresponding to the resulting input power. Further, it must have adequate switching speed and a sufficiently high current gain (β) at the current corresponding to the maximum input power.

Although there are some transistors meeting the above requirements, the selection at lower V_{ceo} or V_{cbo} is much greater. If the inverter is the four-transistor bridge of Fig. 2–13, the maximum collector voltage need only be equal to the maximum supply voltage – not twice that value. Thus, the bridge inverter of Fig. 2–13 requires transistors with V_{cbo} ratings of 528/2 or 264 V rather than 528. A large number of transistors having the other required characteristics are available if the maximum voltage required is 264 V rather than 528 V.

The price paid for the lower-voltage bridge inverter circuit is, of course, the extra cost and space of the additional two transistors as well as the slight cost and space of low-level circuits for driving four rather than two power transistors. In the schemes of Figs. 3–1 and 3–2, the preregulator usually steps down the rectified line voltage to somewhere around the range of 100–125 V. Since this is now regulated, it will remain constant for a 10% line voltage variation. Thus, the two-transistor inverter is usable in these configurations, since the maximum voltage the collectors are subjected to is twice 100 or twice 125 V. Even adding a 20% spike, the maximum voltage rating needed with a preregulator output of 125 V is only 300 V. There are many transistors available with such voltage ratings and all the other required characteristics.

3.1.4 Preregulator-Driven Converter with Postregulation Following Secondary Rectification (Fig. 3–4A)

With additional feedback regulation following the rectifiers after the dc/ac converter, the scheme in Fig. 3–4A provides better regulation than that of Fig. 3–1. In Fig. 3–1 the feedback around the preregulator provided constant input voltage to the dc/ac converter and, hence, its output voltages did not change with ac line changes. But the converter output voltage was not regulated against load-current changes. Only the low output impedance resulting from the low-impedance silicon rectifiers and the square-wave ac (Sect. 2.1.6) made the rectified dc output relatively independent of load-current changes.

It was indicated in Sect. 3.1.1 that output voltage changes with load could be kept constant to ±0.15 V. But in cases in which this is not good enough, the postregulation of Fig. 3–4A results in both line and load regulation adequate to meet many needs. The price paid, of course, is the added space, dissipation, complexity, and cost of the added circuitry of the postregulators.

The added circuitry can be relatively simple and inexpensive. The simplest and fewest-component regulator is the series-pass type (Sect. 1.1). Its greatest drawback is the low efficiency when its input voltage is highest. However, with the preregulator ahead of the dc/ac converter, all dc outputs following converter secondary rectification can be constant to ±0.15 V for line and load changes. Thus, transformer secondary turns can be chosen to yield a voltage about 1.0–2 V greater than the desired postregulator voltage. This is sufficient to put the series-pass transistor above the knee of its V_c–I_c characteristic (Figs. 1–2A and 1–14C) and still adequate to keep the ±0.15-V change at the postregulator input from getting through to its output. With even moderate gain in the postregulator, its output change with load-current changes and ±0.15-V input changes will be negligible.

It was shown in Sect. 1.1 that series-pass efficiency is $V_o/V_{in(max)}$. Then for outputs of 5 and 15 V, efficiencies with dc input voltages a safe and regulated 2 V above the output are $5/7 = 71\%$ and $15/17 = 88\%$, respectively.

If the larger component count of a switching postregulator (Sect. 1.2) is acceptable, even higher efficiencies can be achieved. For any voltage output, efficiency with the switching regulator can be as high as $V_o/(V_o + 1)$ (Sect. 1.2.1). This would yield switching efficiencies at 5 and 15 V of $5/6 = 83\%$ and $15/16 = 94\%$, respectively, at frequencies under 10 kHz. At higher frequencies (in the vicinity of 20 kHz), ac losses in the switching postregulators become significant and efficiency approaches $V_o/(V_o + 2)$, which is identical to that of the series-pass regulator with a preregulated input 2 V above the output. In this case, the switching postregulator offers no advantage over the series-pass type.

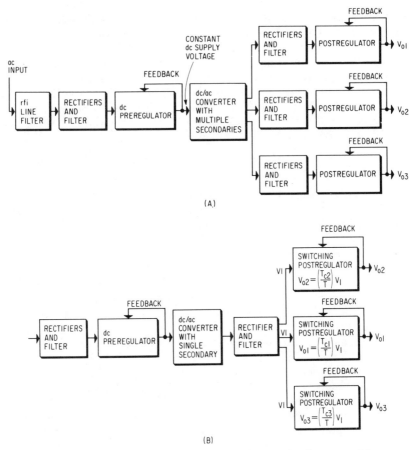

Fig. 3–4. (A) Preregulated converter with postregulated outputs. (B) With switching postregulators, a single secondary-rectified filter can supply all postregulators.

The two-feedback-loop scheme of Fig. 3–4A is much easier to stabilize against oscillation than that of Fig. 3–2, since each separate loop is around a single pair of phase-shifting elements – either a single LC or RC network. There is rarely need to add components to tailor the phase shift frequency characteristics, and thus the total delay through the entire circuit will be less than in Fig. 3–2 and transient response will be better.

Figure 3–4A is preferable to Fig. 3–3 if series-pass postregulators are used. The unregulated dc voltage to the output regulators of Fig. 3–3 makes series-pass regulators unusable except for low-output currents.

If output switching regulators are used at all outputs, the scheme of Fig. 3–4A with its preregulator has little advantage over Fig. 3–3, for each post-regulator can give adequately constant voltage without preregulation and the cost and parts count of the preregulator can be saved. One advantage as discussed in Sect. 3.1.3 is that with a preregulator a two-transistor push–pull dc/ac converter can be used. Without the preregulator, either very high voltage transistors or a transistor bridge inverter must be used.

The main advantage of the scheme of Fig. 3–4A arises in the case in which some of the outputs need be regulated against line input changes and can tolerate output changes of ± 0.15 V for load changes alone. In this case, a postregulator can be used for that output (or possibly two outputs), where output voltage must be extremely constant. In the outputs in which load changes of ± 0.15 are acceptable, the postregulators can be omitted completely. The preregulators and low output impedance seen looking back into the rectified secondary outputs will yield outputs constant to ± 0.15 V without further regulation.

Multiple Output Voltages from Single Rectified Secondary (Fig. 3–4B)

The schemes of Figs. 3–3 and 3–4 can be used with only one transformer secondary winding and one filter capacitor to generate a multiplicity of different output voltages at high efficiency as shown in Fig. 3–4B.

This becomes possible by the use of switching postregulators. The single rectified dc output voltage is made higher (at least 10%) than highest dc output voltage. Then each switching postregulator is operated at its own ratio of closed-switch/open-switch time (Sect. 1.2) to yield the required separate output voltages. This obviously would not be possible with series-pass postregulators, since the lowest output voltage node would have the largest voltage drop across its series-pass element and, hence, a low efficiency. Also, this is possible only if all the outputs have a common output terminal. The diode rectifiers and transformer secondary winding must, of course, have a current rating adequate to carry the sum of all output currents.

3.1.5 Half-Cycle, Width-Modulated Inverter with Rectified Secondary Feedback and Line-Only Regulated Slave Outputs (Fig. 3–5)

This is the scheme of Sects. 2.5, 2.5.1, 2.5.2, and Fig. 2–24. Its characteristics and advantages are fully discussed in those sections. Here it is sufficient to point out that it is competitive with Fig. 3–2. It provides one well-regulated output (V_{o1}) and slave outputs that are regulated against line input changes. Output voltage changes due to load-current change are small because of the low output impedances.

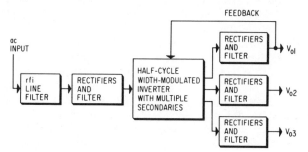

Fig. 3–5. Half-cycle, width-modulated inverter with slaved and line-only-regulated outputs.

The chief advantage of Fig. 3–5 over Fig. 3–2 is higher efficiency and faster transient response. The higher efficiency results because the main power is handled only once; in Fig. 3–2 it is handled with some significant losses in the preregulator and again in the dc/ac converter. The faster response results from the fact that feedback in Fig. 3–5 is over fewer phase-shifting elements than in Fig. 3–2.

As was pointed out in Sect. 3.1.3, one disadvantage of Fig. 3–5 is that the use of an unregulated line voltage (115 V_{ac}) rectified dc voltage to drive the inverter narrows the choice of transistor and inverter types. If a two-transistor push–pull inverter is used (Fig. 2–24), the transistors must have V_{cbo} ratings of greater than 528 V. If higher voltage types are not available, the bridge inverter of Fig. 2–13 must be used, since, in the "off" state, transistors in the bridge inverter must withstand only the maximum dc supply voltage, not double its value, as in two-transistor push–pull inverters.

3.1.6 Half-Cycle, Width-Modulated Inverter with Rectified Secondary Feedback and Postregulated Slave Outputs (Fig. 3–6)

Here V_{o1} is regulated against both line and load variations. The slave outputs are regulated against line changes only directly after rectification. Also, as discussed in Sect. 3.1.2, these outputs can be changed only in multiples of 1 or 2 V, depending on the volts per turn characteristic of the transformer. By adding the postregulators, both load and line regulation is obtained at the slave outputs also.

Further, since the dc input to the slaved postregulators is already regulated against line changes, series-pass postregulators can be used at relatively high efficiencies. Transformer secondary windings can be fixed to give a dc output after rectification that is only 2 V (or in some cases 1 V) above the desired output voltage. Efficiency is then $V_o/(V_o + 2)$ and the simple, low-component count series-pass regulator becomes possible.

3.2   Building Block Combinations of Preregulated dc/dc Converters with Open-Loop Secondary Outputs

3.2.1 Series-Pass Preregulator Implementation of Fig. 3–1

The scheme of Fig. 3–1 can be implemented with acceptable efficiency with a series-pass preregulator (as in Fig. 3–7) because of its relatively high output voltage. Although efficiency would be higher with a switching preregulator, the simplicity and lower component count of the series-pass regulator may be preferable in some applications.

One major drawback to low efficiency is, of course, that it is difficult to get rid of the internally generated heat and limit the temperature rise. To achieve acceptably low temperature rise with high internal dissipation may require large volume heat sinks or forced-air convection cooling. Both of these alternatives result in low-power densities (output watts per cubic inch). Where power densities of 0.5 W/cubic inch or less are acceptable or at output powers under 100 W, the relatively low efficiency of the series-pass preregulator may not be too great a drawback. Efficiency of the scheme of Fig. 3–1 implemented with a series-pass preregulator can be calculated as shown in the following section.

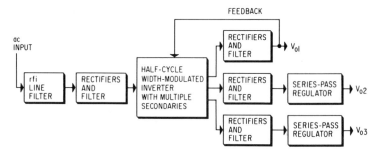

Fig. 3–6. Half-cycle, width-modulated inverter with postregulators at slaved outputs for better load regulation.

Efficiency of "Off-the-Line" Series-Pass Regulator

It was shown in Sect. 1.1.1 that the minimum efficiency of the series-pass regulator occurs at its maximum dc input voltage (maximum ac line voltage in this case) and is given by $E_{\min} = V_o/V_{in(\max)}$.

Now a series-pass regulator fed from the rectified ac line voltage must have a nominal dc voltage sufficiently high so that at the minimum ac line voltage (assumed 10% below nominal), the input voltage at the bottom of the ripple triangle is still safely above the output voltage by about 2 V so that the series-pass element is out of saturation.

For a silicon bridge rectifier driven directly off the ac line into a capacitive filter with no limiting resistor, the peak output voltage at the capacitor is two rectifier diode drops below the peak ac line voltage, or for 115 V nominal line voltage:

$$
\begin{aligned}
V_{P(dc)} &= 1.41(115) - 2V_d \\
&= 1.41(115) - 2 \\
&= 160 \text{ V}
\end{aligned}
$$

where V_d = rectifier diode drop = 1 V.

If there is a small rectifier surge current limiting resistor after the bridge rectifier, drop in this resistor should be taken into account.

It will be shown in Chap. 5, Fig. 5.5, that at 60 Hz, the peak-to-peak triangular ripple voltage at the capacitive filter output is about 8 V peak to peak for a filter capacity of 1,000 μF per dc ampere of load current. Then at a nominal line voltage of 115 V, the dc voltage at the capacitor output (for 1,000 μF/ampere) is

$$
160 - \frac{V_{\text{ripple, peak to peak}}}{2} = 160 - \frac{8}{2} = +156 \text{ V}
$$

The bottom of the ripple triangle is at $(160 - 8)$ or $+152$ V at nominal line voltage and at $(0.9)(152) = +136$ V at 10% low-line voltage. Thus, the series-pass regulated output must be no higher than 2 V below this or at $+134$ V to avoid pass element saturation. To allow for drop in a filter–capacitor surge-limiting resistor, set the series-pass regulator output about 5 V lower than this, or at $+129$ V.

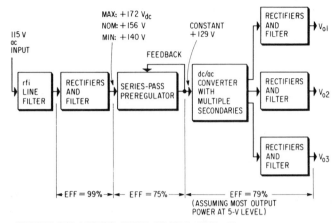

ESTIMATED TOTAL LOW-LEVEL CONTROL AND DRIVE LOSSES = 8%

Fig. 3–7. Series-pass preregulator implementation of Fig. 3–1. Overall efficiency is 54% with most of the output power at a 5-V level.

For a 10% high ac line voltage, the dc output to the series-pass regulator will be 10% above its value at nominal line voltage or at $(1.1)(156) = 172$ V. Thus, series-pass regulator efficiency at maximum line is

$$V_o/V_{in(\text{max})} = 129/172 = 75\%$$

DC/DC Converter Efficiency

Converter efficiency for an input of V_{dc} and an output of V_o is given by Eq. 2–1B as

$$E = [(V_{dc} - 1)/V_{dc}]^2[V_o/(V_o + 1)]E_{tr}$$

Transformer hysteresis losses for a ferrite can be obtained from Fig. 2–6 for low-loss 3C8 (Ferroxcube) material once a specific core and its operating parameters are selected. For currently used 20 kHz operating frequency and 1,500 G peak flux density, hysteresis loss is only 25 mW/cc of core material. It will be shown in Chap. 7 that with such low losses per cubic centimeter, a core at about 300–500 W of output power will have hysteresis losses of under 0.25%.

Transformer copper losses can only be estimated when its windings are designed. In general, at output power levels of up to 500 W, copper losses can be kept down to under 2.5%. Thus, rounded-up transformer copper plus hysteresis losses are $2.5\% + 0.25\% \cong 3\%$ for a transformer efficiency of 97%.

Thus, in Fig. 3–7, for V_{in} of 129 V, V_o of 5 V (assume most of the output power is at a 5-V level), the inverter efficiency is

$$E = (128/129)^2(5/6)(0.97) = 79\%$$

Input Rectifier Diode Efficiency

Earlier in this section it was calculated that the average dc voltage after the rectifier is 172 V at 10% high line voltage. A bridge rectifier with two rectifier diode drops at 1 V each will yield a rectifier efficiency of $100(172/174) = 99\%$.

Total System Efficiency for Scheme of Fig. 3–1 with Series-Pass Preregulator

Total efficiency of Fig. 3–7 is

$E =$ Input rectifier efficiency
  × Series-pass regulator efficiency
  × dc/dc Converter efficiency, including output rectifiers
  × Efficiency of 0.92 due to miscellaneous low-level losses
    of 8%
  $= (0.99)(0.75)(0.79)(0.92) = 53.9\%$

Thermal Significance of Overall Efficiency

By itself, an efficiency number conveys little information. To appreciate its significance, it must be translated into internal dissipation and then into the surface area and volume of the heat sink required to keep the heat sink and semiconductor junction temperature rise to acceptable levels.

Thermal calculations will be covered in detail in Chap. 4. Here, some simple calculations will be done to show the significance of the above-calculated efficiency of 53.9%.

Assume load powers of 50, 100, 300, and 500 W, respectively. For these, the calculated input power is P_o/efficiency and internal dissipation is $P_o/E - P_o$. Then for a reasonably acceptable maximum heat sink temperature rise of 50°C, the required thermal resistance of the heat sink is 50/internal dissipation (°C temperature rise per watt of power dissipation). These data are shown in columns 1 through 5 of Table 3–1.

Now, by jumping ahead to Chap. 4, the heat sink volume required to achieve the thermal resistance of column 5 in Table 3–1 at the power levels of column 4 in Table 3–1 may be calculated. This can be read from Fig. 4–11 if the required thermal resistance normalized to a 10-W power level is known.

The normalized 10-W thermal resistance can be calculated from Fig. 4–8 as follows. In Fig. 4–8, the ratio of thermal resistance at any power level, P, to its value at a 1-W power level is read as θ_p/θ_1 (column 6). Also from Fig. 4–8, the ratio of thermal resistance at a 10-W power level to its resistance at a 1-W power level is read as θ_{10}/θ_1 (column 7). Then the ratio of thermal resistance at a power level P to its resistance at 10-W levels is calculated as

$$\frac{\theta_p}{\theta_{10}} = \frac{\theta_p/\theta_1}{\theta_{10}/\theta_1} \quad \text{(or column 8)}$$

And finally, to achieve the thermal resistance of column 5 at the power levels of column 4, the normalized 10-W thermal resistance is $\theta_p/(\theta_p/\theta_{10})$ or column 5/column 8, as shown in column 9.

Now from Fig. 4–11, at this equivalent 10-W power level thermal resistance, the volume of the required heat sink is read and shown in column 10 of Table 3–1.

This is the required heat sink volume at the power levels of column 4 in Table 3–1 to achieve the thermal resistances of column 5 in Table 3–1. At the power dissipation of column 4, the heat sink volumes of column 10 will result in 50°C temperature rise for those heat sinks. It can be seen that significantly large heat sink volumes are required to keep the temperature rise to 50°C.

Table 3–1. Required Heat Sink Volume for Various Output Powers at 53.9% Efficiency for a Maximum Heat Sink Temperature Rise of 50°C

1	2	3	4	5	6	7	8	9	10
Output power = P_o *(watts)*	*Efficiency* = E *(%)*	*Input power* = P_o/E *(watts)*	*Internal dissipation* = $P_o/E - P_o$ *(watts)*	*Required thermal resistance for temperature rise of 50°C at power level of column 4 = θ_p (°C/watt)*	$\dfrac{\theta_p}{\theta_1}$	$\dfrac{\theta_{10}}{\theta_1}$	$\dfrac{\theta_p}{\theta_{10}}$	θ_{10} *(°C/watt)*	*Required volume of heat sink (cu in.)*
50	53.9	93	43	1.16	0.56	0.70	0.80	1.45	32
100	53.9	185	85	0.59	0.51	0.70	0.73	0.81	70
300	53.9	556	256	0.20	0.43	0.70	0.61	0.33	250
500	53.9	927	427	0.12	0.40	0.70	0.57	0.21	480

A frequent goal in modern power supply design is to achieve an overall load power density of 1 W of load power per cubic inch or better. It can be seen from Table 3–1 that this is just about achievable up to load powers of 100 W. For 100 W of load power with 70 cu. in. required for the heat sink alone, everything else must be packaged in 30 cu. in. Generally, the size of the input and output filter capacitors and the size of the power transformer (even at 20 kHz) make this almost impossible.

Thus, for load powers of 100 W or more, better efficiencies than 53.9% are required if packaging densities of 1 W/cubic inch are to be achieved.

Generally, above 100 W of load power a more efficient building block system using switching rather than a series-pass preregulator would be used. Further, in most systems requiring dissipation of over 75 W of power in a box requiring a packaging density of 1 W/cubic inch, forced-air convection cooling would be used. This can drop the heat sink volume required for a given thermal resistance by a factor of 3–5. And in the usual case, the space for the blower or fan supplying the forced air is not allotted to the power supply but is part of the total system volume. On this basis, power supply packaging densities of 1 and up to 2 W/cubic inch are possible. With water cooling, densities of up to 4 W/cubic inch become feasible.

3.2.2 Series-Switch Step-Down Preregulator Implementation of Fig. 3–1

This is shown in Fig. 3–8. It was seen in Sect. 1.2.1 that the efficiency of the series-switch step-down converter/regulator (Fig. 1–4) is $V_o/(V_o + 2)$ and is independent of the input voltage.

The series-pass preregulator designed in Sect. 3.2.1 to implement the scheme of Fig. 3–1 has an efficiency of $V_o/V_{in\,(max)}$. It was seen in Sect. 3.2.1 that for a nominal ac line voltage of 115 V, the output voltage must be 129 V to avoid saturating the series-pass transistor at the bottom of the ripple triangle at

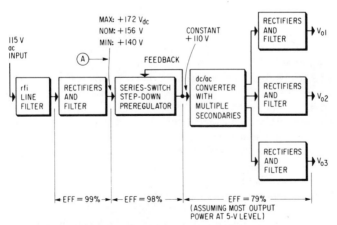

Fig. 3–8. Series-switch preregulator implementation of Fig. 3–1. Overall efficiency is 70% for most of the output power at a 5-V level.

a 10% low-line voltage. Then at a 10% high-line voltage, dc input voltage is 172 V and efficiency at this line voltage is 129/172 or 75%. But the series-switch step-down regulator with its efficiency of $V_o/(V_o + 2)$ (Eq. 1–2A) achieves much better efficiency than this. Since obviously the highest values of V_o yield the greatest efficiency, what are the criteria for selecting V_o? These can be seen as follows:

Since $V_o = V_{in}(T_c/T)$ in the step-down regulator (Sect. 1.2), the open-switch time is $T_o = T - T_c = T - (V_o/V_{in})T = [1 - (V_o/V_{in})]T$. Then as V_o/V_{in} approaches unity, the open-switch time rapidly approaches zero. But the open-switch time cannot be made indefinitely small — it is limited by the storage time in the transistor. Thus, for a storage time of 2 μsec and a switching period of 40 μsec (25 kHz), the maximum value of V_o/V_{in} is

$$\frac{V_o}{V_{in}} = 1 - \frac{T_o}{T} = 1 - \frac{2 \times 10^{-6}}{40 \times 10^{-6}} = 0.95$$

Thus, the highest possible value of V_o is 95% of the minimum value of V_{in}. Now it has been shown in Sect. 3.2.1 that for an off-the-line rectifier with an ac input of 115 V $\pm 10\%$, with a filter capacitor of 1,000 μF/ampere of load current, the bottom of the ripple triangle is at $+136$ V. Then the highest usable output voltage in this step-down switching regulator is $(0.95)(136) = 129$ V.

At this output voltage, the series-switch step-down regulator efficiency is $V_o/(V_o + 2) = 129/131 = 98.5\%$, as compared to a minimum efficiency of 75% for a series-pass regulator generating 129 V.

But in a practical case, such an "off-the-ac" line step-down converter generates an output voltage somewhat less than the above-calculated 129 V. This is feasible, since the step-down regulator efficiency does not fall off significantly with lower-output voltage. The lower-output voltage is chosen because it is often specified that a 10% negative-going transient shall not get through to the output. It is usually assumed that at the bottom of this negative-going transient the minimum open-switch time is no less than 10% of the period to allow for variations in transistor storage time. Then

$$V_o/V_{in} = 1 - T_o/T = 1 - 0.1 = 0.9$$

And with a -10% transient, the bottom of the ripple triangle is at $(0.9)(136) = 127$ V. Then for $V_o/V_{in} = 0.9$, maximum regulated output voltage is $(0.9)(127) = 110$ V.

And at this regulated output from the step-down regulator, its efficiency is still $V_o/(V_o + 2) = 110/112 = 98.2\%$. At 10% high ac input, the dc input to the regulator from the line rectifier is $(1.1)(156) = 172$ V (Sect. 3.2.1). At this input and 110 V output, the switching regulator efficiency is still the same $V_o/(V_o + 2)$ or 98.2%. But note that a series-pass regulator with an input of 172 and an output of 110 V would have an efficiency of only 64%. Thus, assume a switching step-down regulator following the line rectifier. At an output voltage of 110 V, its rounded off efficiency is 98%.

Now the scheme of Fig. 3–1 implemented with a series-pass preregulator of 75% efficiency had a total efficiency of 53.9% (Sect. 3.2.1 and Fig. 3–7). Then all other efficiencies remaining equal, the same scheme implemented instead with a series-switch step-down regulator of 98% efficiency will have a total system efficiency of $53.9 \times 98/75 = 70.4\%$.

Table 3–2.

1	2	3	4	5	5A	5B	6
Output power (watts)	Efficiency = E (%)	Input power (watts)	Internal dissipation (watts)	Heat sink resistance* (°C/watt)	$\dfrac{\theta_p}{\theta_{10}}$ †	Θ Equivalent at 10 W ‡	Heat sink volume§
50	70	71	21	2.38	0.89	2.67	13
100	70	143	43	1.16	0.81	1.43	32
300	70	429	129	0.39	0.69	0.56	110
500	70	714	214	0.23	0.63	0.37	200

* For a sink temperature rise of 50°C.
† Ratio of thermal resistance at power levels of column 4 to thermal resistance at 10-W power level as read from Fig. 4–8.
‡ Equivalent thermal resistance at 10-W power level (= column 5/column 5A).
§ Required heat sink volume for 50°C temperature rise (from column 5B and Fig. 4–11).

Thermal Significance of Improved Efficiency

This is a significant savings in internal dissipation and makes possible power supplies with load power densities of 1 W/cubic inch at relatively high output powers without the use of forced-air cooling. The values of Table 3–1, reproduced with a total system efficiency of 70%, are shown in Table 3–2.

It can be seen in Table 3–2 that a load power density of 1 W/cubic inch is possible up to 500 W of output power without the need for forced-air cooling. Thus, for a power level of 500 W and at a power density of 1 W/cubic inch, the total permissible power supply volume is 500 cu in. With 200 cu in. for the heat sink alone, there remains for all the components, hardware, printed circuit boards, and wiring, an amount 500 − 200 or 300 cu in. This would generally be adequate for a 500-W power supply at a switching frequency of 20 kHz.

3.2.3 Shunt-Switch Step-Up Preregulator Implementation of Fig. 3–1

The scheme of Fig. 3–1, implemented with shunt-switch step-up preregulator of Fig. 1–6B, offers no advantage in efficiency but generates less noise (rfi) at the input rectifier and, hence, requires a smaller rfi filter to keep noise off the ac lines.

It was shown in Sect. 1.3.1 that the efficiency of the step-up regulator is $V_{in}/(V_{in} + 2)$. Efficiency is thus a minimum at minimum dc input voltage. In Sect. 3.2.1, it was shown that for a nominal ac line voltage of 115 V, the minimum dc for 10% low ac input is +156 V. Minimum efficiency of the step-up regulator is, hence, 156/158 = 98.7%. This is practically equal to the efficiency of the step-down regulator calculated in Sect. 3.2.2, and, hence, overall system efficiency will be the same, i.e., 70%.

Output voltage of the step-up regulator should be slightly more (10%) than the peak dc output from the line rectifier at maximum line voltage. Thus, for 115 V nominal ac input, this would be (1.1)(1.1)(1.41)(115)= 196 or about 200 V. Width modulation can easily keep the output dc at 200 V for line variations of ±10% and eliminates the rectifier ripple.

In a two-transistor dc/ac converter, as discussed in Sect. 2.1.9, the off transistor is subjected to twice the dc plus about a 20% spike at transistor turnoff due to transformer leakage inductance. This maximum voltage stress at transistor turnoff is $(1.2)(2)(200) = 480$ V. With a 20% derating below the manufacturer's voltage rating, the transistor should have a V_{cbo} (ensure low base impedances or reverse bias at turnoff) of 480/0.8, or 600 V.

If transistors with this voltage rating and adequate current and switching speed ratings are not available, the bridge dc/dc converter of Sect. 2.2 can be used, since it requires transistors having only half the voltage rating of the two-transistor push–pull converter. It should be noted that the losses in the four-transistor bridge converter are twice that of the two-transistor version. While transformer primary current is equal in the two designs, in the bridge, on each half cycle, this same current flows through two transistors in series rather than through one as in the two-transistor converter.

The advantage of the step-up regulator becomes apparent from the waveforms of the current flow in the input rectifiers. Current waveforms are discussed in detail in Chap. 9, Sect. 9.5.1, and are shown in Fig. 9–30.

Here it will only be noted that (referring to Fig. 1–6B) the current drawn from the dc source through L1 can be made to have a very small ac component by making L1 sufficiently large.

When S1 is closed, the current in L1 flows through S1; when S1 is open the same current flows through D1. When S1 in Fig. 1–6B is closed, the potential across L1 is V_{in}, and the change in current drawn from V_{in} during T_c, the S1 closed time, is $+\Delta I = V_{in}T_c/L1$. For L1 sufficiently large, $+\Delta I$ can be made as small as desired. It usually is made 10–20% of the average current from V_{in}. When S1 is open (for a time T_o), potential across L1 is $(V_o - V_{in})$, and the current in L1 decreases by the same amount that it increased when S1 was closed. Thus,

$$-\Delta I = \frac{(V_o - V_{in})T_o}{L1} = +\Delta I$$

The ac component of current drawn from V_{in} is thus a triangular wave of peak-to-peak current of amplitude, $V_{in}T_c/L_{in}$, which is generally only 10–20% of the average dc current from V_{in}.

In contrast, the series-switch step-down converter/regulator of Fig. 1–4 takes a train of chopped current pulses from V_{in}. These current pulses drop to zero when S1 is open for a time T_o. For a time T_c that S1 is closed they have a peak amplitude about equal to the average output current. Their fast rise and fall times result in troublesome internal crosstalk.

This chopped current drawn from V_{in} results also in more serious noise signals on the ac line. The series step-down converter requires a larger rfi filter than the shunt step-up converter. In some instances, the lesser rfi problem is the deciding factor in selecting the shunt step-up converter over the series step-down converter.

An additional advantage of the step-up converter is that less disastrous effects result from the most common failure mode – a shorted S1 switch. S1 is the power transistor whose normal failure mode is the shorted condition. In the step-down converter of Fig. 1–5, a shorted S1 results in V_o rising to V_{in}. This higher voltage can result in failures of the dc/ac converter transistors, which are the loads for the step-down converter in Fig. 3–1. If the preregulator of Fig. 3–1 is the shunt step-up regulator of Fig. 1–6, a shorted S1 reduces V_o to zero. The output voltage is lost, of course, but shorting of S1 does not cause failure of the dc/ac converter transistors.

3.2.4 Width-Modulated Inverter Preregulator Implementation of Fig. 3–1

This configuration is shown in Fig. 3–9 and is discussed in Sect. 3.1.5. The width-modulated converter is the half-cycle, width-modulated, double-ended converter of Sect. 2.5. The single-ended, transformer-coupled energy storage width-modulated inverter of Sect. 1.4 is generally usable only at low-power outputs because of the unidirectional primary current that requires a large transformer with an air gap to prevent its saturation.

The half-cycle, width-modulated inverter has very much the same circuit configuration as that of a dc/dc converter. The only exception is that the duration of each half cycle is width modulated and, hence, dc transistor losses are $V_{ce(sat)}I_c[T_{on}/(T/2)]$, where $T_{on}/(T/2)$ is the fraction of a half cycle that each transistor is on. These lesser losses than for the conventional converter are balanced by the additional low-level losses in the width control circuitry.

Thus, in Fig. 3–9, assuming 3% transformer losses, the efficiency of the half-cycle, width-modulated inverter from the input rectifier output to the output rectifier output is from Eq. 2–1B (this does not include low-level control and drive losses):

$$E = [(V_{dc} - 1)/V_{dc}]^2 [V_o/(V_o + 1)](0.97)$$
$$= (155/156)^2(5/6)(0.97) = 79\%$$

Now including, as in Sect. 3.2.1, an input rectifier diode efficiency of 99% and an efficiency of 92% due to miscellaneous low-level control circuit losses, the total efficiency of Fig. 3–9 is $(0.99)(0.79)(0.92) = 72\%$.

This is only slightly better than the 70% calculated in Sect. 3.2.2 for a series-switch step-down preregulator driving a conventional dc/dc converter. The lower component count for the width-modulated inverter configuration plus the somewhat better efficiency results in significant advantages over the series-switch step-down preregulator scheme. It should be noted that, with unregulated line-rectified dc input to the width-modulated inverter, transistors with voltage ratings of about 535 V (Sect. 2.2) are required or the bridge inverter of Fig. 2–12 must be used.

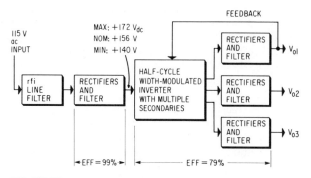

Fig. 3–9. Half-cycle, width-modulated inverter implementation of Fig. 3–1. Overall efficiency is 72% for most of the output power at a 5-V level.

3.3   Building Block Combinations of Preregulated Converters with Rectified Secondary Feedback (Fig. 3-2)

These are the combinations of Fig. 3-2 whose advantages and short-comings were discussed in Sect. 3.1.2. The configuration of Fig. 3-2 can be implemented either with a series-pass preregulator as described in Sect. 3.2.1, the series-switch step-down preregulator described in Sect. 3.2.2, or the shunt-switch step-up preregulator of Sect. 3.2.3.

The efficiency with any of these preregulators will be identical to the corresponding configurations of Fig. 3-1, in which the feedback was around the preregulator output rather than around one of the rectified secondaries of the dc/ac converter (i.e., 54% for the series-pass preregulator, 70% for a series-switch step-down or shunt-switch step-up preregulator). Since feedback in Fig. 3-2 is around one of the outputs—V_{o1}, that output will be very stable for load and line changes. As discussed in Sect. 3.1.2, load changes in the V_{o1} output will cause output voltage changes in the other outputs because of changing V_{o1} rectifier diode drops. And, as discussed in the same section, transient response will suffer because of the single feedback loop around two or more phase-shifting circuits. Since the output filter in a switching regulator is a LC circuit rather than an RC circuit as in a series-pass regulator, implementing Fig. 3-2 with a series-switch step-down or shunt-switch step-up Regulator will result in poorer transient response than with a series-pass preregulator. But, of course, the latter will yield lower overall efficiency.

3.4   Building Block Combinations of Unregulated dc/dc Converter with Postregulated Secondary Outputs (Fig. 3-3)

As indicated in Fig. 3-3 the postregulators can be either series-pass or series-switch step-down regulators. Shunt step-up postregulators can also be used. Efficiencies may be estimated as follows.

3.4.1 Series-Switch Step-Down Implementation of Fig. 3-3 (Fig. 3-10)

In Sect. 1.2.1, it was shown that a series-switch step-down regulator efficiency is $V_o/(V_o + 2)$. Assume (for the worst case) all the output power is at $+5$ V. It matters little whether there is only one or there are many output voltages. For the same total output power, efficiency will not change much, since the low-level control circuits dissipation for three output voltages is not significantly different from that of a single output. Then the efficiency of the switching post-regulators is $V_o/(V_o + 2) = 5/7 = 71\%$.

Now assume the dc/ac converter produces an output of 20 V after secondary rectification. This will be chopped down to 5 V in the output switching regulator. Then from Eq. 2-18, assuming a nominal 154 V input, the dc/dc converter efficiency (assuming 3% loss in the power transformer) is

$$E = [(V_{dc} - 1)/V_{dc}]^2 [V_o/(V_o + 1)](0.97)$$
$$= (155/156)^2(20/21)(0.97) = 91\%$$

Then for an input bridge rectifier efficiency of 99% and low-level control and drive circuit losses of 8%, the total system efficiency of Fig. 3-10 is

E = Series-switch step-down regulator efficiency
  × dc/dc Converter efficiency (A to B)
  × Input bridge rectifier efficiency
  × Low-level control and drive circuit loss efficiency
  = (0.71)(0.91)(0.99)(0.92) = 59%

3.4.2 Series-Pass Postregulator Implementation of Fig. 3–3

The much lower efficiency of the series-pass regulator, especially at 5 V output, makes it almost prohibitive to implement Fig. 3–3 with this element. Nevertheless, for the sake of completeness, the efficiency of such a scheme is calculated. The scheme analyzed is that of Fig. 3–10 with a series-pass output regulator replacing the series-switch regulator.

To prevent input ripple from getting through to the output, the voltage at the bottom of the input ripple triangle at 10% low ac input must be no less than 2 V above the output. Now it will be shown in Chap. 5 (Fig. 5.5) that for 60 Hz, single phase, an input filter capacitor of 1,000 μF/ampere of load current yields a peak-to-peak ripple of 8 V. This, for the rectified input in Fig. 3–10, is a percentage ripple of ±4/156 or ±2.5%.

Such a filter capacitor at the input supply voltage of the dc/dc converter of Fig. 3–10 will thus yield a rectified output ripple of ±2.5%. So if the voltage at the bottom of the ripple triangle is to be 2 V above the output of 5 V, the dc voltage must be set 2.5% above that or at 1.025(5 + 2) = 7.2 V.

Then if the rectified dc at the dc/dc converter output is to be +7.2 V at 10% low line, it is (1.1)(1.1)(7.2) = 8.7 V at +10% high ac line voltage. Series regulator efficiency at high ac line is then 5/8.7 = 57%.

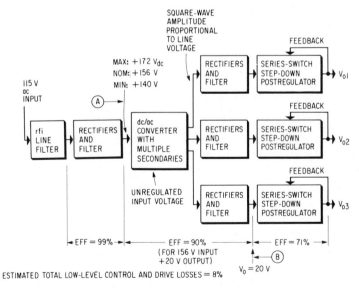

Fig. 3–10. Series-switch step-down output regulator implementation of Fig. 3–3. Overall efficiency is 59% for most of output power at 5-V level.

Now in Fig. 3–10, if the dc/dc converter were designed to give a maximum output voltage of 8.7 V, its efficiency (from Eq. 2–1B) is

$$E = [(V_{dc} - 1)/V_{dc}]^2 [V_o/(V_o + 2)](0.97)$$
$$= (155/156)^2(8.7/10.7)(0.97) = 78\%$$

Then total system efficiency of Fig. 3–10 with the series-switching regulator output replaced by a series-pass device is:

$E =$ Series-pass regulator efficiency
  $\times$ dc/dc Converter efficiency
  $\times$ Input bridge rectifier efficiency
  $\times$ Low-level control and drive circuit loss efficiency
$= (0.57)(0.78)(0.99)(0.92)$
$= 40\%$

It is obvious from the discussion in Sect. 3.2.1 and Table 3–1 that at this low efficiency, at a load power of about 50 W, the heat sink volume required to keep the heat sink temperature rise to 50°C will be about 60 cu in. With so much volume allotted to the heat sink alone, load power density of 1 W/cubic inch is obviously not attainable.

Thus, the scheme of Fig. 3–3 implemented with series-pass post-regulators is only feasible at low output powers for cases in which load power densities of less than 0.5 W/cubic inch are acceptable or in which forced-air convection cooling is available.

3.5   Building Block Combinations of Preregulated dc/dc Converters with Postregulated Secondary Outputs (Fig. 3–4)

This has been discussed in some detail in Sect. 3.1.4. It is most often used with a series-switch step-down preregulator regulating the rectified line voltage down to about 110 V where its efficiency is 98% (Sect. 3.2.2). It can also be used with the shunt-switch step-up regulator providing a regulated 200 V at about the same efficiency (Sect. 3.2.3).

But, as discussed in Sect. 3.2.3, with 200 V to the dc/ac converter, inverter transistors with V_{cbo} ratings of 600 V should be used to allow for +20% spikes at inverter turnoff resulting from transformer leakage reactance. The 600-V rating also permits a 20% derating of the vendors maximum voltage ratings. If such high voltage transistors are not available at the required current and switching speed ratings, the four-transistor bridge inverter of Fig. 2–13 should be used.

3.5.1 Series-Switch Step-Down Preregulator with Series-Pass Postregulator Implementation of Fig. 3–4 (Fig. 3–11)

With preregulated input to the dc/ac converter, the converter secondary voltage can be designed to be a safe 2 V above the desired series-pass output voltage. It will remain constant at that value for line and load variations, and, hence, even at maximum ac line voltage, the series-pass efficiency, which is $V_o/V_{in(max)}$, is for a 5-V output, 5/7 or 71%.

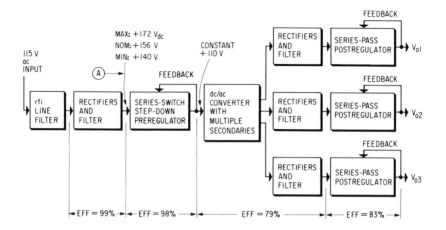

ESTIMATED TOTAL LOW-LEVEL CONTROL AND DRIVE LOSSES = 8%

Fig. 3–11. Implementation of Fig. 3–4A with a series-switch step-down preregulator and series-pass postregulators. Overall efficiency is 59% for most of the output power at a 5-V level with a preregulated 6-V input.

High-current transistors, such as the 2N3771 class, have saturation knees below 1.0 V at currents up to 12 A (Fig. 1–13C). Such a transistor can be used in a series-pass configuration after the preregulated dc/dc converter and operated safely with its dc input only 1 V above the output. In this case, series-pass efficiency to $V_o/(V_o + 1) = 5/6 = 83\%$ for 5 V of output.

Now in Fig. 3–11, assume the series-switch step-down preregulator generates (as discussed in Sect. 3.2.2) 110 V as an input for the dc/dc converter. The converter efficiency as given by Eq. 2–1B is

$$E = [(V_{dc} - 1)/V_{dc}]^2 [V_o/(V_o + 1)]E$$

And for 3% transformer losses,

$$E = (109/110)^2(5/6)(0.97) = 79\%$$

The series-switch step-down converter efficiency is (from Eq. 1–2A)

$$E = V_o/(V_o + 2) = 110/112 = 98\%$$

Then for 99% input rectifier efficiency, and 8% low-level control and drive circuit losses, total system efficiency of Fig. 3–11 is

$$\begin{aligned} E = &\ E(\text{Output series-pass regulator}) \\ &\times E(\text{dc/dc Converter} - 110\text{ V input, 6 V output}) \\ &\times E(\text{Series-switch step-down regulator} - 156\text{ V input,} \\ &\qquad 110\text{ V output}) \\ &\times E(\text{Input bridge rectifier efficiency}) \\ &\times E(\text{Efficiency due to low-level control, drive losses}) \\ = &\ (0.83)(0.79)(0.98)(0.99)(0.92) \\ = &\ 59\% \end{aligned}$$

It is obvious that the low efficiency at the 5-V output is primarily responsible for the lower overall efficiency. In most cases, it is not quite true that all of the output power is at a 5-V level. In those cases, the scheme of Fig. 3–11 can be implemented with about 65–68% efficiency.

3.5.2 Series-Switch Step-Down Preregulator with Series-Switch Step-Down Postregulator Implementation of Fig. 3–4

It was noted in Sect. 3.5.1 that with preregulated dc input voltage, use of a 2N3771 series-pass transistor permits setting regulator input only 1 V above its output. Thus, at 5 V output, efficiency $V_o/(V_o + 1) = 5/6$ or 83%. But in Sect. 1.2.1, it has been shown that the series-switch step-down regulator (considering only dc and ac power transistor losses) has an efficiency of $V_o/(V_o + 2) = 5/7 = 71\%$. From an efficiency viewpoint, there is thus no advantage to be gained by using the series-switch step-down postregulator in the configuration of Fig. 3–4, which has preregulated input to the dc/ac converter.

3.6   Building Block Combinations of Half-Cycle, Width-Modulated Inverters with Line-Only-Regulated Slave Outputs (Figs. 3–5 and 3–12)

This configuration was discussed in Sect. 3.2.6 as a version of the preregulated schemes of Fig. 3–2 in which the preregulator function and the dc/ac converter function are combined into the one half-cycle, width-modulated inverter. It is shown in Sect. 3.2.4 that this combination has an overall efficiency of 72% when most of its output power is at a 5-V level.

3.7   Building Block Combinations of Half-Cycle, Width-Modulated Inverters with Postregulated Slave Outputs (Fig. 3–6)

3.7.1 Series-Pass Postregulators

This was shown in Fig. 3–6 and discussed in Sect. 3.1.6. Overall system efficiency depends on how the output power is divided between V_{o1} (assumed a 5-V output) and V_{o2}, V_{o3}. If most of the output power is in the V_{o1} winding at 5 V output, the efficiency is close to the same 72% discussed in Sect. 3.6. The series-pass postregulators here serve to provide better load regulation and reduce changes in the output at V_{o2}, V_{o3} resulting from load changes in V_{o1}.

The efficiency or internal losses of a system such as in Fig. 3–6 with series-pass postregulators may be compared to the one in Fig. 3–5. For equal voltages and current outputs at V_{o1}, V_{o2}, V_{o3} in both systems, the scheme of Fig. 3–6 has losses exceeding those in Fig. 3–5 by only $(1)(I_{o2} + I_{o3})$. This is so, of course, because the preregulated inputs to V_{o2}, V_{o3} permit their dc levels to be only 1 V above their corresponding outputs. Overall system efficiencies will generally range between 65 and 72%.

3.7.2 Series-Switch Step-Down Postregulators (Fig. 3–12)

With only a 1–2 V drop across the series-pass postregulator (Fig. 3–6), use of more complex switching postregulators might be thought pointless. But in

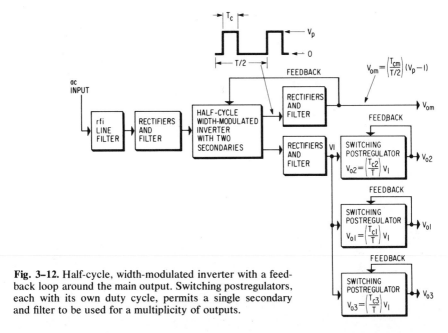

Fig. 3–12. Half-cycle, width-modulated inverter with a feedback loop around the main output. Switching postregulators, each with its own duty cycle, permits a single secondary and filter to be used for a multiplicity of outputs.

some instances, as in Fig. 3–12, in which a single-transformer secondary-rectifier–filter combination provides input for a multiplicity of switching regulators, each with its own duty cycle and output voltages, there might be an advantage. The space saving offered by use of a single-transformer secondary-rectifier–filter might in some applications outweigh the higher component count of three switching postregulators. The single-secondary, rectifier–filter is possible, of course, only with switching postregulators, since series-pass postregulators will operate with large voltage drops and consequently high dissipation across the lower-output-voltage series-pass elements.

Efficiency of configurations such as in Fig. 3–12 can be as high as 72% even with most of the output power at the 5-V level.

3.8   DC Prime Power Systems

All of the block diagram combinations of Fig. 3–1 to 3–6 following the rectifier–filter block are usable when the prime power is dc. In the schemes of Figs. 3–1 to 3–6, the rectified dc is nominally +156 V. In systems in which the prime power is dc, it is usually at a level of +28 or +30 V for aircraft, missile, satellite, or submarine power systems. In occasional applications in vehicles, prime power dc voltage is at a 12-V level.

Efficiency figures calculated in Sects. 3.2 to 3.7 will change with lower dc voltage. Losses will drop 1–3% because input rectifiers and surge current-limiting resistors are eliminated. And the high dc voltage of 156 V (172 V maximum) resulting from rectifying the ac line directly, often forces the use of a four-transistor bridge inverter because of inadequate voltage ratings of transistors necessary for two-transistor inverters. Losses in the four-transistor inverters are, of course, twice that in the two-transistor configuration. Thus, with lower voltage in a dc prime power system, this problem does not arise — two-transistor inverters with their lower losses are always usable.

But with lower dc input, the first building block in most of the configurations of Fig. 3–1 to 3–6 will operate with greater losses at the lower input voltage. Thus, a series-pass first building block has an efficiency of $V_o/V_{in(max)}$. Assume an output voltage 2 V below the lowest input (90% of nominal input) and a maximum input of 110% of nominal input. Then for a dc prime power source voltage of 28 $\pm 10\%$, a series-pass regulator putting out $[(0.9)(28) - 2]$ or 23 V will have an efficiency at maximum line of $23/(1.1)(28) = 23/31 = 74\%$.

Now (Sect. 3.2.1) a series-pass regulator operating off the rectified 115-V ac line voltage can generate an output voltage no higher than $+134$ V (2 V below the bottom of a 2-V ripple triangle at 90% of ac input voltage). At 20% high-line voltage, dc input is 172 V and efficiency is $134/172$ or 78%.

It has been shown (Sect. 1.2.1) that the efficiency of a series-switch step-down regulator at 20 kHz or higher is $V_o/(V_o + 2)$. Thus, if such regulators were used to generate the above output voltages from the same sources ($+23$ from $28 \pm 10\%$ and $+134$ from $156 \pm 10\%$), the former would have an efficiency of $23/25$ or 92%, the latter $134/136$ or 98%.

The dc/dc converter operating off lower dc input voltages also has lower efficiencies. Equation 2–1B gives converter efficiency as

$$E = [(V_{dc} - 1)/V_{dc}]^2 [V_o/(V_o + 1)]E_{tr}$$

Thus, a converter operating off a preregulated 23 V with 3% transformer losses and generating an output of 5 V has an efficiency of

$$E = (22/23)^2(5/6)(0.97) = 73.9\%$$

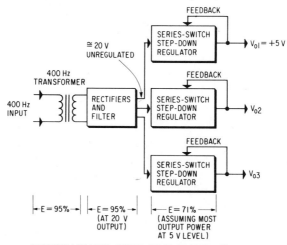

Fig. 3–13. With 400 Hz input power, the low weight and volume of an input power transformer becomes attractive. Overall system efficiency of 59% is easily possible.

And operating off a preregulated 134 V, generating the same 5 V with 3% transformer losses, the converter efficiency is

$$E = (133/134)^2(5/6)(0.97) = 79.6\%$$

One advantage in operating off a dc prime power source is the savings, of course, in the size of the input filter capacitor needed to yield adequately low ripple. It will be shown in Chap. 5, Fig. 5–5, that at 60 Hz in a single-phase, full-wave rectifier, to achieve a peak-to-peak ripple voltage of 8 V requires a filter capacitor of 1,000 μF/ampere of load current out of the filter. Input filter capacitors can in some cases account for as much as 25% of the volume of a power supply.

Further, in designing a series-pass regulator to run off a source with ripple voltage, allowance must be made to ensure that the bottom of the ripple triangle is safely above the output voltage. An 8-V peak-to-peak ripple adds another 4 V across the series-pass element and increases its dissipation by $4I_o$ V.

3.9   Prime Power Systems with 400-Hz Line Frequency

Somewhat more freedom of choice in a block diagram is available when the prime power source is 400 Hz. This is because of the relatively small size of the 400-Hz power transformers and the smaller filter capacitors required to yield adequately low ripple. Use of a 400-Hz transformer whose size is no longer prohibitive provides dc isolation from the ac and often obviates the need for a dc/ac converter. The weight of a 400-Hz transformer is roughly 0.01 lb/watt as compared to about 0.06 lb/watt for 60-Hz units. Some of the possible block diagram combinations that become attractive with 400-Hz input power are described in the next two sections.

3.9.1 Transformer-Isolated Series-Switch Step-Down Regulators (Fig. 3–13)

This scheme competes with the one in Fig. 3–10. In Fig. 3–13, with most of the output power at a 5-V level, the series-switch efficiency is $V_o/(V_o + 2)$ = 5/7 = 71%. With 20 V nominal output from the rectified secondary and a 1-V rectifier drop, the rectifier–filter element has an efficiency of 95%. Assuming 5% losses in the 400-Hz input transformer and 8% low-level drive and control circuit losses, the total system efficiency of Fig. 3–13 is (0.71)(0.95)(0.95)(0.92) = 59%.

The scheme of Fig. 3–10 required a dc/ac converter to supply line-isolated dc input to the separate output switching regulators. Its resulting efficiency (Sect. 3.4.1) is 58%. It probably requires a four-transistor bridge rather than a two-transistor push–pull inverter because of voltage rating considerations (Sect. 2.2). This drops its efficiency down to 56% because of the 1-V drop and ac switching losses (= dc losses) in four rather than two transistors.

Thus, if 400 Hz is available, the scheme of Fig. 3–13 with a low-weight power transformer is more efficient and has fewer components than the scheme of Fig. 3–10.

3.9.2 Power Transformer–Rectifier-Driven Series-Pass Preregulator with a dc/dc Converter with Open-Loop Secondaries (Fig. 3–14)

The configuration is competitive with that of Fig. 3–7. In Fig. 3–14, a 400-Hz line transformer has been added. At about 0.01 lb/watt, it is not too significant in size and weight.

It is shown in Chap. 5, Fig. 5–5, that at 60 Hz, a filter capacitor of 1,000 μF/output ampere (output from the filter) yields a peak-to-peak ripple of about 8 V. Then, at 400 Hz, the same-sized filter capacitor could be used – this would drop the peak-to-peak ripple (60/400)(8) or about 1 V.

With this negligible ripple, the transformer secondary voltage could be chosen to yield a rectified output voltage only 2 V above that of the series-pass regulator at low ac line input. If, as in Fig. 3–7, a series-pass output of +129 V is selected, the rectified output at low ac line voltage is +131 V, at nominal output it is (1.1)(131) or 144 V, and at high line, it is (1.1)(144) or 158 V.

Series-pass regulator efficiency at high line is 129/158 or 82%. This compares with 75% in Fig. 3–7 in which the dc input to the regulator had to be higher to cope with the 8-V peak-to-peak ripple voltage. Now assume 79% efficiency after the series-pass regulator as in Fig. 3–7 and again allow 8% for low-level control and drive circuit losses. Assume again 95% power transformer efficiency and 99% rectifier efficiency (1-V rectifier drop, 140-V nominal output for an efficiency of 139/140 = 99%). Overall efficiency of the scheme of Fig. 3–14 is then (0.95)(0.99)(0.82)(0.79)(0.92) = 56%. This compares to 54% for the scheme of Fig. 3–7. But despite the insignificant gain in efficiency, the scheme in Fig. 3–14 has some advantages over the one in Fig. 3–7. It is still open loop from input of the dc/ac converter to outputs, and thus outputs will still change about ±0.1 V with load changes and a significant amount with line changes.

The chief advantage of the transformer of Fig. 3–14 is that auxiliary secondary windings can be provided. These are often necessary as supplies for

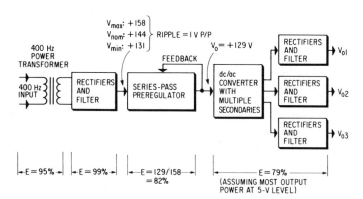

Fig. 3–14. With 400 Hz input, an input transformer is attractive. Open-loop secondaries from an ac/dc converter with a series-pass preregulator input gives adequate regulation and overall system efficiency of 56%.

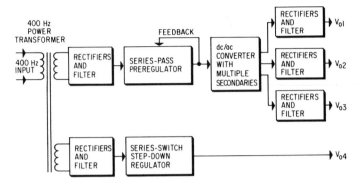

Fig. 3–15. A combination of Figs. 3–13 and 3–14. V_{o4}, coming through a second secondary, minimizes loading on the dc/ac converter and series-pass preregulator.

the control and drive circuitry. Also, leakage inductance in the transformer reduces the transient current pulse drawn by the filter capacitor at turnon.

Possibly, as in Fig. 3–15, a second secondary winding can be used and rectified to serve as an unregulated dc source for a series-switch step-down regulator, whenever the open-loop regulation is insufficient. Although one of the open-loop outputs could also provide such a source, its power would be coming through the dc/ac converter and possibly force the use of the larger inverter transistors.

Generally, 400-Hz line-derived power is less expensive in components, dollars, and power dissipation than power that first must come through a dc/ac converter.

Looked at another way, Fig. 3–15 is really a combination of Fig. 3–13 and 3–14, in which one secondary provides Fig. 3–13-type outputs and another secondary branches out to provide Fig. 3–14-type outputs.

PROBLEMS

3.1 What are the nominal, peak, and minimum dc output voltages from an off-the-line bridge rectifier whose ac input is single-phase 220 V ±10%, 60 Hz? What is the peak-to-peak ripple assuming a filter capacitance of 2,000 μF/load ampere?

3.2 In Prob. 3.1, what is the magnitude of the filter capacitor at 50, 100, 200, and 300 W of rectifier output power?

3.3 In a series-pass regulator in the scheme of Fig. 3–7, with the input of Prob. 3.1, what is the maximum regulated output voltage? What is the efficiency at maximum ac input at this output? What is the efficiency at a regulated output of 225 V?

3.4 In a scheme as in Fig. 3–7, with an ac input of 115±%, a series-pass output of 105 V, a single output of 5 V, 3% transformer losses, and line rectifier efficiency of 99%, what are the efficiencies and internal dissipations for output powers of 50, 100, and 200 W assuming 5% control and drive circuit losses?

3.5 In Prob. 3.4, what would the total system efficiency be if the series-pass regulator was replaced by a series-switch step-down regulator producing the same 105 V output for the dc/ac converter?

3.6 In Prob. 3.5, what would the internal dissipations be for output powers of 50, 100, and 200 W?

3.7 In Prob. 3.6, what are the required heat sink thermal resistances for heat sink temperature rises of 30°C at output powers of 50, 100, and 200 W? What are the normalized 10-W thermal resistance and the corresponding heat sink volumes? What is the available volume for everything but the heat sink to attain load power densities of 1 W/cubic inch?

3.8 In the scheme of Fig. 3–9, with only two outputs of 30 V, and assuming 99% input rectifier efficiency, 97% transformer efficiency, transistor ac losses equal to dc losses, and 95% low-level losses, what are the efficiencies and internal dissipations for 10 A of output current from each of the 30-V outputs?

3.9 In the scheme of Fig. 3–10, with only two outputs of 15 V at 2 A each, and a dc/ac converter designed to give 30 V output to the input of the step-down switching regulator, what is the efficiency and internal dissipation?

  Assume 5% low-level control and drive circuit losses and 3% transformer losses in the dc/ac converter.

3.10 In the block diagram of Fig. 3–11, assume one 5-V output at 5 A, two 15-V outputs at 1 A, and two 30-V outputs at 10 A each. What is

  a. Total series-pass dissipation assuming preregulator keeps series-pass inputs a constant 1 V above the outputs.
  b. Total output rectifier losses at 1 V forward drop per rectifier.
  c. Total load power.
  d. Total power delivered by converter transformer secondary.
  e. Transformer losses assuming 98% transformer efficiency.
  f. Total power input to transformer primary.
  g. Primary current.
  h. Total converter transistor losses assuming ac losses equal dc losses.
  i. Total input power to dc/dc converter.
  j. Switching preregulator efficiency.
  k. Input power to preregulator switch.
  l. Switch losses in preregulator (total ac + dc).
  m. Average input current to preregulator switch.
  n. Input rectifier losses assuming a bridge rectifier.
  o. Total input power from ac line not counting low-level and control circuit losses.
  p. Low-level and control circuit losses assuming 5% of input power.
  q. Total input power.
  r. Overall efficiency.

4
Elements of Thermal Design

4.0   Introduction

Electronics designers achieve satisfactory power supply circuit designs by a combination of paper and pencil analysis and breadboarding to pick up the more subtle and unpredictable transient, spiking, and ac waveform problems. These circuit designers, however, pay insufficient attention to the thermal design and packaging. Even with a successful, working breadboard, the majority of failures with a fully packaged supply is very often the result of an inadequate thermal design.

In this chapter, the elements of thermal design will be taken up. Analysis will not be rigorous, since exact temperature predictions within a supply can be done only by complex computer analysis. By the relatively simple analysis considered herein, critical temperatures can be calculated to within approximately 5 to 10°C.

4.1   Maximum Permissible Temperature and
Temperature Deratings

The first task in a thermal analysis is to set goals as to what the maximum permissible temperatures will be for various components in order to prevent early catastrophic failures and achieve long-time reliability.

The majority of problems arise with semiconductor elements. Manufacturers' maximum junction temperatures must be adequately derated to allow for inexact temperature calculations, overlooking the worst combinations of load current and high device voltage, which causes highest power dissipation and thus highest temperature. Often, the worst combinations of voltage and current are unknown at the start of a power supply design because the system design has not firmly established the dynamic load current versus time profile.

Junction temperatures must be derated not only to avoid catastrophic failures resulting from greatly exceeding the manufacturer's maximum ratings but also because there is a statistical probability of failures occurring even if maximum temperature ratings are not exceeded. This probability of failure depends strongly on how close to the maximum permissible junction temperature the devices operate.

This failure rate or number of failures per 10^{+6} hr is given as a function of operating junction temperature in tables such as the Mil Handbook 217A (Fig. 2–7). From such tables, device temperatures, and the total number of devices of various types, a decision can be made as to how much to back off from the manufacturer's maximum specified junction temperature in order to achieve a total system's mean time between failures (MTBF) requirement. This can be seen as follows.

Consider a power supply or system having N_{t1} transistors of type T1, N_{t2} transistors of type T2, N_r resistors, N_d diodes, N_c capacitors, and N_m magnetic elements (inductors or transformers). Then from the aforementioned Mil Handbook 217A, the number of failures per million hours is read as a function of their operating temperatures. If these failures per million hours are respectively N_{ft1}, N_{ft2}, N_{fr}, N_{fd}, N_{fc}, and N_{fm}, then the total number of failures in the entire power supply per million hours is

$$N_{\text{total}} = N_{t1}N_{ft1} + N_{t2}N_{ft2} + N_rN_{fr} + N_dN_{fd} + N_cN_{fc} + N_mN_{fm}$$

The MTBF, which has specified limits for almost all military and high-reliability commercial equipment, is then given by

$$\text{MTBF (hr)} = \frac{10^{+6}}{N_{\text{total}}}$$

To achieve the required MTBF, device operating temperature must be set low enough to yield a sufficiently low failure rate from the Mil 217A failure rate tables.

In general, it will be found this is not the limiting criterion on transistor junction temperature. It will be found — especially when the number of transistors and diodes is small — that MTBF requirements can usually be met with junction temperatures quite close to the vendor's maximum specified value of 200°C for silicon devices.[1]

It is rather the unpredictable circuit and operating mode conditions that dictate a lower temperature. Things like odd load or line transients, high voltage and current overlap at turnoff of switching devices, second breakdown, component parameter tolerances building up, and uncertainty in temperature calculations make it necessary to set a lower temperature limit than that needed to meet the MTBF specification.

Various companies, programs, and individuals have their own philosophies as to what constitutes safe derating factors for the most temperature-sensitive elements — semiconductors. In the very competitive commercial power supply market, policy is often to permit worst-case maximum transistor and diode temperature to reach 200°C for silicon devices whose manufacturer's maximum rating is 200°C.

---

[1] There is no single catastrophic failure occurring precisely at 200°C for silicon devices. That temperature is defined as "maximum" in the industry, since it has been found that devices beyond that temperature have suffered an economically unacceptable "failure" rate after a 1,000-hr life test. "Failure" is generally taken as a 20% degradation of a significant parameter such as current gain (B) or collector leakage current (I_{ceo} or I_{cbo}), although these specific numerical failure criteria may vary from vendor to vendor.

This is poor design practice and, in equipment in which failures and shutdowns are costly in dollars and perhaps lives, cannot be tolerated. There is no industry-wide concensus as to what constitutes reliable maximum silicon junction temperatures, but a fairly common practice is to limit the worst-case silicon device junction temperatures to 135–150°C for "high-reliability" commerical equipment, 125–135°C for conventional military equipment, and 105°C for ultrareliable military or space equipment.

4.2   Temperature Calculations and Thermal Resistance Concept

A large variety of temperature calculations can be simplified and performed using the concept of "thermal resistance" as shown in Fig. 4–1.

In this concept, the path of heat flow or power is known or approximated and is taken as analogous to current in an electrical circuit. Various thermal resistance elements in the heat-flow path are taken analogous to electrical resistance.

Temperature drop or gradient across an element is analogous to voltage drop across a resistor. Then, just as voltage drop is calculated by

$$V \text{ (volts)} = [I \text{ (amperes)}] [R \text{ (ohms)}]$$

so is temperature gradient across an element of thermal resistance θ, through which a power P is flowing, calculated by

$$\Delta T \text{ (°C)} = [P \text{ (watts)}] [\theta \text{ (°C/watt)}] \tag{4–1}$$

The actual value of thermal resistance of an element is a complex function of the heat-flow path through it and is accurately calculable only if the exact heat-flow path is known. In contrast, if a voltage is applied across the ends of a wire of length L, area A, electrical resistivity ρ, its resistance is easily calculated as $R = \rho (L/A)$. This is so, of course, because the ends of the wire are equipotential surfaces and current flow path is along the wire.

In the heat-flow situation, if, say, there is a metal chassis with a number of heat-dissipating transistors distributed at random over it and cooling it by cold plates at one end of the chassis, the problem is one of heat flow in three dimensions and not easily solvable without simplifying approximations.

The problem is very similar to the calculation of currents and voltages in a mesh of interconnected electrical resistances with many nodes. Such thermal calculations are easily done by computer using a thermal model in which various

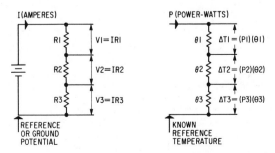

Fig. 4–1. The concept of thermal resistance simplifies thermal calculations.

nodes are established and simplifying approximations of the thermal resistance between nodes are made.

In most instances, simplifying approximations as to heat-flow paths and thermal resistances can be made and temperatures calculated to an accuracy of about 10°C without computer calculations.

Thus, calculations or measurements of the thermal resistances in the paths to a reference point of known temperature, permits calculation of semiconductor junction temperature (or that of any point in the path) from Eq. 4–1. If the semiconductor is at the top of a string of elements of thermal resistances $\theta_1, \theta_2, \theta_3, \ldots$, through which flow powers $P_1, P_2, P_3, \ldots$, then its junction temperature for a reference point temperature of T_r is (as in Fig. 4–1)

$$T_j = T_r + P_1\theta_1 + P_2\theta_2 + P_3\theta_3 + \cdots \qquad (4\text{–}2)$$

Either T_r is the known temperature of the ambient air if cooling takes place

EXTRUSION TYPE		SURFACE AREA PER IN. OF LENGTH	OVERALL WIDTH	OVERALL DEPTH	WEIGHT PER IN. OF LENGTH
2501		20.7 sq in.	4 in.	1-1/16 in.	0.10 lb
2502		33.3 sq in.	4 in.	1-9/32 in.	0.13 lb
2503		42.3 sq in.	5-1/8 in.	1-1/4 in.	0.19 lb
2504		18.3 sq in.	4 in.		0.08 lb
2505		28.6 sq in.	4 in.	1-1/4 in.	0.12 lb
2506		39.1 sq in.	5-1/8 in.	1-1/4 in.	0.13 lb
2508		15.6 sq in.	4-3/4 in.	7/16 in.	0.08 lb
2509		22.8 sq in.	4-3/4 in.	11/16 in.	0.11 lb
2510		10.9 sq in.	2-7/8 in.	11/16 in.	0.06 lb
2517		36.3 sq in.	4-3/4 in.	1-1/4 in.	0.14 lb
2518		54.6 sq in.	6-1/4 in.	2 in.	0.27 lb

Fig. 4–2A. Some typical heat-sink extrusions. (*Courtesy* Astrodyne, Inc.)

by radiation and convection, or it may be that of a coolant at known temperature if cooling is by conduction to a cold plate kept at a fixed temperature by a circulating liquid coolant.

4.3   Transistor Junction Temperature Calculations

4.3.1 Junction Temperatures for Heat-Sink-Mounted Transistors

In most cases, for power supplies up to 1,000 W of output power, the dissipated heat is ultimately disposed of by radiation and convection to the ambient air from a "heat sink." Heat sinks are aluminum extrusions with large area fins to increase their heat-radiating efficiency (decrease their thermal resistance).

For power dissipations up to 100 W, the heat sink area and volume necessary to achieve reasonably low temperature rise (50°C or less) are sufficiently small so that natural convection cooling is adequate. Above 100 W, for maximum ambient temperatures above 60°C, forced convection or fan cooling is often necessary.

Heat sinks come in a variety of shapes, sizes, and fin designs (Fig. 4–2). They are generally specified by the vendor in thermal resistance (°C/watt) from their surface to the ambient air temperature for a fixed extrusion length—generally 3 in. They may also be obtained in any length for various-shaped extrusions. To permit thermal designs with greater extrusion lengths (and, hence, larger area and lower thermal resistance), the vendor specifies the heat sink in surface area per running inch length of extrusion. Thermal resistance is primarily a function of surface area and power level. Thus, from curves such as in Figs.

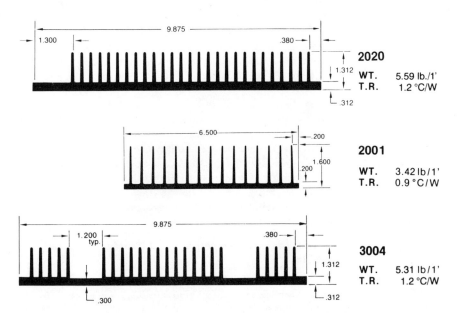

Fig. 4–2B. Additional extrusion types; thermal resistance (TR) is for a 3-in. length at a power level causing 50°C temperature rise. (*Courtesy* Aham, Inc.)

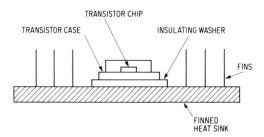

Fig. 4–3. Thermal resistances involved in transistor junction temperature calculations: heat sink to ambient air, heat sink to transistor case through insulating washer, and transistor junction to case.

4–7 and 4–8, thermal resistance for any area and power level can be calculated, or, given a desired thermal resistance at any power level, the required heat sink area may be calculated from Figs. 4–7 and 4–8.

When thermal resistance is given by the vendor for his standard running length of 3 in., since it is dependent on power level, it is generally quoted at that power level resulting in a 50°C temperature rise.

The transistors are generally mounted on the heat sink or on a bracket attached to it and having low thermal contact resistance to the heat sink. They may also be mounted on the chassis itself and the heat sink attached to the chassis with a low thermal contact resistance between chassis and heat sink.

In the temperature calculation of Eq. 4–2, the thermal resistances involved can be seen from Fig. 4–3. First, there is the thermal resistance of the heat sink to the ambient air. This is calculated from its total area and power level from Figs. 4–7 and 4–8. Usually, the transistor case must be electrically isolated from the chassis or heat sink. This requires an insulating washer—generally mica, anodized aluminum, plastic film, or silicone rubber. Thermal resistance through the washer, from the bottom of the transistor case to the top of the heat sink, generally ranges from 0.4 to 1.0°C/watt for TO3 transistor case insulating washers.

Thermal resistances from transistor junction to the bottom of the case (θ_{jc}) is specified by the vendor for most transistors and diodes. It ranges from 0.75–1.5°C/watt for transistors in TO3 cases to 5–7°C/watt for TO66 case devices, 45–60°C/watt for TO5 case devices (with some newer types as low as 6.6–17.5°C/watt), and 83–145°C/watt for TO18 case devices. The actual value of θ_{jc} depends on the transistor chip size and the thermal resistances involved in the manner by which the chip is attached to the transistor case. The quoted θ_{jc} values represent the average of present-day chip sizes and chip attachment means.

Design Example: Junction Temperature and Heat Sink Area Calculation

For a specific case in Fig. 4–3, assume an ambient air temperature of 70°C, thermal resistance from heat sink to ambient air (θ_{hsa}) of 2°C/watt, thermal resistance through the insulating washer (θ_{iw}) of 0.7°C/watt, and a TO3 case transistor with a resistance from junction to case (θ_{jc}) of 1°C/watt. Assume also that there are four transistors mounted on the heat sink with each dissipating

8 W. Then from Eq. 4–2, since 32 W flows into the heat sink, 8 W through each insulating washer, and 8 W through each transistor junction to case resistance:

$$T_j = T_r + 4P_t\theta_{hsa} + P_t\theta_{iw} + P_t\theta_{jc}$$
$$= 70 + 4(8)(2) + 8(0.7) + 8(1) = 147.6°C$$

where P equals power dissipation per transistor.

As discussed in Sect. 4.1, this would be too high for reliable military designs, in which the goal is to limit maximum junction temperatures to 105°C. To lower junction temperatures, a larger area heat sink with lower thermal resistance can be chosen.

The design procedure more frequently is first to establish the maximum transistor junction temperature, to calculate the required thermal resistance from Eq. 4–2, and then, using Figs. 4–7 and 4–8, to calculate the necessary heat sink area to achieve the required thermal resistance. This can be seen as follows.

For a maximum junction temperature of 105°C, from Eq. 4–2,

$$105 = 70 + 4(8)\theta_{hsa} + 8(0.7) + 8(1)$$

or $$\theta_{hsa} = (105 - 70 - 5.6 - 8)/32$$
$$= 21.4/32 = 0.67°C/watt$$

Thus, a heat sink of 0.67°C/watt at a 32-W power level is required. From Fig. 4–8, at 32 W, the heat sink thermal resistance is 0.59 times as large as its thermal resistance at a 1-W power level. Thus, the normalized 1-W thermal resistance is 0.67/0.59 = 1.13°C/watt. From Fig. 4–7, this requires a heat sink of 439 sq in.

4.3.2 Thermal Resistance/Thermal Conductivity/Geometry Relationships

The basic relationship in heat transfer by conduction is shown in Fig. 4–4. Consider an element with two faces of area A, separated by a length L. If the two faces are kept at temperatures $T1$ and $T2$, respectively, and all the heat or power flowing into the first face flows out through the second, then the power flowing through the element is

$$P = (KA/L)(T2 - T1) \tag{4–3}$$

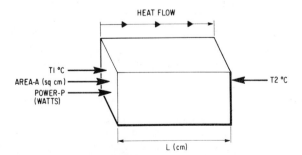

HEAT FLOW

TI °C
AREA-A (sq cm)
POWER-P
(WATTS)

T2 °C

L (cm)

Fig. 4–4. Basic heat transfer relation. $(T2 - T1) = PL/KA$; for K in watts per °C per square centimeter per centimeter; L in centimeters; A in square centimeters; P in watts; and $(T2 - T1)$ in °C.

	Thermal conductivity	
Material	(Watts/sq cm/cm/°C)	(Btu/hr/sq ft/°F)
Air	0.00024	0.0138
Aluminum	2.25	130
Aluminum oxide	0.20	11.6
Beryllium oxide	2.08	120
Brass	1.06	61.3
Copper	4.01	232
Epoxy laminate	0.0030	0.17
Ferrite	0.063	3.64
Glass (borosilicate)	0.010	0.58
Gold	3.39	196
Iron	0.71	41.0
Kovar alloy	0.17	9.82
Mica	0.0043	0.25
Nichrome	0.132	7.63
Nickel	0.62	35.9
Silicon	0.83	48.0
Silicone rubber (G.E. type RTV)	0.0026	0.15
Silver	4.19	242
Stainless steel	0.16	9.25

Fig. 4–5. Thermal conductivity of materials in common use in electronics.

The proportionality constant K is referred to as the "thermal conductivity." For P in watts, A in square centimeters, L in centimeters, and $(T2 - T1)$ in °C, K has the dimensions of watts per °C per square centimeter per centimeter. In terms of heat flow, since 1 cal/sec equals 4.187 W, Eq. 4–3 states that if the opposite faces of area A (in centimeters) separated by L (in centimeters) are maintained at a temperature differential of $(T2 - T1)$°C, the heat flow between the two faces is $P/4.187$ cal/sec for a power flow of P watts between the two faces.

Equation 4–3 can be interpreted in another way. If a power of P watts flows through two faces of A (square centimeters), which are separated by a length L (centimeters) of material of conductivity K, the temperature difference between these faces will be given by

$$T2 - T1 = \Delta T = PL/KA$$

and the thermal resistance of the element in °C/watt is

$$\Delta T/P = L/KA \qquad °C/watt \qquad (4-4)$$

where L is in centimeters and A in square centimeters.

Thermal conductivity K is most often quoted in engineering handbooks in units of Btu per hour per square foot per foot per °F. The conversion factors between the two units are

$$K(\text{watts/sq cm/cm/°C}) = 0.0173K(\text{Btu/hr/sq ft/ft/°F})$$

From Eq. 4–4, thermal resistance of elements of various lengths, areas, and thermal conductivity can be calculated. In the usual case, the heat-flow path is not well defined in length and cross-sectional area, but simplifying approximations as to average cross-sectional area and path length generally make it possible to calculate thermal resistance to about 10% from Eq. 4–4.

Values of thermal conductivity for some materials in common usage in the electronics field are shown in Fig. 4–5.

4.3.3 Thermal Resistance Calculation for a Potted Toroidal Core Transformer in a Cylindrical Hole in a Heat Sink

As an example of the type of simplifying approximations used in thermal resistance calculations, consider the transformer of Fig. 4–6A.

The transformer is wound on a ferrite toroid (core 144T500 of Fig. 8–1). The toroid has an OD of 2.90 in., an ID of 1.53 in., and a height of 0.50 in. The copper windings are wound uniformly around the toroid, which is then encapsulated in a thin-walled aluminum can using a silicone rubber (G.E. type RTV of Fig. 4–5) potting material. Assume that the potting material completely surrounds the wound core with silicone rubber wall thickness of 0.1 in. between the inside wall of the aluminum can and the copper windings.

Now assuming that the transformer is cooled by inserting it in a hole in a massive aluminum block or heat sink kept at a reference temperature of T_r, the transformer can fit snugly within the hole so that there is no thermal re-

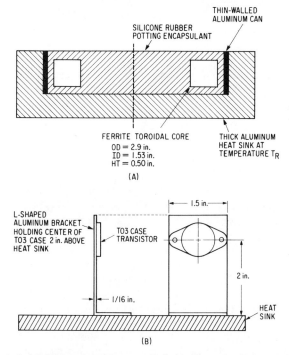

Fig. 4–6. (A) Thermal resistance calculation for a toroidal core transformer potted in silicone rubber in aluminum can inserted in a cylindrical hole in a large-mass heat sink. (B) Thermal resistance calculation for an L-shaped aluminum bracket.

sistance between the outside of the can and inside of the hole, and the power dissipation in the transformer is all in the copper windings and any hysteresis losses can be neglected. The copper windings having high thermal conductivity can be assumed to be an isothermal surface.

The windings can dissipate their heat in all directions – up through the top of the can through 0.1 in. of encapsulant by conduction and then by radiation to the ambient air. But this path will have a high thermal resistance, since the radiating area is small – it is essentially the annular projection of the top of the toroid. This area is approximately $(\pi/4)(\overline{OD}^2 - \overline{ID}^2) = (\pi/4)[(2.9)^2 - (1.5)^2]$ = 4.8 sq. in. It will be seen in Sect. 4.4.1, Fig. 4–7, that such a radiating surface area has a thermal resistance to the ambient air of 26°C/watt.

Heat can also flow out radially by conduction through the 0.1 in. of encapsulant around the outer periphery of the toroidal winding, through the thin-walled aluminum can, and to the inside of the hole in the block, which is kept at a fixed temperature.

This latter path is a lower thermal resistance path, since there is then no other temperature gradient once the heat flows radially out through the 0.1 in. of encapsulant. The heat will thus take this lower thermal resistance path and it can be assumed all of it will flow radially out through this outer "cylinder" of potting material.

This cylinder has a wall thickness of 0.1 in., average diameter of 2.90 + 0.1 or 3.0 in., and a height of about 0.5 in. (the height of the toroidal winding). In Eq. 4–4, this represents a heat-flow path length of 0.1 in. or 0.254 cm. The effective area through which the heat flows is

$$A = \pi DH = \pi(3)(0.5) = 4.7 \text{ sq in.} = 30.4 \text{ sq cm}$$

Then for a silicone rubber thermal conductivity of 0.0026 W/sq cm/cm/°C, from Eq. 4–4, the thermal resistance of the copper windings to the heat sink is

$$\frac{\Delta T}{P} = \frac{L}{KA} = \frac{0.254}{0.0026(30.4)} = 3.2°C/\text{watt}$$

4.3.4 Thermal Resistance of TO3 Transistor on L-Shaped Aluminum Mounting Bracket

As a second illustration of the application of Eq. 4–4, consider a TO3 case transistor mounted on a $\frac{1}{16}$-in.-thick L-shaped bracket as in Fig. 4–6B. Assume that the center of the TO3 case is 2 in. above heat sink on which the foot of the bracket is mounted.

The heat-flow path is not easily definable. It is difficult to state precisely the width of the path along the long dimension of the TO3 case. As a close approximation, let the width down the bracket to the heat sink be the width to the ends of the TO3 case (1.5 in.), since the TO3 base is quite thick and, hence, is an isothermal surface. It is fairly correct to say the average path length of heat flow vertically down the bracket is equal to the height of the center of the TO3 case or 2 in. Once the heat reaches the foot of the bracket, it spreads out laterally, since the foot area is large, and the foot of the bracket can then be assumed at the same temperature as the base of the heat sink.

Then thermal resistance of the bracket to heat sink is that of a segment of aluminum of area (1/16)(1.5) = 0.094 sq in. or 0.60 sq cm and 2 in. or 5.08 cm in length. From Eq. 4–4, its thermal resistance is (for aluminum conductivity of 2.25)

$$\frac{\Delta T}{P} = \frac{L}{KA} = \frac{5.08}{2.25(0.60)} = 3.8°C/\text{watt}$$

4.3.5 Thermal Resistance of a 2-Mil Mica-Insulating Washer for a TO3 Case

A last illustration of the usefulness of Eq. 4–4 is in the calculation of the thermal resistance of the often-used 2-mil-thick mica-insulating washer between a TO3 transistor case and a heat sink. The area of the base of a TO3 transistor case is approximately 5 sq cm. Thus, the thermal resistance of the mica washer normal to its face is that of a section 5 cm in area and 2 mils (5 $\times$ 10^{-3} cm) thick. From Fig. 4–5, mica conductivity is 4.3 $\times$ 10^{-3}. Then from Eq. 4–4, the thermal resistance should be

$$\frac{\Delta T}{P} = \frac{L}{KA} = \frac{5 \times 10^{-3}}{(4.3 \times 10^{-3})(5)} = 0.23°C/\text{watt}$$

but thermal resistance measurements on such a 2-mil mica washer show it to have a thermal resistance of 0.8–1.0°C/watt.

This discrepancy can be explained by air spaces or "voids" between the mica surfaces and those of the transistor base and heat sink. The cases and heat sink surfaces are not perfectly flat and, hence, do not mate uniformly with the mica across the entire 5 sq cm area of the mica face. It can be seen in Fig. 4–5, that the thermal conductivity of air in cgs units is 2.4 $\times$ 10^{-4} as compared to 4.3 $\times$ 10^{-3} for mica. Hence, an air space whose width is that of the mica itself (5 sq cm) and only one-tenth its thickness or 0.2 mil will have a thermal resistance of

$$0.23 \left(\frac{1}{10}\right)\left(\frac{4.3 \times 10^{-3}}{0.24 \times 10^{-3}}\right) = 0.4°C/\text{watt}$$

Thus, a 2-mil TO3 mica washer with a 0.2-mil equal area air gap in series calculates to have a total thermal resistance of 0.23 + 0.40 or 0.63°C/watt. This compares to average measured values ranging from 0.8 to 1.0°C/watt.

In the above calculation of the resistance of a 0.2-mil-thick air gap, it was assumed it had the thermal conductivity of air. But this is not quite as correct as the air conductivity of 2.4 $\times$ 10^{-4} is for air free to move and carry heat away by convection. In a void under the mica, the air is trapped and, hence, its conductivity may be considerably less than 2.4 $\times$ 10^{-4}. Thus, even smaller-area, thinner "air" gaps than postulated above can account for the difference between the calculated value of 0.23°C/watt for mica alone and the actual measured value of 0.8–1.0°C/watt.

Usually, in using a mica insulating washer, a metal oxide filled silicone "thermal grease" is used on both mica faces to fill the "air gaps." This generally reduces the thermal resistance from 0.8–1.0°C/watt to about 0.4°C/watt.

The above thermal resistance calculation of a "thin air gap" points out the importance of having good, flat mating surfaces between parts if a low thermal resistance is to be maintained.

The same problem exists in achieving low thermal resistance between a transistor chip and the case to which it is bonded. Small voids can easily increase the vendor's quoted junction to case thermal resistance. Since there is not 100% inspection measurement of thermal resistance for all transistors on a production line, small voids can go undetected. Thus, the vendor's specified junction to case thermal resistance is not assured for any one specific transistor. Problems such as these make it necessary to derate the maximum permissible junction temperature below the vendor's specified maximum value of 200°C.

4.4   Heat Sink Fundamentals

Heat sinks come in a vast variety of shapes, sizes, and fin spacings[2] (Fig. 4–2) to achieve lowest thermal resistance in a given volume. A discussion of the detailed thermal processes involved and the relative merits of various fin shapes and spacings is beyond the scope of this book. A useful summary treatment of the forces at work is given by Astrodyne.[2]

Heat sinks work primarily by conduction of heat from their fin surfaces to the layer of air immediately adjacent to the fins. As the air warms up, it expands and rises, resulting in a thin skin or boundary layer of air moving vertically upward past the surface of the fins. As the warmed air rises, other cooler air moves in to take its place. The result is a circulating thin boundary layer of air taking up its heat from the fins, moving upward and then outward away from the fin to deliver this heat to the farther-away mass of air not in contact with the fins.

It is obvious that the more fins and, hence, more surface area there is, the greater is the number of circulating thin boundary layers of air and the greater is the number of calories removed per second. Increasing the height of a fin slows down the velocity of the boundary layer and decreases the number of calories it can carry away per second. Thus, a heat sink with tall fins is not as efficient as one with the same fin area but shorter in height.

Further, it is qualitatively obvious that the higher the temperature of the fins, the higher the temperature of the boundary layer, and, hence, the higher its velocity and the more heat that is carried away per second. Thus, the thermal efficiency of a heat sink increases (or its thermal resistance decreases) at higher power levels where its operating temperature is higher.

4.4.1 Thermal Resistance/Heat Sink Area Relationship

The detailed design of a heat sink must consider many factors. Heat transfer efficiency depends on the thickness and thermal conductivity of the boundary layer, the velocity of the air particles as a function of distance from the fin, the interaction of boundary layers from adjacent fins, and the height and height-to-spacing ratio of the fins and total fin area.

The exact numerical relationships between heat sink thermal resistance and fin area, shape, size, and power level is complex and unnecessary to present

[2] Aavid Engineering Inc., Laconia, N.H., "Extruded Heat Sink Catalog"; Aham Corp., Azusa, Calif., "Heat Sinks and Standard Extrusions"; Astrodyne, Inc., Wilmington, Mass., "Heat Transfer and Dissipation Devices" and "Heat Transfer Designs for Electric Equipment"; IERC, Burbank, Calif., "Heat Sinks and Extrusions"; Thermalloy Corp., Dallas, Texas, "Heat Sinks and Electronics Cooling Catalog"; Wakefield Engineering, Inc., Wakefield, Mass., Heat Sink Catalogs Nos. 102, 1966; J. H. Dununu Astrodyne, Inc., Wilmington, Mass., "Heat Transfer Designs for Electronic Equipment"; J. H. Dununu Astrodyne, Inc., Wilmington, Mass., "Design Parameters For Fin Spacing."

here. An empirical approach has been taken, though. The thermal resistance versus heat sink area for a large variety of different vendors' heat sinks has been plotted and is shown in Fig. 4–7. The curve holds surprisingly well over a heat sink area range of 5,000 sq in. down to the case areas of TO5 and TO18 transistor packages (areas of 0.35 and 0.14 sq in., respectively). This corresponds to a thermal resistance of 0.21°C/watt at 5,000 sq in. and 300°C/watt for the 0.14 sq in. area of TO18 transistor package.

The curve is an average curve drawn through the quoted thermal resistances for the quoted areas. It holds at a power level of 1 W delivered to the heat sink. It also holds quite accurately whether the heat sink is actually a finned device, such as those of Fig. 4–2, or the exposed sides of a box whose surface area is equal to that of the finned heat sink. If the heat sink is finned, it holds for the fins in a vertical plane only. With fins horizontal, thermal resistance may increase by 10–20%. The curve of Fig. 4–7 over most of its length follows the relation $\theta_1 = 80A^{-0.70}$, where A is in square inches and θ is in °C/watt.

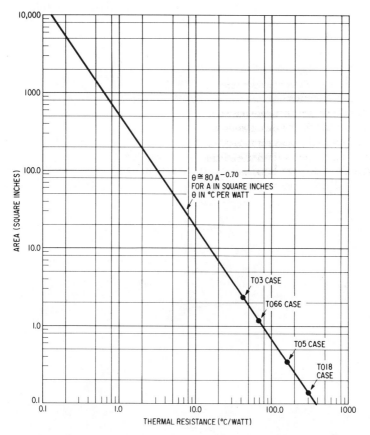

Fig. 4–7. Thermal resistance versus total heat sink area. Total area means area of both sides of a flat plate or includes both sides of a fin in a finned heat sink. Curve is at a power dissipation of 1 W. Use multiplying factor of Fig. 4–8 for other power levels.

Although theoretically thermal resistance is a function of fin height, for the heights encountered in the unusual commercially available heat sinks ($\frac{1}{2}$ to 3 in.), thermal resistance is primarily determined by the total fin area, as shown in Fig. 4–7, not the fin height.

4.4.2 Thermal Resistance/Heat Sink Power Level Relationship

The curve of Fig. 4–7 holds for power levels into the heat sink of 1 W. To convert to thermal resistance at any other power level, the multiplying factors of Fig. 4–8 are used. Figure 4–8 gives the ratio of thermal resistance at any power level to its resistance at the 1-W level as read from Fig. 4–3. The relationship of Fig. 4–8 is purely empirical, having been derived from a study of a large variety of various commercially available heat sinks. It holds to within 5–10% over the range of 1–1,000 W.

As discussed in Sect. 4.4, thermal resistance decreases with power level because of the higher temperature gradient between the heat sink and ambient air. This results in higher velocity of air in the boundary layer and, hence, better heat transfer efficiency. It might be thought then that the normalization curve of Fig. 4–8 would be a function of the absolute value of heat sink area, for a large-area heat sink at a given power level would run cooler than a small-area one. Hence, the normalizing curve of Fig. 4–8 should fall off less steeply for a large-area heat sink than for a small-area one.

Nevertheless, a survey of vendors' data on thermal resistance versus power level does not indicate a significant difference in the slope of Fig. 4–8. That curve can thus be taken as representative for heat sink areas ranging from about 0.1 to about 5,000 sq in.

Figure 4–8 is represented analytically by the expression $K1 = P^{-0.15}$ A useful set of curves can be generated from Figs. 4–7 and 4–8. Since in Fig. 4–7, $\theta = 80 A^{-0.70}$ then the thermal resistance at any power level P as a function of its power level and area is

$$\theta_P = \theta_1 K1 = 80A^{-0.70}P^{-0.15}$$

And the temperature rise at any power level P is

$$\Delta T = P\theta_p = 80A^{-0.70}P^{+0.85} \tag{4-5}$$

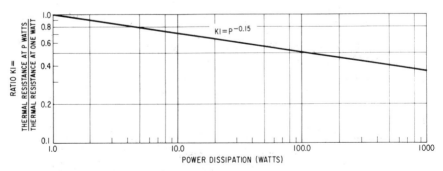

Fig. 4–8. Normalized thermal resistance versus power dissipation in heat sink.

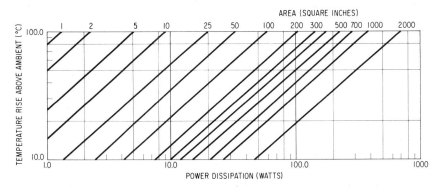

Fig. 4–9. Heat sink temperature rise versus power dissipation for various heat sink areas. (From Eq. 4–5: $\Delta T = 80 A^{-0.70} \times P^{+0.85}$)

Equation 4–5 is plotted in Fig. 4–9 for various power levels at a number of different often-used heat sink areas.

Figures 4–7 and 4–8 taken together give a heat sink temperature rise accurate to within 10°C. Fin shape and spacing does affect thermal resistance, but this is a second-order effect. Some vendors with proprietary fin shapes claim 10% or even up to 30% decrease in thermal resistance compared to conventional heat sinks of the same total area. But, generally, there is a price paid for this in that the heat sink must be used with all its surfaces in a vertical plane.

Design Example: Heat Sink Selection for Specific Power Dissipation and Permitted Temperature Rise

As an example of the use of Figs. 4–7 and 4–8, select a heat sink to permit a maximum of 40°C temperature rise with a maximum of 200 W dissipated in it. The selection is made as follows:

1. Required 200-W level thermal resistance = 40/200 = 0.2°C/watt.
2. From Fig. 4–8, thermal resistance at 200 W is 0.45 times as great as its 1-W thermal resistance. Hence, the 1-W normalized thermal resistance is 0.2/0.45 ≐ 0.44°C/watt.
3. From Fig. 4–7, for 0.44°C/watt at a 1-W power level, a heat sink surface area of 1,700 in. is required.
4. From Fig. 4–2, select a heat sink with the largest number of square inches of surface area per running inch length of heat sink. (Vendors' catalogs of Sect. 4.4 have a larger selection.) But from Fig. 4–4 choose an Aham Inc. type 3004 heat sink, which has an area of 67.1 sq in./inch of length. For 1,700 sq in. of area, a total length of 1,700/67.1 = 25.3 in. is needed.

4.4.3 Forced Convection Cooling of Heat Sinks

Fan or forced convection cooling of the heat sink can lower its thermal resistance. For initial design purposes, it is convenient to have some guidance as to what decrease in thermal resistance can be achieved for various air-flow rates in cubic feet per minute (cfm).

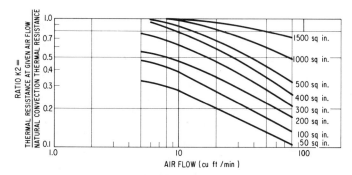

Fig. 4–10. Ratio of thermal resistance at given air flow to natural convection thermal resistance versus air flow in cubic feet per minute (cfm). Natural convection thermal resistance taken at power level that yields 50°C temperature rise.

But such a normalizing curve is not universal. The percentage decrease in thermal resistance for a given cfm is greater for a small-area heat sink than for a larger one. This is so because a large-area heat sink already has large movements of its boundary layers and small forced convection flows in cfm do not provide a large percentage increase in air flow above the natural convection flow.

Nevertheless, some guidance can be provided by normalizing curves for various ranges of heat sink area. This is shown in Fig. 4–10. There the ratio

$$K2 = \frac{\text{Thermal resistance at given air flow}}{\text{Natural convection thermal resistance at a 50°C } \Delta T \text{ power level}}$$

is plotted against air flow in cfm. The natural convection thermal resistance is taken at a power level yielding a 50°C temperature rise. Curves are shown for heat sink areas ranging from 50 to 1,500 sq in.

It is seen that for a 50-sq-in. heat sink, 20 cfm of cooling air can yield a thermal resistance 0.20 times as great as its value under natural convection conditions. In contrast, as discussed above, a 500-sq-in. heat sink at 20 cfm has its thermal resistance decreased to only 0.67 times its value under natural convection conditions.

Figures 4–7 to 4–10 are used to calculate the thermal resistance of any given heat sink area at any power level and any volume of cooling air. Thus, if the heat sink area is given, its 1-W thermal resistance can be read from Fig. 4–7. Its natural convection thermal resistance at any other power level is obtained by using the proper multiplying factor read from Fig. 4–8, or temperature rise for any heat sink area and power level can be read directly from Fig. 4–9. Finally, its thermal resistance with forced-air cooling is found for any heat sink area from Fig. 4–10, where it is given in terms of the natural convection thermal resistance at the power level resulting in a 50°C temperature rise. This latter is read from Fig. 4–9.

Figure 4–10 is an empirical relation and represents the average of measurements on what a large number of heat sink vendors achieve. Taken together, Figs. 4–7, 4–8, and 4–9 yield temperature estimates accurate to 8–10°C.

This is sufficiently accurate to provide guidance in an initial design. A more precise prediction for a given heat sink area and cfm of cooling air must depend on exact measurements by the heat sink manufacturer.

Design Example: Required cfm of Cooling Air for Desired Temperature Rise

In the design example of Sect. 4.4.2, it was seen that under natural convection conditions a heat sink area of 1,700 sq in. is required to limit the temperature rise to 40°C with 200 W flowing into the heat sink.

Now consider what can be achieved with forced-air cooling. Assume a heat sink area of 500 sq in. and calculate the required volume of cooling air:

1. For ΔT of 40°C at 200 W, the required thermal resistance is 40/200 = 0.2°C/watt.
2. For 500 sq in. area, Fig. 4–9 shows the thermal resistance for 50°C temperature rise under natural convection is 50/100 = 0.5°C/watt. Then for this to drop to 0.2°C/watt, a $K2$ factor in Fig. 4–10 of 0.2/0.5 or 0.4 is required. Now Fig. 4–10 shows at 500 sq in. area, a $K2$ factor of 0.4 is obtained at 54 cfm of cooling air.
3. From Fig. 4–2, for 500 sq in. of heat sink, using an Astrodyne heat sink type 2506 (39.1 sq in./inch of length), a length of 500/39.1 = 12.7 in. is required.

It is to be noted that, to achieve the required air flow, the fan output air must be ducted into the entrance to the heat sink, and sufficient air pressure must be available from the fan to overcome the heat sink's air flow resistance. The heat sink vendor generally specifies the required pressure differential to achieve a given air flow.

4.4.4 Heat Sink Thermal Resistance/Volume Relationship

It might initially be thought that increasing the heat sink fins indefinitely by spacing them closer together would increase total area and decrease thermal resistance indefinitely. But a point is reached at which the boundary layers providing the cooling interfere with one another, and little further decrease in thermal resistance results from closer fin spacing.

Most vendors have designed their heat sinks for optimum spacing and then the only way to decrease thermal resistance is to add more fin area either in height or width of the heat sink. This then increases volume of the outer envelope of the heat sink. Hence, for any given thermal resistance, the total volume occupied by the outer envelope of the heat sink is relatively constant.

An empirical curve showing thermal resistance for a given heat-sink envelope volume is shown in Fig. 4–11. It is for a 10-W power level in the heat sink. For any other power level, thermal resistance should be converted to resistance at the 10-W power level using Fig. 4–8 as discussed in Sect. 3.2.1. Volume of the heat sink can then be read from Fig. 4–11, which is a purely empirical curve derived from the available volume/thermal resistance data in the data sheets of a large number of vendors.

Figure 4–11 is often valuable in estimating whether the specifications of a power supply in cubic inches can be met when one takes into account the volume required by the heat sink alone.

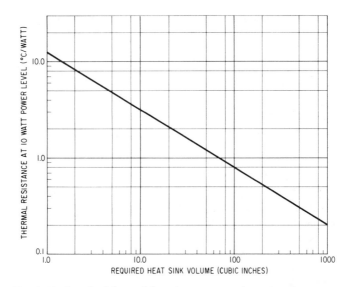

Fig. 4–11. Required heat sink volume versus thermal resistance at a 10-W power level. For other wattages, convert to the equivalent 10-W power level from Fig. 4–8.

4.5   Transistor Power Dissipation Ratings

Vendors generally specify maximum transistor power dissipation at 25°C case temperature for power transistors. For lower-power (generally TO5, TO18 case) transistors, maximum power-dissipation capability is also specified at 25°C ambient temperature.

These maximum power-dissipation specifications are often misunderstood or misinterpreted. The maximum dissipation for a 25°C case temperature is that power dissipation which will bring the transistor junction temperature to its maximum value (usually 200°C) if the case is kept firmly at 25°C by a heat sink. Thus, for the specified θ_{jc} (Junction-to-case thermal resistance), the maximum permissible dissipation is given by

$$T_{j(\text{max})} - 25 = 200 - 25 = PD_{\text{max}}\theta_{jc} \tag{4-6}$$

Or $$PD_{\text{max}} = 175/\theta_{jc}$$

If, as in Sect. 4.3.1, transistor junction temperature is to be permitted to go no higher than 105°C, the maximum permissible power dissipation for a 25°C case is

$$PD_{\text{max}} = (105 - 25)/\theta_{jc} = 80/\theta_{jc} \tag{4-7}$$

If the transistor were mounted by itself on a heat sink whose thermal resistance from heat sink to ambient air was θ_{hsa}, and the heat sink (as often specified) was in a maximum ambient air environment of 70°C, then for a 105°C maximum junction temperature:

$$T_{j(\text{max})} = T_a + \theta_{hsa}PD_{\text{max}} + \theta_{iw}PD_{\text{max}} + \theta_{jc}PD_{\text{max}} \tag{4-8}$$

Or $$105 = 70 + PD_{max}(\theta_{hsa} + \theta_{iw} + \theta_{jc})$$

where θ_{hsa} is the heat-sink-to-ambient thermal resistance, θ_{iw} is the insulating washer thermal resistance, and θ_{jc} is the transistor-to-case thermal resistance.

It is instructive to see how PD_{max} varies for the conditions of Eqs. 4–6 to 4–8. Thus, for the 2N3771 (an often-used transistor for series-pass applications) with $\theta_{jc} = 1.17°C/watt$, $\theta_{iw} = 0.8°C/watt$, and $\theta_{hsa} = 3°C/watt$, for the conditions of Eq. 4–6,

$$PD_{max} = 175/1.17 = 150 \text{ W}$$

(i.e., the maximum power-dissipation specification is derived from the above.) For the conditions of Eq. 4–7,

$$PD_{max} = 80/1.17 = 68.4 \text{ W}$$

And, finally, for the conditions of Eq. 4–8,

$$PD_{max} = \frac{35}{3.0 + 0.8 + 1.17} = \frac{35}{4.97} = 7.0 \text{ W}$$

Thus, the "150-W" rating for the 2N3771 has become 7.0 W for the realistic conditions of Eq. 4–8.

It is finally instructive to examine the maximum power-dissipation capability of the 2N3771 if it were mounted on a printed circuit (PC) board with no heat sink other than the surface area of its TO3 case. Figure 4–7 shows for the approximately 2.4-sq-in. area of a TO3 case, its case-to-ambient air thermal resistance is 42°C/watt. Then for a junction-to-case thermal resistance of 1.17°C/watt, the total resistance from junction to air is $1.17 + 42 = 43$ °C/watt. Thus, the transistor would reach 200°C junction temperature and very likely fail at a power dissipation of only

$$PD_{max} = 175/\theta_{ja} = 175/43 = 4.1 \text{ W}$$

4.5.1 Junction-to-Ambient Air Thermal Resistance

Low-power transistors are often mounted on a printed circuit board without heat sinks. It is generally necessary to perform junction temperature calculations to meet some maximum specified limit. These calculations are easily done by recognizing that the junction-to-ambient thermal resistance (θ_{ja}) is equal to the junction-to-case resistance (θ_{jc}) plus the case-to-air resistance (θ_{ca}) or

$$\theta_{ja} = \theta_{jc} + \theta_{ca} \tag{4-9}$$

Values of θ_{ja} for various transistor cases can be read from Fig. 4–7. Values of θ_{jc} are always quoted in the vendor's specification or calculated by Eq. 4–6 from the vendor's maximum dissipation specification at 25°C case temperature.

In Fig. 4–8 it can be seen that θ_{ca} for TO5 and TO18 cases is about 160 W and 300°C/watt, respectively. If these are too high, there are available a large number of clip-on heat sinks that can bring θ_{ca} down to the region of 25°C/watt for TO18 devices, and as low as 8°C/watt for TO5-type devices. From Eqs. 4–9 and 4–2 and with known power dissipations, junction temperatures for any possible configuration may be calculated.

4.6   Power Transistor Insulating Washers

These washers (Sect. 4.3.1) have always presented problems of various kinds. They have been made with a variety of materials, each of which has some type of drawback. To make good thermal contact and avoid air gaps (Sect. 4.3.5), a high conductivity thermal silicone grease is often used. This is messy to apply, and often the grease can dry out. The washers have been made of beryllium oxide for good thermal conductivity, but these often crack under applied torque at installation or under vibration. Anodized aluminum has been used but scratches on its surface result in shorts through the washer.

The most frequently used material is 2-mil mica. Without grease, a TO3 washer has a thermal resistance of about 0.8°C/watt on the average, but this can be considerably larger with cracks parallel to the plane of the washer.

Silicone rubber-insulating washers have recently become available.[3] They come in relatively large thicknesses: 12 mils as compared to 2 mils for mica. But they are compressed under installation pressure, and for TO3 case washers yield thermal resistances of 0.50°C/watt without the nuisance of grease application. Because of the rubber elasticity, they provide cushioning and prevent air gaps between the mating surfaces.

4.7   Temperature Rise/Air-Flow Rate Calculations for Fan Cooling of Power Supply Cabinets

When the power supply is in an enclosed cabinet, or when an enclosed cabinet contains an entire electronic subsystem, a fan is often used to cool the entire cabinet. The initial question that arises is: How many cfm of air must be drawn through the cabinet to remove a specified amount of heat dissipated in the cabinet and achieve a desired temperature differential between inlet and outlet air?

Often vendors quote neat little equations for specifying the cfm, but it is instructive to see how the relation of cfm, power dissipation, and temperature differential is derived.

Assume a power P in watts is dissipated in a cabinet and that power is to be transferred in calories to a mass of air that will be removed at a rate so that the heat equivalent of the input watts is equal to the calories per second removed by the air. Then,

input calories per second = output calories per second.

Now $1 \text{ W} = 1 \text{ J/sec} = 1/4.185 \text{ cal/sec}$

Input equivalent of P (watts) = $P/4.185$ cal/sec. Now if Q calories are delivered to a mass m_g (grams) of specific heat s (calories/gram/°C), its temperature will rise Δt(°C). Or

$$Q = m_g s(\Delta t)$$

But $m_g = 454 m_p$ (454 g equal 1 lb)
$$= 454 N D$$

---

[3] Berquist Co., Inc., Minneapolis, Minn.

where m_p is the mass in pounds, D is density in pounds per cu ft $= 0.07$ for air at 40°C, and N is the number of cubic feet of the air to be removed. For $s =$ the specific heat of air $= 0.238$ cal/g/°C

$$Q = 454(0.07)(0.238)(N\Delta t)$$
$$= 7.56 N \Delta t$$

And if N cubic feet of air are removed per second, this is $Q/T = 7.56\ N_s \Delta t$ calories per second, where N_s is the number of cubic feet of air per second.

For the input calories per second to equal the output calories per second,

$$P/4.185 = 7.56 N_s \Delta t$$

If the number of cubic feet of air moved out per minute is $N_m = 60\ N_s$, then

$$\Delta t = 60\ P/4.185(7.56)N_m$$

Or $\qquad \Delta t = 1.89\ P/N_m$ $\hfill$ (4–10)

This states that for a power P in watts, dissipated in the cabinet, if the fan moves N_m cubic feet per minute through the cabinet, the temperature rise between inlet and outlet air is $1.89\ P/N_m$ in °C.

It should be noted, of course, that for Eq. 4–9 to hold, the air mass must actually absorb the calories equivalent generated by the P W. That is, the air mass must be ducted past the heat-generating elements, which must transfer their heat to the moving air mass by means of fins.

PROBLEMS

4.1 A transistor in a TO3 case is rated at a maximum junction temperature of 200°C. It has a maximum rated power dissipation of 150 W at a case temperature of 25°C.
    a. What is its junction temperature at an internal dissipation of 150 W and what is its junction-to-case thermal resistance?
    b. Assume that rather than being attached to a heat sink, it is mounted on a printed circuit board where its only radiating area is that of the TO3 case alone. What will its junction temperature be in an ambient of 25°C with only 5 W of internal dissipation?

4.2 Calculate the maximum junction temperature for a transistor dissipating 15 W operating in a location where the maximum operating ambient air temperature is 50°C. Assume the following:
    a. Heat sink thermal resistance $= 0.3$°C/watt.
    b. Insulating washer thermal resistance $= 0.5$°C/watt.
    c. Transistor-junction-to-case thermal resistance $= 1.5$°C/watt.
    d. Total of 200 W flowing into heat sink.

4.3 What value of thermal resistance must a heat sink have under the following conditions?
    a. Maximum transistor junction temperature $= 125$°C.
    b. Total power into heat sink, 300 W.
    c. Transistor thermal resistance $= 1.4$°C/watt.
    d. Insulating washer thermal resistance $= 0.5$°C/watt.
    e. Maximum ambient air temperature $= 60$°C.
    f. Maximum transistor power dissipation $= 18$ W.

4.4 It is desired to pipe heat from one location to another through some cylindrical "heat pipes." Assume there is space for six paralleled solid copper rods, each 0.25 in. in diameter and 12 in. long. What is the thermal resistance of the group of heat pipes?

4.5 Assume a heat sink bottom surface does not make contact over its full area with the chassis on which it rests. Assume its bottom area is 4 × 4 in. and there is a 0.0002-in. air gap between the chassis and bottom of the heat sink. What is the thermal resistance of the air gap?

4.6 A heat sink has an area of 100 sq in. What is its thermal resistance at 1-, 50-, 100-, and 200-W power levels?

4.7 If the heat sink area of Prob. 4.6 is doubled, what are the corresponding thermal resistances?

4.8 If the heat sink area of Prob. 4.6 is quadrupled, what are the corresponding thermal resistances?

4.9 For a 100-sq-in. heat sink, what power level results in a 50°C temperature rise? What is the thermal resistance at the 50°C temperature rise?

4.10 Repeat Prob. 4.9 for 200-, 300-, 400-, and 500-sq in. heat sinks.

4.11 For a 300-sq-in. heat sink, what is the natural convection thermal resistance at a 50°C temperature rise and what is the power level resulting in that temperature rise? For the same heat sink, what is the thermal resistance at 20, 30, 40, and 50 cfm of cooling air and the temperature rise at these cooling rates for power dissipations of 200 and 300 W?

4.12 How many cfm of cooling air is required to keep the temperature rise in a cabinet to 10°C with a total of 1,000 W of dissipation inside the cabinet?

5
Elements of Rectifier Design

5.0   Introduction

Rectifier diodes and filter elements, for either ac power frequency input or high-frequency inverter output use, are not very failure prone and do not generally present significant design problems.

The design decisions consist mainly of selecting rectifiers with adequate peak inverse voltage, maximum forward current, and power dissipation and turn-on surge current ratings. Forward voltage drop and slope of the V–I curve is predetermined once a silicon diode of the proper maximum current rating is chosen. Most silicon rectifier forward voltage drops will range around 1.0 ± 0.2 V if properly chosen.

Manufacturers' maximum limits for these parameters should be derated adequately for reliability and a safe worst-case design. Rectifiers for high-frequency inverter output use must be of the high-speed type and must be specified for reverse recovery time after a pulse of forward current of prescribed amplitude.

The effect of input voltage and current transients on the power supply itself, its input source, and crosstalk to other elements in a system must be considered. Filter capacitors, whether at the input in an off-the-ac-line rectifier or reflected into the primary in transformer input supplies, present a zero impedance load before they reach full charge. Their effects – especially if an input switch is thrown at the peak of the ac sine wave in 208-V ac line sources – should be examined. The initial high-input current surge may blow input fuses, open circuit breakers, exceed rectifier surge current ratings or generate crosstalk, and change states of flip-flops in parts of the system that may already be turned on.

Thermal calculations on the rectifiers must be performed and a heat sink design done which ensures safe rectifier junction temperature at the worst-case power dissipation in the rectifiers.

Rectified ac line filters are almost always of the capacitive input type. Input filter capacitors generally occupy a large fraction of the power supply volume and must be chosen carefully. Their manufacturers' maximum voltage rating should be derated to withstand safely the highest input voltage transient at the highest steady-state input voltage.

127

CONFIGURATION	CIRCUIT	V_{in}	$V_{o(peak)}$	V_o dc	PEAK INVERSE VOLTAGE PER DIODE	RMS RIPPLE VOLTAGE	FUNDAMENTAL OUTPUT RIPPLE FREQUENCY*	OUTPUT WAVEFORM
	SINGLE-PHASE HALF WAVE	V_{rms}	$1.41\,V_{rms}$	$\frac{1}{\pi}V_{o(peak)}$ $=0.45\,V_{rms}$	$1.41\,V_{rms}$	$0.54\,V_{rms}$	$1\,F_L$	
	SINGLE-PHASE CENTER TAP	V_{rms}	$1.41\,V_{rms}$	$\frac{2}{\pi}V_{o(peak)}$ $=0.90\,V_{rms}$	$2.82\,V_{rms}$	$0.43\,V_{rms}$	$2\,F_L$	
	SINGLE-PHASE BRIDGE	V_{rms}	$1.41\,V_{rms}$	$\frac{2}{\pi}V_{o(peak)}$ $=0.90\,V_{rms}$	$1.41\,V_{rms}$	$0.43\,V_{rms}$	$2\,F_L$	
	THREE-PHASE WYE V_{rms} LINE TO NEUTRAL	V_{rms}	$1.41\,V_{rms}$	$1.17\,V_{rms}$	$2.45\,V_{rms}$	$0.21\,V_{rms}$	$3\,F_L$	
	THREE-PHASE BRIDGE V_{rms} LINE TO LINE	V_{rms}	$1.41\,V_{rms}$	$1.35\,V_{rms}$	$2.45\,V_{rms}$	$0.057\,V_{rms}$	$6\,F_L$	

*F_L = LINE FREQUENCY

Magnitude of the capacitance must be selected by a calculation whose inputs are the maximum permissible peak-to-peak ripple voltage at the highest dc load current and lowest line frequency.

Value of the average dc output voltage from the rectifier–filter combination must be calculated at maximum ac input voltage for series-pass regulator designs. In such regulators, series-pass transistor dissipation is a maximum at maximum ac input voltage, and this dissipation must be calculated for a safe thermal design.

Value of the minimum voltage at the bottom of the ripple triangle at minimum line voltage must be calculated to ensure that the series-pass regulators either directly off the rectified ac line or at the rectified secondary output of a line transformer still have a minimum of 2 V across the collector-emitter junction of the series-pass element to avoid saturation.

Values of the highest voltage at the top of the ripple triangle at maximum steady-state input voltage must be calculated for the highest specified line voltage transient. This becomes important — especially in off-the-ac-line rectifiers with 208 V input — since this peak voltage is applied directly across the collector-emitter junction of series-switch step-down switching regulators (Fig. 1–4), and there are a limited number of power transistors that can survive such voltages — generally above 400 V. Details of such design calculations and problems are presented in this chapter.

5.1   Rectifier Circuits and Output–Input Relationships for Resistive Loads

Rectifiers for present-day power supplies are almost always followed by large capacitive input filters that charge up to voltages close to the peak of the ac sine wave and have ripple voltage outputs proportional to dc load current. Thus, the conventional charts showing output dc voltages and ripple for pure resistive loads are not too pertinent. Nevertheless, since output characteristics with a capacitive filter are related to characteristics with a pure resistive load, output–input relationships with latter-type loads are shown in Fig. 5–1.

It can be seen from the waveforms in Fig. 5–1 that with a purely resistive load and no filter capacity the rectified output moves from the peak of the ac sine wave down to zero volts in single-phase rectifiers. The dc or average value of these waveforms is shown in column 5. For most applications, a relatively smooth, ripple-free dc voltage is required.

Filter capacitors at the output provide the energy storage to supply current to the loads in the interval between rectified peaks.

If the voltage is to be held up by the filter capacitor for the full time between rectifier peaks, it is seen in Fig. 5–1 that in the half-wave rectifier, the capacitor must supply full load current for a full cycle of the line frequency or 16.6 msec for 60 Hz.

For the single-phase, full-wave center tap or bridge, the filter capacitor must supply load current by itself for a half cycle or 8.3 msec at 60 Hz. In the

Fig. 5–1. Characteristics of often-used rectifier circuits with an unfiltered resistive load.

three-phase, line-to-neutral, half-wave "wye," peaks come at intervals of one-third of a period and the filter capacitor must supply current for 16.6/3 or 5.5 msec. Finally in the three-phase, full-wave bridge, the filter capacitor supplies the full load current for one-sixth of a cycle or 16.6/6 or 2.8 msec at 60 Hz line frequency.

It is these time intervals and the load currents that determine the size of the filter capacitor required to yield any specified peak-to-peak ripple.

5.2   Capacitive Input Filters

In most present-day supplies, filters are of the capacitive input type. The waveform at the output of a single-phase, full-wave rectifier with resistive load and a capacitive filter is shown in Fig. 5–2. Without the filter capacity, the rectified output waveform would follow the dotted line down to zero.

On the first positive half cycle after turnon, say, as A goes sinusoidally positive, the capacitor C_o follows it upward without a time delay, since the impedance of silicon diodes is small. C_o thus rides up with A, lagging only one diode drop or 1 V behind A. As A reaches its peak and starts moving down its sine wave, if capacitor C_o has been chosen large enough to supply the load current by itself, diode D1 becomes reverse biased, C_o stays up near the peak it had reached, and the anode of D1 simply moves down, increasing its reverse bias.

Now C_o is chosen large enough to supply the full load current for the entire half cycle until B rises high enough to forward bias D2. Then transformer end B replenishes the small charge C_o had lost on the previous half cycle in supplying the load current by itself. B also supplies some of the load current during the small conduction interval T_c when D2 is forward biased.

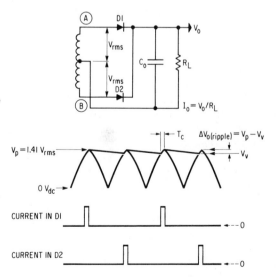

Fig. 5–2. Ripple output voltage and rectifier diode current in a single-phase, full-wave rectifier with capacitive input filter.

5.2.1 Output Ripple/Filter Capacitance and Load-Current Relationship

During most of the half cycle, C_o is large enough so that it can supply the full load current with only a negligible voltage droop. Thus, during each half cycle when C_o is supplying current, that current is substantially constant. For a constant current I_o in a capacitor C_o, its rate of change of voltage is given by $dV/dt = I_o/C_o$.

The exact time interval during which C_o alone supplies current is fixed by the permissible peak-to-peak ripple voltage. The peak of the ripple triangle, V_p, can be assumed to be at the peak of the ac sine wave (assuming negligible rectifier diode drop). For ripple valley voltage of V_v, the filter capacitor conduction angle is, from Fig. 5-2, $\theta_c = 90° + \arcsin V_v/V_p$. The duration of time during which the filter capacitor supplies the load current by itself in a 60-Hz, single-phase, full-wave rectifier is $T_c = (\theta_c/180)(8.33)$ msec.

Filter capacitor conduction angles and times are shown in Fig. 5-3 for various values of V_v/V_p. Generally, ripple voltages will not be permitted larger than about 10% of V_p. From Fig. 5-3, for peak-to-peak ripple voltages of 0.1 V_p, it is seen that the filter capacitor conduction time is 7.14 msec for a 60-Hz, single-phase, full-wave rectifier. But, in general, in calculating the required magnitude of the filter capacitor, for simplicity it is often assumed it must carry current for the entire half cycle or 8.33 msec. This provides margin for capacitor tolerance and variation with temperature. Then assuming full half-cycle conduction angle for the filter capacitor, the peak-to-peak ripple is

$$\Delta V_o = (I_o/C_o)T/2 \qquad (5-1)$$

For a permissible droop or peak-to-peak ripple of ΔV_o, the size of the required capacitor is

$$C_o = (I_o/\Delta V_o)T/2 \qquad (5-2)$$

and at 60 Hz,

$$C_o = (I_o/\Delta V_o)(8.33 \times 10^{-3}) \text{ farads} \qquad \text{(for } I_o \text{ in amperes} \qquad (5-3)$$
$$\text{and } \Delta V_o \text{ in volts)}$$

Peak ripple voltage (V_p)	Ripple valley voltage (V_v)	Peak-to-peak ripple voltage ($\Delta V_o = V_p - V_v$)	Filter capacitor conduction angle ($90° + \arcsin V_v/V_p$)	Filter capacitor current carrying time for 60-Hz single-phase, full-wave (msec)
V_p	0.95 V_p	0.05 V_p	161.8°	7.48
V_p	0.90 V_p	0.10 V_p	154.2°	7.14
V_p	0.85 V_p	0.15 V_p	148.2°	6.86
V_p	0.80 V_p	0.20 V_p	143.1°	6.62
V_p	0.75 V_p	0.25 V_p	138.6°	6.41

Fig. 5-3. Filter capacitor conduction angle and current carrying time in 60-Hz, single-phase, full-wave rectifier with capacitive input filter.

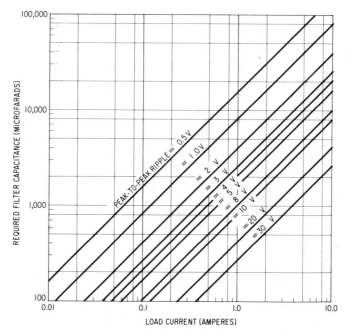

Fig. 5–4. Required filter capacity versus dc load current. For various peak-to-peak ripple voltages in a 60-Hz single-phase center-tap or bridge rectifier, as calculated from Eq. 5–3 under the following conditions: peak-to-peak ripple less than 10% of output voltage, and capacitor assumed to carry a dc load current for a full half cycle.

Equation 5–3 has been plotted in Fig. 5–4 for various permissible peak-to-peak ripple voltages. It applies, of course, only for a "constant" current or for a small ΔV_o — say, no more than 10% of the absolute output voltage. Also, it applies only for 60 Hz. For other frequencies, ripple at various load currents and filter capacitors is calculated from Eq. 5–2.

5.2.2 Filter Capacitance Proportional to Load Current

Equation 5–3 or Fig. 5–4 can be used to select the required value for the filter capacity for any desired peak-to-peak ripple at any load current, but a more convenient way of handling or remembering what Eq. 5–3 states is to make the filter capacity proportional to load current. Then from Eq. 5–3

$$\Delta V_o = (I_o/C_o)(8.33 \times 10^{-3})$$

And for $C_o = kI_o$,

$$\Delta V_o = (8.33 \times 10^{-3})/k \qquad (5\text{–}4)$$

The proportionality constant k will generally range from 1,000 to 4,000 μF/ampere of load current for a line frequency of 60 Hz and from 500 to 2,000 μF/ampere for a line frequency of 400 Hz. Equation 5–4 is plotted in Fig. 5–5. A usual value of k for 60 Hz single-wave rectifiers is 3,000 μF/ampere of load current. From Fig. 5–5, it is seen this results in 2.75 V peak-to-peak ripple voltage.

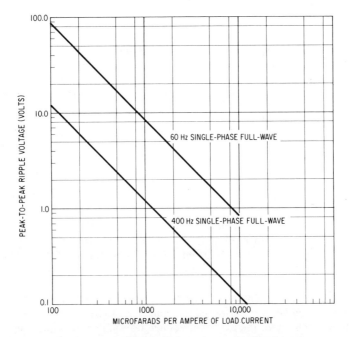

Fig. 5–5. Peak-to-peak ripple voltage versus microfarads per ampere of load current for a single-phase, full-wave rectifier with capacitive input filter. Plotted from Eq. 5–4.

It can be assumed the peak of the ripple triangle is one silicon diode or 1 V below the positive peak of the ac sine wave at the anode of the rectifier diode for positive-rectified outputs. For negative-rectified outputs, the ripple triangle peak is 1 V above the negative sine wave peak. For a peak-to-peak ripple of ΔV_o the average or dc output at the top of the filter capacitor is

$$V_{\mathrm{dc}} = V_p - \Delta V_o/2 = 1.41\, V_{\mathrm{rms}} - 1 - \Delta V_o/2 \qquad (5\text{–}5)$$

5.3 Rectifier Diode Characteristics and Ratings

The significant rectifier ratings for any proposed application are the peak repetitive reverse voltage $V_{rm(rep)}$, average rectified forward current I_o, nonrepetitive forward surge current $I_{fm(surge)}$, I^2t rating, and junction-to-case thermal resistance θ_{jc}. These ratings together with the forward volt–ampere characteristics must be considered in any rectifier application.

5.3.1 Peak Repetitive Reverse Voltage Rating (V_{rm}) and Input Transients

This is the maximum anode-to-cathode reverse voltage that the vendor specifies shall be allowed across the diode. Good worst-case design practice is to derate the vendor's specified value. Here too there is no industry concensus on what constitutes safe derating factors. An often-used factor is 0.6–0.7, i.e., no more than 0.6–0.7 of the manufacturer's rated maximum voltage shall be permitted across the rectifier repetitively.

Most manufacturers[1] add a transient reverse voltage specification. This is the momentary reverse voltage the device can withstand on a nonrepetitive basis. Some vendors specify it as being no more than 5 msec in duration, while others have it as a single half cycle of a 60-Hz sine wave. This transient reverse voltage limit is generally twice the normal reverse voltage rating for rectifiers with reverse ratings up to 200 V. From 200 to 1,000 V, the transient specification ranges from 1.75 down to 1.33 times the normal reverse voltage rating.

Very little information is obtainable as to exactly how often such a "nonrepetitive" transient voltage can be applied. It is surely more than once in a lifetime of the device, but nothing is known about the cumulative effect of such transients.

The amplitude and duration of power line transients vary widely and depend on the nature of the prime power source. Transients are spelled out most specifically for military power sources. Thus, equipment to be used on navy ships are often specified to be able to withstand transients described in Mil Standard 1399, "Interface Electric Power Standards for Shipboard Systems" (Fig. 5–6). Equipment powered from DOD (Department of Defense) mobile electric generator sets must withstand transients described in Mil Standard 1332A (Fig. 5–7). There are various classes of prime power sources described in these documents – each having its own transient characteristic. All characteristics of these sources are too varied and numerous to be presented here in detail, but a short summary of the expected voltage transients and voltage regulation is given in Figs. 5–6 and 5–7.

The transients spelled out in Fig. 5–6 are to be assumed superimposed on the worst-case, steady-state voltages. Thus, for a type 1 navy power source, the steady-state tolerance for a single phase of a three-phase system is $\pm7\%$. A voltage transient of $\pm18\%$ superimposed on this makes the worst power line voltage $(7 + 18)$ or $+25\%$ above its nominal value. The waveform during this voltage transient is the normal sinusoid but of an amplitude 25% above its nominal value. The duration of this transient from Fig. 5–6 is 2 sec – long enough to charge the filter capacity to 25% above its normal value. Thus, in the single-phase center-tap rectifier with a capacitive input filter, the peak inverse voltage per rectifier diode is $2.82V_{rms(nom)}$. With a $+25\%$ transient, the maximum reverse voltage the rectifier diode is subjected to is $(1.25)(2.82)V_{rms}$ or $3.5V_{rms(nom)}$.

Also from Fig. 5–7, it can be seen that a 3-kW DOD generator has $\pm5\%$ regulation, $\pm4\%$ long-term stability, and a $+30\%$ transient lasting 4 sec at rejection of full-rated load. This adds up to a possible peak of $(5 + 4 + 30)$ or 39% above normal rms voltage. The rectifier diode can thus be subjected to a possible peak inverse voltage of $2.82V_{rms(max)} = (2.82)(1.39)V_{rms(nom)}$ or $3.9V_{rms(nom)}$ lasting for 4 sec.

Since the price and size of rectifier diodes do not change significantly with increased reverse voltage rating, diodes with adequate margin against the worst-case voltage transients should be selected. There are various transient suppression schemes available, but these generally require a series voltage dropping element (inductor or possibly a resistor) and a shunt element having low impedance above some threshold level. Such schemes are space consuming and

---

[1]RCA, 1N1200A rectifier family. Motorola, Inc., MR1120 rectifier family.

Electrical Power System Characteristics

Characteristic	Power Source Type		
	Type I	*Type II*	*Type III*
Nominal utilization voltage (V_{rms})	440 or 115	440 or 115	440, 115, or 115/200
Nominal frequency (Hz)	60 or 400	60 or 400	400
Steady-state voltage			
a. Steady-state tolerance band			
1. Average of 3-phase voltages	±5%	±1%	±$\frac{1}{2}$%
2. Phase voltage for single-phase			
of 3-phase system	±7%	±2$\frac{1}{3}$%	±1$\frac{1}{6}$%
b. Unbalance	3%	2%	1%
c. Voltage modulation	2%	2%	1%
d. Waveform			
1. Total harmonic distortion	5%	6%	3%
2. Maximum single harmonic	3%	4%	2%
3. Deviation factor	5%	5%	5%
Voltage transient			
a. Voltage transient limits	±18%	±18%	±5%
b. Recovery time (sec)	2	0.25 @ 400 Hz and 0.75 sec @ 60 Hz	0.25
Spike voltage (volts)	2500 (peak)	2500 (peak)	2500 (peak)
Steady-state frequency			
a. Tolerance band	±5%	±5%	±$\frac{1}{2}$%
b. Modulation limits	$\frac{1}{2}$%	$\frac{1}{2}$%	$\frac{1}{2}$%
Frequency transient			
a. Frequency transient limits	±3%	±3%	±1%
b. Recovery time (sec)	2	2	0.25
Typical power interruption time (sec)	0.5–20	0.5–20	0.5–3

Fig. 5–6. Transient and steady-state voltage characteristics of Navy shipboard power sources as per Mil Standard 1399A.

not practical for transients as wide as a half cycle of 60 Hz, since the series inductance becomes too large.

For narrow transients (under about 1 msec), a series inductor (the input rfi filter) and a thresholding shunt element, such as a pair of back-to-back power zener diodes[2] become feasible. Another possible shunt element is a nonlinear resistor such as "Thyrite"[3] a proprietary G.E. material in which current is proportional to some high power (up to seventh power) of the applied voltage. Thyrite comes as resistors in the shape of rods and discs with various power and resistance ratings. Application notes on the use of Thyrite in transient suppression circuits are available from the vendor.

Equipment designed to be powered from commercial power lines should be designed for the worst expected transients on these lines. Surprisingly, utility companies do not offer much information on the worst expected transients.

---

[2] Motorola Application Note AN-461, "Transient Suppression with Power Zener Diodes."

[3] General Electric Co., Apparatus Dept., Schenectady, N.Y., "Thyrite — A Non-Linear Resistance Material."

Voltage Characteristics (Maximum or Minimum Limits)

Characteristic	Precise (Class 1)		AC Utility (Class 2)					
	KW-DED		KW-DED	KW-GED		KW-DED		
	15–60	100–200	0.5–1.5	3–5	10	5–10	15–200	500–1500
Regulation (%)	1	1	5	5	4	3	3	2
Steady-state stability (variation; bandwith %)								
a. Short term (30 sec)	1	1	2	2	2	2	2	1
b. Long term (4 hr)	2	2	4	4	4	4	4	2
Transient performance								
a. Application of rated load								
1. Dip (%)	15 @ 60 Hz and 12 @ 400 Hz	15 @ 60 Hz and 12 @ 400 Hz	30	30	20	20	20	20
2. Recovery (sec)	0.5	0.5	4	4	4	3	3	3
b. Rejection of rated load								
1. Rise (%)	15 @ 60 Hz and 12 @ 400 Hz	15 @ 60 Hz and 12 @ 400 Hz	30	30	20	20	20	30
2. Recovery (sec)	0.5	0.5	4	4	4	3	3	3
c. Application of simulated motor load (twice rated current)								
1. Dip (%)	30 @ 60 Hz and 25 @ 400 Hz	30 @ 60 Hz and 25 @ 400 Hz	N/A	N/A	40	35	40	N/A
2. Recovery to 95% rated voltage (sec)	0.7	0.7	N/A	N/A	5	5	5	N/A

Fig. 5–7. Transient and steady-state voltage characteristics of DOD mobile electric power generators as per Mil Standard 1332A.

Transients are put onto power lines not by the generators themselves alone, but by high-current motor-type loads turning on and off. The amplitude and duration of such load-caused transients depend on the size and source impedance of the local power line transformers and load-current changes. Factory environments with large and frequent motor switching loads have larger transients than office, residential, or light industry environments.

In general, a safe design for equipment powered from commercial power lines should assume line voltage transients (envelope of the normal ac sine wave) of $\pm 15\%$ above the normal steady-state voltage tolerance, which is usually $\pm 10\%$. Duration of such transients should be assumed at 2–4 sec.

5.3.2 Rectifier Peak Reverse Voltages with Capacitive Input Filters

The peak inverse voltages per rectifier shown in Fig. 5–1 hold unchanged for single-phase rectifiers with capacitive input filters. For the three-phase circuits of Fig. 5–1, with capacitive input filter, peak inverse voltage per rectifier increases from 2.45 to $2.82V_{rms}$.

5.3.3 Maximum Average Forward-Rectified Current (I_o)

This is the maximum permissible value of the average load or diode current in a half-wave rectifier with resistive load and no capacitive filtering. In a full-wave center-tap or bridge rectifier, the total load current can be twice the specified value, since this amounts to the same average current per diode.

This current is specified generally at 150°C case temperature and is that average current in resistor loaded half-wave rectifier service (where $I_{average} = (1/\pi)I_{peak}$ which results in the maximum specified junction temperature for the specified thermal resistance from junction to case.

In multiphase rectifiers, since conduction takes place over only part of a half cycle, the ratio of peak to average current is greater, and since heating effect is proportional to the square of the current, the heating effect or rms value of a narrow large-amplitude current waveform is greater than that of a smaller wider current waveform of the same average value.

Hence, maximum average forward current limits for the same rectifier diode are lower for multiphase rectifier service. Correspondingly, the forward current limit is greatest for dc (or half-cycle, square-wave current pulses in the rectifier).

This can be seen in Fig. 5–8A for a typical 12-A I_o rectifier family — the Motorola MR 1120. Values of I_o are only a guide in the initial selection of the rectifier diode for its current rating. The final criterion is the junction temperature that will be permitted under worst-case load conditions.

Junction temperature is calculated just as for a transistor (Sect. 4.3.1) from the ambient temperature, power dissipation, and thermal resistances. Thus,

$$T_{j(max)} = T_a + PD_{HS}\,\theta_{hsa} + PD_D(\theta_{iw} + \theta_{jc}) \tag{5-6}$$

where $T_{j(max)}$ is the maximum junction temperature, T_a is the maximum ambient temperature, PD_{HS} is the total power dissipated in heat sink (all rectifier diodes if they are on the same heat sink), θ_{hsa} is the thermal resistance from heat sink to ambient air, PD_D is the power dissipation per rectifier diode, θ_{iw} is the thermal

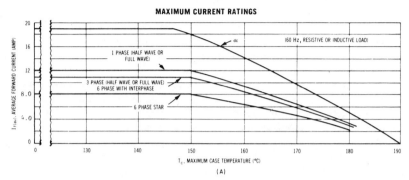

Fig. 5–8A. Maximum average current ratings showing lower permissible currents for multiphase rectifiers because of the higher rms currents for shorter conducting periods. (*Courtesy* Motorola, Inc.)

resistance of diode insulating washer, and θ_{jc} is the thermal resistance of diode junction to case.

Power dissipation per diode is read from Fig. 5–8B for the type of rectifier — single or multiphase, sine wave ac or dc if input is a square wave. The average forward current is, of course, the current per diode. Thus, in a center-tap or bridge rectifier, the forward current per diode for entering Fig. 5–8B is one-half the dc output current. In the three-phase line to neutral "wye" or three-phase bridge, the current at which Fig. 5–8B is read is one-third the dc output current. The curves of Fig. 5–8B apply only for resistive loads without capacitive filters.

A decision must be made as to how high rectifier diode temperatures shall be permitted to go. Although the vendors establish 190–200°C as maximum limits for ac line frequency rectifiers, a good worst-case design should derate this. A frequent derating factor for rectifier junction temperatures is 65–70% of the vendor's specified maximum value.

5.3.4 Rectifier Diode Dissipation with Capacitive Input Filters and Sine-Wave Power Input

It is of interest to examine the rectifier diode dissipation with a capacitive input filter. For with large filter capacitors to keep peak-to-peak ripple low, the rectifier diode current, as can be seen in Fig. 5–2, is a narrow, high-amplitude spike. This has a high rms value and the question arises as to whether the diode junction temperature limit will be exceeded. Junction temperature calculations are done as in the following example.

Assume a 30-V, 5-A, single-phase power supply with center-tap transformer. Choose a peak-to-peak output ripple of 2 V. From Fig. 5–4, at 5 A load current, for 2 V peak-to-peak ripple, the required filter capacitor is 21,000 μF. Assume the ripple is centered about 30 V, i.e., output moves from $+31$ to $+29$. Thus, in Fig. 5–2, the peak of the sine wave is at $+31$ V at 90° of phase angle. Conduction starts at $+29$ V on a sine wave whose peak is at $+31$. Conduction then starts at a phase angle θ such that

$$29 = 31 \sin \theta \quad \text{or} \quad \theta = 69.3°$$

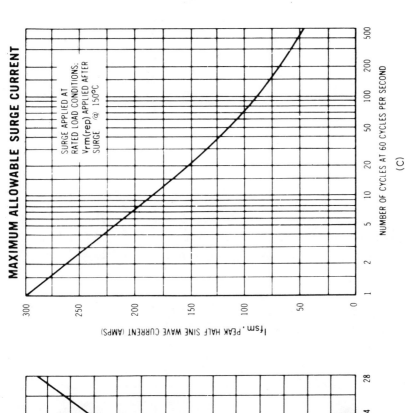

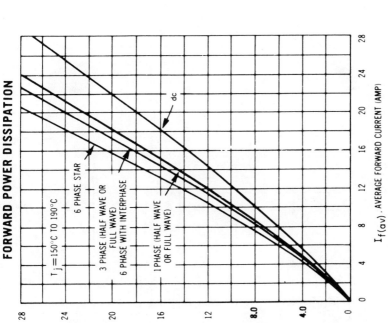

Fig. 5–8 B and C. Significant characteristics of a typical 12-A power frequency rectifier: the MR1120. (*Courtesy* Motorola, Inc.)

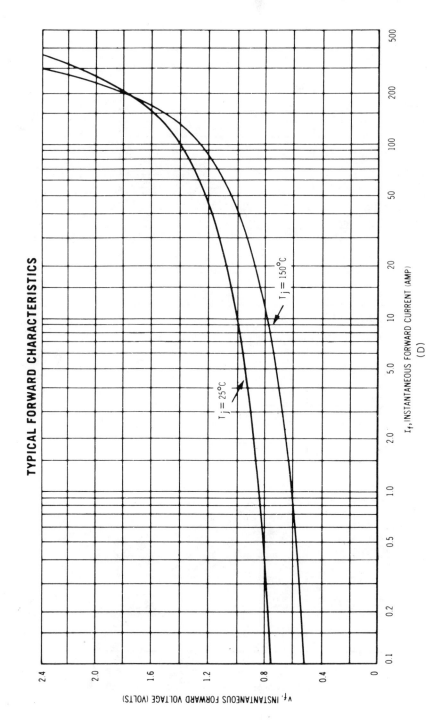

Fig. 5–8D. Significant characteristics of a typical 12-A power frequency rectifier: the MR1120. (*Courtesy* Motorola, Inc.)

Duration of the conduction interval is $90 - 69.3$ or $20.6°$. This corresponds to a time (for 60-Hz line frequency) of $(20.6/180)$ 8.3 $= 0.95$ msec.

The transformer, during this 0.95-msec conduction interval, must move a 21,000 μF capacitor up from $+29$ to $+31$ V. This requires an average current of

$$I = \frac{c\Delta V}{\Delta t} = \frac{(21,000 \times 10^{-6})(2)}{0.95 \times 10^{-3}} = 44.2 \text{ A}$$

During this interval, the rectifier diode must carry this 44.2 A plus the 5 A of load current, or a total of 49.2 A.

From Fig. 5–8D, at 49.2 A, the rectifier forward drop is about 1.1 V at a junction temperature of about 140°C. Peak power dissipation during this 0.95-msec interval is then

$$PD = 49.2(1.1) = 54 \text{ W}$$

And this occurs for each diode only 0.95 msec out of every 16.6. Average power is then

$$54(0.95/16.6) = 3.09 \text{ W}$$

And for thermal resistance of junction to case, θ_{jc} of 2°C/watt, the junction rises $3.09(2) = 6.18°$C above the case. This presents no thermal problem. Consider that in Eq. 5–6 it is desired to keep the junction temperature to 140°C. Then in an ambient of 70°C, with $\theta_{iw} = 1$°C/watt, $\theta_{jc} = 2$°C/watt, and two rectifier diodes on the heat sink, its required thermal resistance is from Eq. 5–6: $140 = 70 + 2(3.09)\theta_{hsa} + 3.09(1 + 2)$ or $\theta_{hsa} = 9.8$°C/watt.

And from Fig. 4–8, the K 1 ratio at 9.8 W is 0.7 or the normalized 1-W thermal resistance is $9.8/0.7 = 14°$C/watt. Then from Fig. 4–7, the required heat sink area is only 11 sq in.

It is of interest to note the rectifier diode dissipation for the same situation without a filter capacitor. From Fig. 5–8B, it is seen that for 5 A total dc output or 2.5 A average forward current per rectifier diode, the diode dissipation would be only about 1.8 W. The 3.09 W calculated above is, of course, due to the narrow, large-amplitude spike of current taken by the filter capacitor at the top of the sine wave.

5.3.5 Nonrepetitive Peak Surge Current [$I_{fm \text{(surge)}}$]

This is defined as the peak allowable single half sine wave (duration 8.3 msec) of current spaced in time between the normal maximum amplitude current half sine waves in a 60-Hz, single-phase rectifier. The rms value of this current waveform is the rms value of a half-cycle sine wave within one full cycle. For a peak amplitude I_p, the rms value of this permissible fault current is $I_{rms} = I_p/2$.

Another way of describing this permissible fault current, then, is to say that over any 16.6-msec interval, there can be any waveform of current whose rms value over that 16.6 msec is one-half the peak specified half sine wave.

Thus, for the Motorola MR1120 (Fig. 5–8C), the specified maximum nonrecurrent peak surge current is 300 A. The rms value of this is $I_p/2$ or 150 A. The $I_{fm \text{(surge)}}$ spec thus also permits a square wave of current of 150 A for the full 16.6 msec.

The surge current rating also permits larger number of surge pulses at the 60-Hz rate but of lesser amplitude. This is shown in Fig. 5–8C. High-energy surge pulses can occur at initial turnon, especially with capacitive input filters, when the main power switch is closed at the peak of the input power sine wave.

Directly-off-the-ac-line rectifiers fed from a 208-V ac line source can have trouble with inrush surges exceeding these limits. The usual rfi line filter in series with the rectifier diodes serves to limit inrush current surges.

If there is no such limiting impedance, it is essential in any new design to measure input surges with an oscilloscope and current probe. If limits are exceeded, either a small resistor shorted out by a relay contact after a short time delay may be added. Or it may be more economical in space and dollars not to limit the current surge at all, but simply to go to the rectifier diode with the next higher current rating, since rectifier diodes are quite inexpensive.

There generally is no problem with inrush current surges on rectifiers fed from transformers, for transformer leakage inductance is usually sufficient to provide the limiting action.

5.3.6 I^2t Rating

This is a measure of the maximum energy deliverable to the diode in a single high-current pulse. It is the maximum permissible product of the square of the rms current and its time duration.

I^2t rating is simply another way of expressing the "nonrepetitive peak surge current" $I_{fm(\text{surge})}$ rating and is derivable from it. Thus, in Sect. 5.3.5, it was pointed out that the rms value of $I_{fm(\text{surge})}$ over a full period of 60 Hz is $\frac{1}{2}I_{fm(\text{surge})}$. This rms current can be carried for a full cycle of 60 Hz. Hence, the equivalent I^2t rating is $(\frac{1}{2}I_{fm(\text{surge})})^2(0.0166)$ and its units are square amperes $\times$ seconds.

Thus, the Motorola MR1120 has an $I_{fm(\text{surge})}$ rating of 300 A. Its I^2t rating is then $(300/2)^2(0.0166) = 375$ A^2-sec. This is precisely the value quoted for I^2t in the device data sheets.

5.4   Circuit Considerations

5.4.1 Bridge Versus Center-Tap Rectifiers

The first decision to be made in single-phase rectifiers is the type of circuit configuration: full-wave center tap or full-wave bridge. The half-wave rectifier, especially at power line frequencies, is usable only for low-output currents, for the filter capacitor must supply load current for almost the full cycle of 16.6 msec as contrasted to 8.3 msec for full-wave rectifiers. From Eq. 5–2 it can be seen this requires twice the filter capacitance for the same ripple output voltage. Nevertheless, for high-frequency, square-wave output rectifiers, the half-wave circuit is an economical and often overlooked circuit.

The bridge, center-tap, and half-wave rectifier configurations are shown in Fig. 5–1.

The bridge and center-tap configurations each has its own merits. Because it has two rather than four rectifier diodes, the center-tap circuit dissipates less power, requires less space, and is more economical than the bridge. But for the same dc output voltage, it requires diodes with twice the peak inverse voltage rating. Because the impedance looking back into the rectifier from the load is that of one diode rather than two in series, the center-tap circuit has lower output impedance.

The center-tap circuit results in a larger transformer, since it has twice as many secondary turns for the same dc output voltage. The rms current in the single winding in a bridge is twice that of the current in either half of the center-tap circuit, since the single-bridge winding conducts on each half cycle. Thus, for the same coil current density or temperature rise, the bridge transformer wire size must be greater. Despite this, the bridge circuit, because it has half the number of turns of the center tap, still results in a smaller transformer — this is perhaps its chief advantage.

5.4.2 Three-Phase, Full-Wave Versus Half-Wave, Line-to-Neutral "Wye" Circuits

These rectifier circuits are shown in Fig. 5–1. Usually when three-phase "delta" input is available, the rms line-to-line voltage is 208 V. With a capacitive output filter, the peak dc output voltage is $(1.41)(208) = 293$ V.

If "neutral" is available in a 208 "line-to-line" system, the line-to-neutral voltage is $208/\sqrt{3} = 120$ V. In a three-phase, half-wave "wye" rectifier with capacitive input filter, this yields a dc output of $1.41(120)$ or 169 V.

Now if a dc/dc converter is driven from the dc output of an "off-the-line" rectifier, the inverter transistors, which are subjected to at least twice the dc, will have to withstand $2(1.41)(208)(1.1)$ or 646 V for a 10% high-line, full-wave bridge rectifier. With a half-wave "wye" line rectifier, the transistors are subject to only $169(2)(1.1)$ or 372 V.

There are not many transistors that can withstand with adequate safety margin a dc voltage of 646 V. Thus, if a full-wave bridge rectifier is used, a four-transistor bridge (Sect. 2.2) or a two-transistor half bridge (Sect. 2.3) with bulky capacitors would have to be used. Or alternatively, a series-switch step-down preregulator (Sect. 1.2) would have to be used to step the dc voltage down to roughly 150 V. With 150 V in a two-transistor push–pull dc/dc converter, the power transistors are subjected to 300 V in the off state. This leaves an adequate safety margin for the many available transistors with a 375-volt V_{cer} rating — especially with preregulated dc input.

Thus, the lower available voltage from the three-phase, half-wave, line-to-neutral "wye" rectifier, which yields lower dc output voltage, gives greater degree of freedom in a power supply system design and generally results in fewer components.

5.4.3 Peak and Valley dc Output Voltages for Various Rectifiers with Capacitive Input Filters

Figure 5–9 shows, for useful reference, the peak dc output voltage from directly-off-the-ac-line rectifiers with capacitive input filters. These voltages are shown for commonly used rectifier circuits and common ac line input voltages.

Voltage at the bottom of the ripple triangle is below the peaks by the amplitude of the peak-to-peak ripple. Ripple amplitude is fixed by filter capacity and dc load current and is calculated from Eq. 5–1, where $(T/2)$ is taken as the time between sine wave peaks for the type of rectifier (Sect. 5.1).

Peak dc output voltages are of interest to verify that no semiconductor or capacitor is subjected to a dangerous voltage stress at the highest transient

	Nominal rms input voltage (volts)	Peak dc output voltage (volts)				
Circuit		Nominal ac input	10% high-line input	10% transient above 10% high line	10% low-line input	−10% transient below 10% low line
Single-phase, bridge						
115 line to line	162	178	196	146	131	
120 line to line	169	180	205	152	137	
220 line to line	310	341	375	279	251	
Three-phase, half-wave, "wye"						
115 line to neutral	162	178	196	146	131	
120 line to neutral	169	186	205	152	137	
Three-phase, full-wave, bridge						
208 line to line	293	323	354	264	237	

Fig. 5–9. Peak dc output voltages for commonly used rectifier circuits on common ac line voltages in off-the-ac-line rectifiers.

superimposed on the highest steady-state input voltage. Minimum voltage outputs are examined to ensure that, at the lowest point on the ripple triangle at the largest negative-going transient below the lowest steady-state voltage, series-pass regulator input voltages are still a minimum of 2 V above their desired outputs.

5.4.4 Rectifier Circuits for Various Output Voltage Combinations

A number of frequently occurring, useful rectifier circuits can be obtained by combinations of voltage doubling and bridge or center-tap rectifier configurations. Some of the frequently used ones are presented here in a qualitative fashion.

Conventional Full-Wave Doubler

This is shown in Fig. 5–10C. The circuit is derived from the full-wave bridge. On the half cycle when A is positive relative to B, D2 charges C2 in the polarity shown to a peak voltage $1.41V_{rms}$. On the next half cycle when B is positive relative to A, D1 charges C1 in the polarity shown to $1.41V_{rms}$.

The load is connected between the positive end of C2 and negative end of C1. It is seen the voltages across C1 and C2 add in series to a voltage of $2.82V_{rms}$.

Full- and Half-Output Voltage from Bridge Rectifier

It is often necessary to have an output voltage lower than the full output from a rectifier. This can always be done with an additional transformer winding, of course, but Fig. 5–10A shows how it may be done with only a center tap on a winding for a bridge rectifier.

In Fig. 5–10A, diodes D1–D4 form the conventional bridge rectifier. A load with capacitive filter C2 is bridged between the transformer center tap and the D2–D4 junction. C_o charges up to the conventional $1.41V_{rms}$ of a bridge rectifier. But diodes D4 and D2 act as a full-wave, center-tap rectifier and charge C2 up to $1.41V_{rms}/2$. V_{o1} and V_{o2} have a common negative terminal and are both positive with respect to that terminal.

If R_{L2} is bridged between the center tap and the D1–D3 junction, V_{o1} and V_{o2} will have a common positive terminal, although the voltage magnitudes will be unchanged.

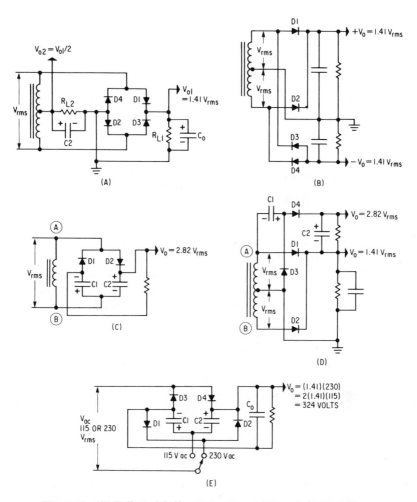

Fig. 5–10. (A) Full- and half-output voltages from a bridge rectifier. (B) Equal positive- and negative-output voltages from the same center-tap transformer winding. (C) Conventional voltage doubler. C1 and C2 are charged to $1.41V_{rms}$ on alternate half cycles. Their outputs are in series across the load. (D) Normal and double voltage from the same center-tap transformer. (E) Same output voltage for 115- or 230-V ac input by a simple linkage change.

Positive and Negative Outputs from the Same Center-Tap Rectifier Winding

It is often necessary to have equal positive and negative voltages about a common ground point. This is simply achieved as in Fig. 5–10B with diodes D1 and D2 providing the rectified positive output. Diodes D3 and D4 are reversed in polarity and provide the rectified negative output. Each transformer half winding now conducts on every half cycle, not on alternate half cycles as in a single-ended rectifier. Coil wire size must be chosen to take this into account.

Normal- and Double-Output Voltage from Single Center-Tap Winding

Often in a full-wave, center-tap rectifier it is necessary to have a voltage level above the normal output without adding an additional transformer winding.

This can be done as in Fig. 5–10D. Diodes D1 and D2 and both transformer halves about the center tap comprise the standard center-tap rectifier yielding an output voltage of $1.41V_{rms}$.

Diodes D3 and D4 and capacitors C1 and C2 form a half-wave voltage doubling circuit. When A is negative relative to B, D3 charges C1 up to a potential of $1.41V_{rms}$ in the polarity shown. On the next half cycle, A goes positive relative to ground by $1.41V_{rms}$ and lifts the negative end of C1 up with it. Thus, the positive end of C1 is raised to $2.82V_{rms}$ and charges the top end of C2 up to that potential via D4.

Rectifier with Identical Output Voltage for Either 115- or 230-V Input

Power line voltage in England and many European countries is standardized at 230 V. It is often necessary that equipment to be sellable for either the 115-V American or 230-V European market must be usable at either location by only a simple linkage change. This is easily done with equipment having power transformer input by providing a tap on the primary.

But with most modern power supplies having directly-off-the-ac-line rectifiers, a scheme such as in Fig. 5–10E can be used. The output will always be 324 V, as if there were a bridge rectifier off the 230-V ac line.

For $230V_{ac}$, the linkage shown is thrown to the 230-V position. This throws in diodes D1 and D2, which together with D3 and D4 comprise a bridge rectifier and yield $(1.41)(230) = 324$ V. When input voltage is 115 V, the linkage is thrown to "115," and C1 and C2 together with diodes D3 and D4 comprise a voltage doubler—exactly as in Fig. 5–10C. Diodes D1 and D2 are back biased and effectively out of the circuit. Output voltage at C_o is $2(1.41)(115) = 324$ V.

5.5   Multiplier Circuits

There is a frequent requirement (as for CRT circuitry) for voltages in the range of 10,000–25,000 V at currents in the low milliampere range. Such voltages are generated by half-wave "voltage multipliers" of the type shown in Fig. 5–11.

The basic principle in such multipliers is to have a stack of capacitors in series and force equal voltage increments across each one. An array of auxiliary

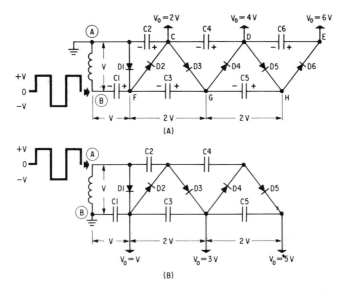

Fig. 5–11. (A) A voltage multiplier multiplying peak voltage at B by even numbers. (B) A voltage multiplier multiplying peak voltage at A by odd numbers.

capacitors and diodes is used to drop equal voltage increment on the string of series capacitors.

Thus, in Fig. 5–11A, assume across transformer secondary A–B, a square wave of $\pm V$ volts with respect to ground. On the first half cycle when point B is negative relative to A, diode D1 charges C1 to a peak voltage of V in the polarity shown. On the next half cycle, B moves positive relative to A by an amount V, pushing the right-hand end of C1 up to $+2V$. C1 thus charges C2 up to $+2V$ via diode D2.

On the third half cycle, B is again negative relative to A by V and C1 again charges up to $+V$ with the polarity shown. Also on this half cycle, since D1 conducts, clamping to ground, the left-hand end of C3 is pulled down to ground.

Now C2 charges C3 up to $+2V$ via diode D3. On the fourth half cycle, B moves up to $+V$, pushing the right-hand end of C1 up to $+2V$ to replenish the charge of $2V$ on C2. Also the right-hand end of C3 is pushed up to $+4V$. This puts a charge of $2V$ across C4 via diode D4. Now the right-hand end of C4 is at a potential of $4V$ above ground.

On the next half cycle, in a similar way, C4 charges C5 up to $2V$ via diode D5 and on the sixth half cycle, when B moves to $+V$, the right-hand end of C1 moves up to $+2V$ to replenish the charge on C2, the right-hand end of C3 moves up to $+4V$ to replenish the $+4V$ potential on C4. The right-hand end of C5 then charges the right-hand end of C6 up to $+6V$ via diode D6.

Potentials of $+2V$, $+4V$, and $+6V$ are available at points C, D, and E. The maximum voltage any diode or capacitor is subjected to is $2V$ volts.

If voltage multiplication by an odd number is desired, point B is grounded as in Fig. 5–11B. Then, in a similar way, it can be shown, that potentials at F, G, and H are respectively V, $3V$, $5V$, etc.

5.5.1 Selection of Multiplication Ratio

Multiplier stacks are notoriously troublesome because of the possibility of arcing at potentials in the range of 10,000–20,000 V. Diodes and capacitors should be subjected to no more than half their manufacturer's rated specifications. Small high-voltage diodes with peak inverse voltage ratings of 6,000 V are easily available at reasonable prices. If, say, 6,000-V diodes are used, since they are subjected to $2V$ and we wish no more than a 3,000-V stress to appear on each diode, then $2V = 3,000$ or $V = 1,500$ V.

And for 15,000-V output, a $\times 10$ multiplier would be used. The transformer secondary voltage would have to be $\pm 1,500$ V. Other multiplier ratios are, of course, usable with correspondingly higher voltage capacitors and rectifiers. Higher voltage diodes and capacitors are generally larger in volume and an engineering compromise has to be made involving overall size, safe voltage derating factors and number of components. Multiplier ratios between 4 and 12 are common for voltages between 12,000 and 18,000 V.

5.5.2 Resistive Isolation of Multiplier Capacitor Ladder

Because of the usual large step-down turns ratio between the secondary and primary of the high-voltage transformer, the capacitive load of the first multiplier capacitor C1 reflects as a very large capacitive load into the primary when power is first turned on and before C1 is charged up. Thus, assume the primary of the high-voltage transformer operates from a 30-V supply for the dc/dc converter. Then for peak secondary volts of 1,500, the turns ratio is $1,500/30 = 50$, and C1 reflects into the primary as a capacitor of $(C1)(50)^2 = 2,500C1$. At an inverter frequency of about $20KC$, C1 is usually in the range of 0.01–0.03 μF. Thus, the 0.01 μF capacitance of C1 reflects into the primary as 25–75 μF. This slows up the fall time of the inverter collectors at initial turnon and can result in inverter failure. To avoid such turn-on failures, a resistor should be placed in series between the transformer secondary and C1.

PROBLEMS

5.1 A 60-Hz, single-phase, center-tap rectifier output is to supply 5 V average output with a peak-to-peak ripple voltage of 10% of its average value. Assuming a capacitive filter, what is the required capacitance to achieve this ripple for an output load resistance of 10 ohms?

5.2 A 50-Hz, single-phase bridge rectifier is to have an average output voltage of 30 V when loaded with 15 ohms. What is the required filter capacitance for a peak-to-peak ripple output of 4 V?

5.3 What is the transformer's required nominal rms voltage either side of center tap and what is the maximum reverse voltage stress for the rectifier diodes of Prob. 5.1? Assume the supply is subjected to a +20% line transient lasting 2 sec if the ac voltage immediately prior to the transient was +10% high.

5.4 Repeat the exercise in Prob. 5.3 for Prob. 5.2.

5.5 A bridge rectifier operating directly off the 115-V ac line delivers an output power of 200 W. With a capacitive filter, what size must the capacitor be for the output ripple to be 4-V peak to peak?

6

Series-Pass Regulators

6.0 Introduction

The block diagram of the basic regulator is shown in Fig. 1–1, and its operation and shortcomings were discussed in Sect. 1.1. It was shown that for an optimum design, minimum efficiency, which occurs at maximum input voltage, is given by Eq. 1–1:

$$\text{Minimum efficiency} = \frac{V_o}{V_{in(\max)}} = \left(\frac{l - 0.01\text{T}}{l + 0.01\text{T}}\right)\left(\frac{V_o}{V_o + 2}\right)$$

T is the plus or minus percent tolerance around the nominal value of input voltage. Efficiencies for various values of output voltage for ±5, 10, and 15% tolerances were calculated and shown in Fig. 1–2. It was noted that, when the effect of ripple voltage is considered, efficiency is even less than shown in Fig. 1–2.

It is the low efficiency, especially at low-output voltage, that has led to the introduction of various types of switching regulators whose efficiency is higher and relatively independent of the input voltage.

Nevertheless, the series-pass regulator is still widely used and is a valuable and often essential element of modern supply systems. Its various characteristics and design procedures are covered in detail in this chapter.

6.1 Line-Voltage-Regulation Calculation

Elements of the series-pass regulator are shown in Fig. 6–1. Input voltage is voltage divided across the load R_L and the series pass element Q1 in proportion to their resistances. A sampled fraction of the output voltage is compared in the difference amplifier to a constant reference voltage V_r. The difference amplifier, usually followed by a current amplifier, controls the base of the series-pass element in a negative-feedback loop. As the output tends to change, either because of changes in output load resistance or input voltage changes, the difference amplifier produces an output current change. This change is amplified by the current amplifier and delivered to the base of Q1 in such phase as to change its resistance in the direction that will keep the output voltage at a constant level.

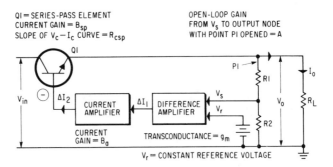

Fig. 6–1. In the series-pass regulator, line regulation or $\Delta V_o/\Delta V_{in}$ $= [(R1 + R2)/R2](1/R_{csp}g_mB_aB_{sp}) = [(R1 + R2)/R2](R_L/R_{csp})(1/A)$.

The negative-feedback loop tends to force the sampled fraction V_s to be equal to the constant reference voltage. Output voltage is then

$$V_o = V_r\left(\frac{R1 + R2}{R2}\right)$$

which can be shown as follows. In Fig. 1–1:

R_{csp} = Dynamic impedance or slope $\Delta V_c/\Delta I_c$ of the V_c-I_c curve (as shown in Fig. 1–2A, and 1–14C) at the operating points in V_c-I_c.

g_m = Transconductance of the difference amplifier at its operating point in V_c-I_c is $\Delta I 1/\Delta(V_s - V_r)$.

A = Open-loop voltage gain from input of the difference amplifier with point P1 open to V_o.

V_r = Constant reference voltage.

β_a = Current gain of any current amplifier following the difference amplifier.

β_{sp} = Current gain of the series-pass element.

Then

$$V_o = \frac{V_{in}R_L}{R_L + R_{csp}} - A\left(\frac{V_oR2}{R1 + R2} - V_r\right)$$

Or

$$V_o\left(1 + \frac{R2A}{R1 + R2}\right) = V_{in}\left(\frac{R_L}{R_L + R_{csp}}\right) + V_rA$$

And

$$V_o = \frac{V_{in}\left(\dfrac{R_L}{R_L + R_{csp}}\right)}{1 + \left(\dfrac{R2}{R1 + R2}\right)A} + \frac{V_rA}{1 + \left(\dfrac{R2}{R1 + R2}\right)A} \tag{6-1}$$

$$= \frac{V_{in}\left(\dfrac{R_L/R_{csp}}{1 + R_L/R_{csp}}\right)}{1 + \dfrac{AR2}{R1 + R2}} + \frac{V_rA}{1 + \dfrac{AR2}{R1 + R2}}$$

Now in the usual case

$$\frac{R_L}{R_{csp}} < 1 \quad \text{and} \quad \left(\frac{R2}{R1 + R2}\right)A \gg 1$$

Then
$$V_o = \frac{V_{in}R_L(R1 + R2)}{R_{csp}AR2} + \frac{V_r(R1 + R2)}{R2} \cong V_r\left(\frac{R1 + R2}{R2}\right) \qquad (6\text{-}2)$$

The line-voltage-regulation change or output voltage per unit change of input voltage is obtained from Eq. 6–2.

$$\frac{\Delta V_o}{\Delta V_{in}} = \left(\frac{R_L}{R_{csp}}\right)\left(\frac{R1 + R2}{A\,R2}\right) \qquad (6\text{-}3)$$

The open-loop gain A is the gain from input of the difference amplifier to the output node with point P1 (Fig. 6–1) opened. This gain is often an easily known or measured value, and it is convenient to express line regulation in terms of it. Frequently, the feedback amplifier of Fig. 6–1 is not as shown: a difference amplifier with a known transconductance, followed by current amplifiers. Rather, it is often an operational amplifier with known voltage gain driving the series element as an emitter follower. In such a case, $\Delta V_o/\Delta V_{in}$ is best expressed in terms of the open-loop gain, A.

But when the feedback amplifier is as in Fig. 6–1, a voltage-to-current transducing-difference amplifier followed by current amplifiers, A is best expressed thus:

$$A = \Delta V_o/\Delta V_s$$
$$= R_L\Delta I_o/\Delta V_s$$
$$= \frac{R_L\Delta V_s g_m\beta_a\beta_{sp}}{\Delta V_s}$$

Or
$$A = R_L g_m\beta_a\beta_{sp} \qquad (6\text{-}4)$$

And substituting this into Eq. 6–3,

$$\Delta V_o = \left(\frac{\Delta V_{in}}{R_{csp}(g_m)(\beta_a)(\beta_{sp})}\right)\left(\frac{R1 + R2}{R2}\right) \qquad (6\text{-}5)$$

6.1.1 Operating Point Effect on Line Regulation

It is seen from Eq. 6–3 or 6–5 that line regulation or change in output voltage per unit change in dc input is inversely proportional to R_{csp}, the slope $(\Delta V_c/\Delta I_c)$ of the series-pass element. This slope can be read from the V_c-I_c curve such as in Fig. 1–2A and 1–14C.

The 2N3055 series of Fig. 1–2A is usually used as the series-pass element up to output currents of 3–5 A; above that the 2N3771 series is most often used. The V_c-I_c curves show that values of R_{csp} strongly depend on operating point and become quite small and result in poor line regulation if operation is permitted to move into the region of the knee of the curve.

Thus, the slope of the 2N3055 at $I_c = 3.0$ A, $V_c = 2$ V is, as nearly as can be measured in Fig. 1–1B, equal to 10 ohms. Beyond the knee, the V_c-I_c curve is considerably flatter. Taking R_{csp} from the slope between 2 and 20 V at about 3.0 A, it is seen to be about 100 ohms.

Thus, for open-loop gain A unchanged, small input voltage changes with an operating point just below the knee will yield output changes 100/10 or 10 times greater than if operation is kept beyond the knee in the V_c-I_c curves.

The higher-current 2N3771 series has a low R_{csp} beyond its knee. Thus, in Fig. 1–14C it is seen that the slope after the knee from about 1.0 to 4.5 V at 10 A is about 4.5 ohms. It is thus clear from Eq. 6–5 that, to achieve low output changes for a given input change, with the 2N3771, values of g_m, β_a, and β_{sp} must be relatively high.

It is of interest to calculate input change attenuation from Eq. 6–5 in a typical case. Thus, in that equation, assume $(R1 + R2)/R2 = 2$, a usual case, and assume the following average values: $R_{csp} = 4.5$ ohms, $g_m = 0.03$ A/volt for the difference amplifier, $\beta_{sp} = 20$, and $\beta_a = 30$. Then from Eq. 6–5,

$$\Delta V_o = \Delta V_{in}\left(\frac{2}{(4.5)(0.03)(30)(20)}\right)$$
$$= 0.025\Delta V_{in}$$

or
$$\Delta V_o = 1/40\Delta V_{in}$$

Often an attenuation of 1/40 of the input change is insufficient and larger values of g_m or additional stages of current amplification (higher β_a) must be used. Higher transconductance in the difference amplifier is more economically achieved; these will be discussed in Sect. 6.5.2.

6.1.2 Line-Voltage Regulation with Darlington Series-Pass Element

If, as in Fig. 6–2, a Darlington driver amplifier Q_d is used to increase current gain, it might be thought that this would result in increased output voltage change for a given input change. For now, if there is an input change ΔV_{in}, there are current changes into the output node via the finite collector-to-emitter impedance of both Q1 (the main series-pass element) and also via Q_d its Darlington driver. But the current via Q_d is amplified by the β of Q_{sp}, resulting in greater current change in the output node and, hence, a greater output voltage change than without the Darlington driver. Actually, the opposite is true. Adding the Darlington driver makes the output less sensitive to input changes. This can be seen as follows: Let current gains of the series-pass element and its Darlington driver be β_{sp} and β_d, respectively. The collector-emitter impedances (slope of V_c-I_c curves at their operating points) are R_{csp} and R_{cd}, respectively.

Then for a given input voltage change, ΔV_{in}, since the output voltage is kept relatively constant by the negative feedback, the current change into the output node if there were not negative feedback would be

$$\Delta I_o = \Delta I \text{ [due to } R_{csp} \text{ alone]} + \beta_{sp}(\Delta I \text{ [due to } R_{cd}\text{]})$$
$$= \frac{\Delta V_{in}}{R_{csp}} + \beta_{sp}\left(\frac{\Delta V_{in}}{R_{cd}}\right)$$

In order for the output voltage to remain relatively constant, a very small voltage change must be permitted at the output mode. This small output voltage change is just enough so that, when the voltage change is divided down by R1 and R2, the resulting current change $\Delta I1$ due to g_m of the difference amplifier, β_a, β_d, and β_{sp} just tends to cancel the ΔI_o given above for the output current change had there been no negative feedback. Thus

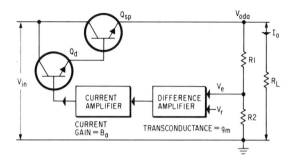

Fig. 6–2. A Darlington series-pass element gives better line regulation despite Q_{sp}-multiplying-Q_d collector-current changes arising from line-voltage changes.

$$\Delta I1 = \Delta V_{oda}\left(\frac{R2}{R1 + R2}\right)g_m\beta_a\beta_d\beta_{sp} \cong \Delta I_o$$

where V_{oda} is the output voltage change with the Darlington driver (Fig. 6–2). Then for ΔI_o as above, equating the above relations,

$$\Delta V_{oda} = \left(\frac{\Delta V_{in}}{R_{csp}g_m\beta_a\beta_d\beta_{sp}}\right)\left(\frac{R1 + R2}{R2}\right) + \left(\frac{B_{sp}\,\Delta V_{in}}{R_{cd}g_m\beta_a\beta_{sp}\beta_d}\right)\left(\frac{R1 + R2}{R2}\right) \tag{6–6}$$

Equation 6–6 can be compared to ΔV_o of Eq. 6–5; the output change of the original circuit of Fig. 6–1 without the Darlington drivers. Thus

$$\Delta V_{oda} = \frac{\Delta V_o\;[\text{Eq. 6–5}]}{\beta_d} + \Delta V_o\;[\text{Eq. 6–5}]\left(\frac{R_{csp}}{R_{cd}}\right)\left(\frac{\beta_{sp}}{\beta_d}\right) \tag{6–7}$$

The Darlington driver operates at an output current of I_o/β_{sp} and will consequently have a larger current gain than β_{sp}. Generally, it can be expected that β_{sp} at its normal operating current level of 1–5 A will have minimum current gains of about 20–30. The Darlington driver at its lower current will have a current gain β_d in the range of 40–50. Further, the Darlington driver, being a lower-current device, will have a higher value of collector-emitter impedance than the series-pass element. Values of R_{csp}/R_{cd} will generally range around 0.1 or less. Then in Eq. 6–7,

$$\Delta V_{oda} \cong \Delta V_o\;[\text{Eq. 6–5}][1/45 + 0.1(25/45)]$$
$$\cong 0.088(\Delta V_o\;[\text{Eq. 6–5}])$$

or the output voltage change for a given input voltage change with the Darlington driver series-pass element (Fig. 6–2) is about 0.088 times as great as for the case of the non-Darlington configuration of Fig. 6–1.

6.2 Load-Current-Regulation Calculation

Output voltage change for a given load change $(\Delta V_o/\Delta I_o)$ at constant V_{in} may be calculated for the series-pass regulator of Fig. 6–1 as follows:

Assume a given output current change ΔI_o. To achieve this current change, there must be a small voltage change ΔV_a at the input to the difference amplifier. This voltage change multiplied by g_m of the difference amplifier and $\beta_a\beta_{sp}$ of the current amplifier and series-pass amplifiers, respectively, must be great enough to achieve the specified output current change. Thus,

$$\Delta I_o = \Delta V_s g_m \beta_a \beta_{sp}$$

$$= \left(\frac{R2}{R1 + R2}\right) \Delta V_o g_m \beta_a \beta_{sp} \qquad (6\text{--}8)$$

or $\qquad \Delta V_o = \left(\frac{R1 + R2}{R2}\right)\left(\frac{\Delta I_o}{g_m \beta_a \beta_{sp}}\right)$

And for an open-loop voltage gain (V_s to V_o) of $A = g_m \beta_a \beta_{sp} R_L$

$$\Delta V_o = \left(\frac{R1 + R2}{R2}\right)\left(\frac{R_L}{A}\right)\Delta I_o \qquad (6\text{--}9)$$

6.3   Series-Pass Regulator Efficiency with Rectified ac Input Voltage

Minimum efficiency of an optimally designed series-pass regulator with ripple-free dc input voltage was calculated in Sect. 1.1. This efficiency is given by Eq. 1–1 as

$$E_{\min} = \left(\frac{1 - 0.01T}{1 + 0.01T}\right)\left(\frac{V_o}{V_o + 2}\right) = \frac{V_o}{V_{in(\max)}}$$

where T is the percentage tolerance in dc input voltage. This efficiency is based on the freedom to select the dc input voltage so that when it is at its low tolerance limit it is still only 2 V above the desired output voltage. The above efficiency is that resulting when the dc input is at its high tolerance limit and is the minimum resulting efficiency as efficiency is $V_o/V_{in(\max)}$.

Obviously, if V_o is fixed and $V_{in(\text{nom})}$ is fixed at a level such that, at its low tolerance limit, it is more than 2 V above the output, efficiency will be less than indicated in the above expression. Nothing can then be done about increasing efficiency; it is simply $V_o/V_{in(\max)}$ where $V_{in(\max)}$ is the high tolerance limit of the dc input voltage. Generally, $V_{in(\text{nom})}$ may not be lowerable to the value yielding highest efficiency, since it may be used as the supply source for other loads or series-pass elements requiring a higher voltage.

Limiting input voltage so that at its minimum it is still 2 V above the output is forced on the designer by the V_c–I_c curves of the series-pass element. From Fig. 1–2A and 1–14C, it is seen that these curves have a knee at about 1–2 V. Operation must not be permitted to fall below the knee as current gain decreases and the decreasing collector-emitter impedance results in poor line regulation (R_{csp} in Eq. 6–6). This knee occurs at different collector-emitter voltages for different transistors and at different current levels for some transistors. Thus, in Fig. 1–2A for the 2N3055 series, the knee ends at about 2 V at the 3-A level. In Fig. 1–14C it is seen to end at about 1 V at a 10-A level for the 2N3771 series.

But for a safe design, calculations will be based (as in Eq. 1–1) on keeping the dc input voltage when it is at its minimum value, a solid 2 V above the output. This, of course, can be done when the raw dc input is the rectified secondary output from a transformer simply by choosing the proper number of turns on the secondary winding.

When the prime power source is a battery, its output voltage can, of course, only be changed in multiples of the voltage of a single cell—1.5–2.0 V. The efficiency of Eq. 1–1 can be obtained for a given output voltage by selecting the battery voltage to be at its minimum, 2 V above the desired output. With a fixed battery voltage, arbitrarily lower or higher regulated output voltage can be obtained with a series-pass regulator by using it to generate a preregulated dc that is 2 V below the low tolerance limit of the battery. This preregulated dc can then be used to drive a dc/dc converter in some of the configurations discussed in Chap. 3 and Sect. 3.8.

But in the usual case, input to a series-pass regulator comes either from a rectifier–filter combination directly off the ac line or from a rectifier–filter following a properly selected secondary voltage on a transformer.

In either case, the efficiency indicated by Eq. 1–1 is not achievable because allowance must be made for the ripple voltage at the filter output as seen in Fig. 6–3. It is the bottom of the ripple triangle that must be kept 2 V above the desired regulated output voltage.

For a peak-to-peak ripple voltage of V_r and the bottom of the ripple triangle at $V_o + 2$, the average voltage at the output of the filter capacitor is $V_o + 2 + V_r/2$. It should be this value at minimum ac input voltage.

Now the dc voltage is proportional to the ac input. Assume the tolerance in the ac input voltage is $\pm T\%$. Then its values at minimum and maximum ac input voltages are $(1 - 0.01T)V_{dc(nom)}$ and $(1 + 0.01T)V_{dc(nom)}$, where $V_{dc(nom)}$ is the dc voltage at nominal line input. Then the ratio of maximum-to-minimum dc voltage at the filter capacitor output is

$$\frac{V_{dc(max)}}{V_{dc(min)}} = \frac{1 + 0.01T}{1 - 0.01T}$$

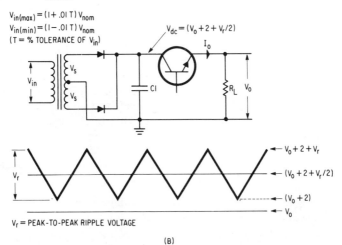

V_r = PEAK-TO-PEAK RIPPLE VOLTAGE

(B)

Fig. 6–3. With rectified ac input to a series-pass regulator, the bottom of the ripple triangle must not be less than 2 V above the output at minimum ac input.

Then the maximum dc voltage from the filter capacitor, when the transformer secondary turns has been chosen so as to have the bottom of the ripple triangle 2 V above the output at minimum ac input, is

$$V_{dc(max)} = \left(\frac{1 + 0.01T}{1 - 0.01T}\right)\left(V_o + 2 + \frac{V_r}{2}\right) \tag{6-10}$$

And maximum series element dissipation is

$$PD_{max} = (V_{dc(max)} - V_o)(I_{o(max)}) \tag{6-11}$$

or

$$PD_{max} = \left[\left(\frac{1 + 0.01T}{1 - 0.01T}\right)\left(V_o + 2 + \frac{V_r}{2}\right) - V_o\right]I_{o(max)} \tag{6-12}$$

Since all the output current flows continuously in series through the series-pass element, the minimum efficiency occurring at maximum dc input is

$$\begin{aligned}
E_{min} &= \frac{P_o}{P_{in(max)}} = \frac{V_o I_o}{V_{dc(max)} I_o} \\
&= \frac{V_o}{\left(\dfrac{1 + 0.01T}{1 - 0.01T}\right)\left(V_o + 2 + \dfrac{V_r}{2}\right)} \\
&= \left(\frac{1 - 0.01T}{1 + 0.01T}\right)\frac{V_o}{V_o + 2 + \dfrac{V_r}{2}} \tag{6-13}
\end{aligned}$$

Assuming losses in the rectifier diodes can be calculated as if they carried the output current continuously at a constant 1-V drop, minimum efficiency including rectifier diode losses is

$$E_{min} = \frac{V_o}{\left[\dfrac{(1 + 0.01T)(V_o + 2 + V_r/2)}{(1 - 0.01T)}\right] + 1} \tag{6-14}$$

Now it has been shown in Chap. 5, Fig. 5–4, that at 60 Hz line frequency, for a filter capacitor of 1,000 μF/ampere of load current, output ripple is 8 V peak to peak. Then assuming an 8-V peak-to-peak ripple, efficiency is calculated from Eq. 6–14 for various output voltage and various assumed ac line voltage tolerances. Results are shown in Fig. 6–4. Peak-to-peak ripple voltage is inversely proportional to filter capacitance per ampere of load current, and for values other than 1,000 μF/ampere the appropriate value can be used in Eq. 6–14 to calculate efficiency.

Comparing Figs. 6–4 and 1–3, it is seen that ripple at the rectifier–filter output and the 1-V rectifier drop has considerably decreased the efficiency below that achievable from a ripple-free source.

6.3.1 Selection of Transformer Secondary Voltage for a Maximum Efficiency Pass Regulator for Fixed Output Voltage

In the previous section, it was shown that the bottom of the ripple triangle, in a capacitive filter must be no less than 2 V above the output voltage at minimum ac input.

Now with a low-impedance silicon rectifier and a simple capacitive filter, the peak at the ripple triangle will not lag behind the peak of the ac sine wave.

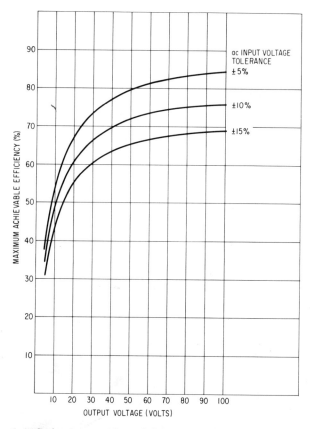

Fig. 6–4. Series-pass regulator fed from transformer rectifier filter. Conditions: (1) For series element input coming from filter capacity output containing ripple. (2) Filter capacity of 1,000 μF/ampere of load current yielding 8-V peak-to-peak ripple at 60 Hz with full-wave rectifier and capacitive filter. (3) Transformer secondary voltage selected so that valley point of ripple triangle is 2 V above output at ac input voltage at its low-tolerance limit. (4) Indicated efficiency is that for ac input voltage at its high-tolerance limit, and, considering losses in series-pass element and rectifier diodes only, control circuit losses are negligible. Calculated from Eq. 6–14.

Then for a peak-to-peak ripple voltage of V_r and an ac line voltage tolerance of $\pm T\%$, 1-V rectifier diode drop, since peak voltage after the rectifier must equal $(V_o + 2 + V_r)$ when the ac line voltage is low (see Fig. 6–3), then

$$(1 - 0.01T)V_{\text{rms(nom)}}(1.41) - 1 = V_o + 2 + V_r$$

or

$$V_{\text{rms(nom)}} = \frac{V_o + 3 + V_r}{1.41(1 - 0.01T)}$$

$$= 0.786(V_o + 3 + V_r) \qquad \text{for } T = \pm 10\% \qquad (6\text{–}15\text{A})$$

$$= 0.744(V_o + 3 + V_r) \qquad \text{for } T = \pm 15\% \qquad (6\text{–}15\text{B})$$

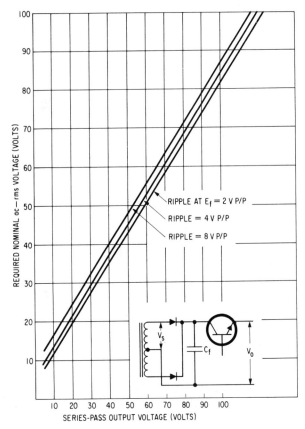

Fig. 6–5. Required rms input voltage (V_s) either side of a center tap in a full-wave rectifier versus series-pass output voltage for a maximum efficiency series-pass regulator with ac line input tolerance of $\pm10\%$. This is for voltage at valley point of ripple triangle equal to ($V_o + 2$) at low-tolerance-limit input voltage. Plotted from Eq. 6–15A.

Equation 6–15A is plotted in Fig. 6–5 for various values of peak-to-peak ripple voltage.

It should be noted nevertheless that Eqs. 6–15A and 6–15B give the ac input series regulator output relationship for regulators requiring no resistive elements in series either at the input or output. A short-circuit protective feature to be discussed in Sect. 6.8.2 adds a current-sensing series resistor. The use of parallel series-pass elements to increase output current requires series resistors from each element to the common output node to ensure equality of current sharing. Often, a small series resistor is inserted ahead of the input filter capacity to limit turn-on current surges.

Such series elements do increase the required ac input voltage but generally by no more than 1–2 V. They also decrease the efficiency somewhat below that indicated in Fig. 6–4.

6.4   Series-Pass Transistor Configurations

The series-pass elements, which are the electronically variable impedances between collectors and emitters of power transistors, can be implemented in many different ways with single- or compound-transistor configurations.

In single-transistor configurations, outputs can be taken from the emitter or collector and the elements may be either npn or pnp devices. Compound series-pass elements may be npn or pnp Darlington circuits with outputs taken either from emitter or collector. Compound combinations with a pnp transistor driver controlling an npn power output stage or an npn driver–pnp power output stage have certain advantages and are often used. The various combinations and areas of application will be discussed here.

6.4.1 Single-Transistor Series-Pass Elements

Figure 6–6 shows the possible single-transistor series pass configurations. When negative terminals of the dc input source and regulated output are common the schemes of Fig. 6–6A or 6–6B are usable. With positive terminals of the input and regulated output common, configurations of Fig. 6–6C or 6–6D are used.

Most often the circuit used is determined by the availability at an acceptable price of transistors with adequate voltage, current, and power dissipation ratings. Because of the details of transistor technology, it is easier to make high-current, high-power transistors in a npn version and, consequently, the circuits of Fig. 6–6A or 6–6C are more often used.

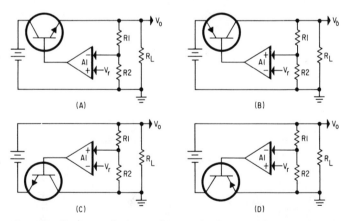

Fig. 6–6. Common single-transistor series-pass regulator configurations. (A) Emitter-loaded npn series-pass regulator. (B) Collector-loaded pnp series-pass regulator. These are used when the negative terminal of the dc input source is common with the negative output terminal. (C) Collector-loaded npn series-pass regulator. (D) Emitter-loaded pnp series-pass regulator. These are used when the positive terminal of the dc input source is common with the positive output terminal.

In all the circuits of Fig. 6–6, line regulation is given by Eq. 6–3:

$$\frac{\Delta V_o}{\Delta V_{in}} = \left(\frac{R_L}{R_{csp}}\right)\left(\frac{R1 + R2}{AR2}\right)$$

where A is the total open-loop gain from the input of the difference amplifier to the output node with R1 disconnected from V_o.

Load regulation in the circuits of Fig. 6–6 is given by Eq. 6–9:

$$\frac{\Delta V_o}{\Delta I_o} = \left(\frac{R1 + R2}{R2}\right)\left(\frac{R_L}{A}\right) = \text{output impedance} = R_o$$

6.4.2 Base Drive Problems with Single-Transistor Series-Pass Elements

Another factor affecting the choice of one of the configurations in Fig. 6–6 is the nature of the required current drive to the base of the series-pass elements. The emitter follower configurations of Figs. 6–6A and 6–6D are more cumbersome to drive and will potentially dissipate more power than the collector-loaded stage of Fig. 6–6B or 6–6C.

Thus, in Fig. 6–6A there must be available a point of higher dc potential than the base of the output stage, to supply current into the base. The only point at higher dc potential than the base is the collector as in Fig. 6–7A, but, as we have seen in the efficiency discussions of Sect. 6.3, it is desirable to keep the collector potential as close to the emitter (and, hence, to the base also) as possible. It was seen in Sect. 6.3 that an efficient design will attempt to keep collector-to-emitter potential at 2 V at low ac line input. This is a collector-to-base potential of $(2 - V_{be})$ V.

Now assume as in Fig. 6–7A that the required base current comes via a small collector-to-base resistor R_b. If R_b is small enough to supply the necessary base drive at low ac line voltage, that same resistor will supply considerably more current into the base node at high ac input voltage. For $V1$ is actually the rectified output of an ac source that is proportional to the ac input voltage. The bottom end of R_b will presumably remain fixed in potential as the ac input voltage

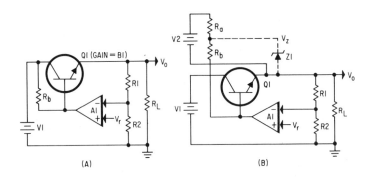

Fig. 6–7. (A) Base drive from a point at same potential as series-pass collector usually results in increased series-pass dissipation. (B) A supply $V2$ floating on V_o and a zener diode as a constant supply source results in decreased series-pass dissipation.

changes because it is one base emitter drop (or 0.7 V) above the output, which remains relatively constant.

Thus, ac input voltage changes will result in relatively large current changes in R_b. If a significant fraction of this current change enters the base of Q1, it is multiplied by β of Q1 and appears as an output voltage change.

Of course, the negative-feedback network senses this output change and via the high-gain amplifier produces an opposing current change that mostly absorbs the current change in R_b and tends to keep the output constant. Nevertheless, there is an output voltage change that is greater, the smaller R_b and $V_1 - V_o$ are.

This can be seen quantitatively as follows (see Fig. 6–7A):

$$\Delta V_o = \Delta I_b \beta 1 R_L - \Delta V_o \left(\frac{R2}{R1 + R2}\right) A 1$$

where $A1$ is the open-loop gain from the input of the difference amplifier to the output node. This is essentially the same as gain to the base of Q1 as its base-emitter gain is unity, since it is an emitter follower. Then

$$\Delta V_o = \frac{\Delta I_b \beta 1 R_L}{1 + [R2/(R1 + R2)]A1} = \frac{\Delta V1 \beta 1 (R_L/R_b)}{1 + [R2/(R1 + R2)]A1}$$

Or

$$\Delta V_o \cong \Delta V1 \beta 1 \left(\frac{R_L}{R_b}\right)\left(\frac{R1 + R2}{R2 A1}\right) \tag{6–16}$$

since

$$\left(\frac{R2}{R1 + R2}\right) A1 \gg 1$$

Now

$$\frac{R_L}{R_b} = \frac{V_o/I_o}{(V1 - V_o)/I_b} = \frac{V_o}{(V1 - V_o)\beta 1}$$

and substituting this into Eq. 6–16

$$\Delta V_o = \Delta V1 \left(\frac{V_o}{V1 - V_o}\right)\left(\frac{R1 + R2}{A1R2}\right) \tag{6–17}$$

It can be seen in Eq. 6–17 that if $V1 - V_o$ is made small to avoid high dissipation in Q1, a given $\Delta V1$ will be multiplied at the output by a factor larger than unity, $V_o/(V1 - V_o)$. The negative-feedback effect degenerates this by multiplying a factor less than unity, $(R1 + R2)/A1R2$. Now if $A1$ is made sufficiently large, small values of $V1 - V_o$ can be tolerated. Still, for a given value of $A1$, smaller values of $V1 - V_o$ result in greater output changes for a given input change.

6.4.3 Improved Current Source Drive for Series-Pass Elements

A series-pass base drive scheme that avoids most of the problems of Fig. 6–7A is shown in Fig. 6–7B. Here the voltage $V1$ can be made as close to V_o as possible so as to minimize the power dissipation in Q1. As discussed in Sect. 6.3, $V1$ will be selected so that at its lower tolerance limit, at the bottom of the ripple triangle, the valley point of the ripple voltage, is still 2 V above the output.

Now base drive for Q1 is taken not from $V1$ but from a low-current supply $V2$ (derived by rectifying the output of a small secondary winding on the input transformer) floating with its negative terminal on V_o. $V2$ can now be made a relatively high voltage without increasing dissipation as the current taken from it $(I_o/\beta 1)$ is small.

$V2$ is selected to be large compared to V_{be} of Q1 so that temperature changes in V_{be} do not significantly change the current to the Q1 base. And as can be seen from Eqs. 6–16 and 6–17, large values of R_b reduce output voltage changes for a given input voltage change.

Drive to the base of Q1 can be still further improved and made completely independent of input voltage variations by using a zener as the voltage-regulated source for the base driver as shown in Fig. 6–7B.

Here, the zener voltage is chosen relatively large compared to V_{be} — usually 5 V or so. R_b is chosen so that at its maximum tolerance limit, it can supply the maximum required Q1 base drive with a minimum zener voltage.

Thus, for resistor, zener diode, and $V2$ tolerances of T_r, T_z, T_{V2}, respectively, and for a nominal zener voltage V_z,

$$(1 + 0.01T_r)R_b = \frac{(V_z - V_{be})_{min}}{I_{b(max)}}$$

$$= \frac{(1 - 0.01T_z)V_z - V_{be(max)}}{I_{o(max)}/\beta 1_{min}}$$

Or
$$R_b = \beta_{min}\frac{(1 - 0.01T_z)V_z - V_{be(max)}}{(1 + 0.01T_r)I_{o(max)}} \qquad (6\text{--}18)$$

R_a is chosen so that at the minimum value of $V2$ and maximum value of V_z, the minimum current available via R_a is at least 2 mA (to keep the zener conducting above its knee) greater than the maximum current demanded by R_b. Thus

$$I(R_{a(min)}) = I(R_{b(max)}) + 0.002$$

Or
$$\frac{(1 - 0.01T_{V2})V2 - (1 + 0.01T_z)V_z}{(1 + 0.01T_r)R_a} = \frac{(1 + 0.01T_z)V_z - V_{be(min)}}{(1 + 0.01T_r)R_b} + 0.002$$

And

$$R_a = \frac{[(1 + 0.01T_{V2})V2 - (1 + 0.01T_z)V_z](1 - 0.01T_r)R_b}{(1 + 0.01T_r)[(1 + 0.01T_z)V_z - V_{be(min)} + 0.002(1 - 0.01T_r)R_b]} \qquad (6\text{--}19)$$

6.4.4 Constant-Current Transistor Drive for Series-Pass Elements

An alternative method of providing a constant-current base drive source independent of ac line voltage changes is shown in Fig. 6–8A. The scheme does not require the additional "floating" power supply of Fig. 6–7B and provides a constant current without substantially increasing the collector voltage and, hence, dissipation of series-pass element Q1.

The circuit of Fig. 6–8A uses the constant current available from the collector of an emitter follower which has a constant voltage from its base to the "top" end of the emitter resistor. Emitter current in Fig. 6–8A is kept constant by the constant voltage $V1$ derived by the resistor divider network across a zener diode hanging down from the Q1 collector. The diode D1 is inserted in series in the R1–R2 divider network to cancel out temperature variations in the base-emitter drop of the emitter follower. Thus

$$I_{e(Qa)} = \frac{V1 - V_{be}}{R_e}$$

$$V1 = V2 + V_{D1}$$

and for $I_{(D1)} = I_{(R3)} + I_{(base\ Qa)} \ll I_{(R1,R2)}$

$$V1 = V_{Z1}\left(\frac{R1}{R1 + R2}\right) + V_{D1}$$

Then
$$I_{e(Qa)} = \frac{V_{Z1}\left(\frac{R1}{R1 + R2}\right) + V_{D1} - V_{be(Qe)}}{R_e}$$

And since the base-emitter junction drop V_{be} is closely equal to the diode drop and, even more important, tracks it with temperature:

$$I_{e(Qa)} \cong \frac{V_{Z1}R1}{R_e(R1 + R2)}$$

and
$$I_{(collector\ Qa)} = \frac{\beta}{\beta + 1}I_{e(Qa)} \cong I_{e(Qa)} \qquad \text{for } \beta > 1$$

$$\cong \frac{V_{Z1}R1}{R_e(R1 + R2)} \tag{6-20}$$

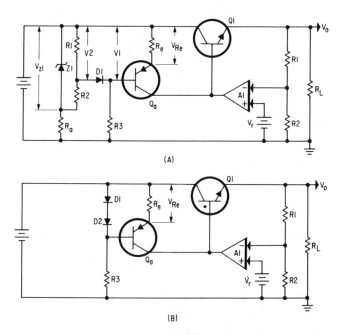

Fig. 6–8. (A) A constant current supply for the series-pass base reduces dissipation. (B) A simpler constant-current source for the series-pass base.

For current in Q_a to remain constant (emitter follower action) collector saturation must be avoided. Thus, at the highest base-emitter potential in Q1, and lowest Q1 collector voltage, the collector of Q_a should not be permitted to move positive relative to its base. Now

$$V_{ce(Q1)} = V_{be(Q1)} + V_{ce(Q_a)} + V_{R_e}$$

And if the base and collector potentials of Q_a are equal at the lowest input voltage, $V_{ce(Q1)} = V_{be(Q1)} + V_{be(Q_a)} + V_{R_e}$ and permitting $V_{ce(Q1)} = 2.1$ V at minimum input

$$V_{ce(Q1)} = 2.1 = 0.9 + 0.7 + V_{R_e}$$

Then $V_{R_e} = 2.1 - 0.9 - 0.7 = 0.5$ V

Then for an output current in Q1 of I_o, the necessary current in Q_a, $I_{(Q_a)} = I_{o(Q1)}/\beta_{(Q1)}$. Then the magnitude of R_e is $R_e = V_{R_e}/I_{(Q_a)} = 0.5\beta_{(Q1)}/I_{o(Q1)}$.

Now for a preselected zener voltage, V_{Z1} from Eq. 6–20, the ratio R1/(R1 + R2) is selected as

$$\frac{R1}{R1 + R2} = \frac{I_{e(Q_a)}R_e}{V_{Z1}} = \frac{0.5}{V_{Z1}}$$

and finally the absolute magnitudes of R1 and R2 are chosen so that I_{R1} or I_{R2} $\gg I_{D1}$ or

$$I_{R1} \text{ or } I_{R2} \gg I_{R3} + I_{e(Q_a)}/\beta_{(Q_a)}$$

in order for voltage $V2$ to be dependent on the magnitude of R1 or R2 only.

A simpler circuit that is almost as good is shown in Fig. 6–8B. Here the drop in diode D2 roughly equals the drop in the base-emitter diode of Q_a and tracks it in temperature. Since

$$V_{D1} + V_{D2} = V_{be(Q_a)} + V_{R_e}$$

and $$V_{D2} \cong V_{be(Q_a)}$$

then $$V_{R_e} = V_{D1} \cong 0.6 \text{ V} = R_e I_{e(Q_a)}$$

and for a desired output current I_o in Q1,

$$I_{(\text{base Q1})} = \frac{I_{o(Q1)max}}{\beta_{Q1(min)}} \cong I_{e(Q_a)} = \frac{0.6}{R_e}$$

or $$R_e = \frac{0.6\beta_{Q1(min)}}{I_{o(Q1)max}}$$

Now since V_{D1} decreases with temperature and it is this voltage that fixes the Q_a emitter current, that current will decrease with increasing temperature. But since β of Q1 increases with increasing temperature, less base drive is required at higher temperatures. Thus, the temperature-varying base drive for Q1 may not be a very great drawback.

6.4.5 Complementary Transistor Drive for Series-Pass Elements

A very useful circuit configuration (Figs. 6–9A and 6–9B) uses a complementary-type inverter amplifier as the base drive source for the series-pass element.

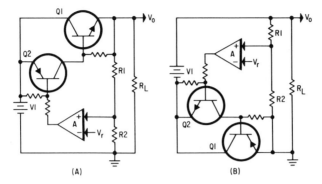

Fig. 6–9. Complementary-type driver stages permit lower series-pass collector-emitter voltages and reduce dissipation. (A) A pnp driver feeding an npn emitter follower output stage. (B) An npn driver feeding a pnp emitter follower output stage.

The circuit is most often used as in Fig. 6–9A with a pnp low-current inverter amplifier driving the base of a high-current npn emitter follower output stage.

The value of the circuit is that a very large current can be obtained from the same power supply feeding the collector of the output stage. This large current is available without increasing the collector-emitter potential (and thus dissipation) of the output stage. Thus, in Fig. 6–9A the collector-base potential of Q1, which is also the emitter-collector potential of Q2, can be permitted to go as low as 0.6 V. A lesser voltage will saturate Q2 and lower its gain. Then

$$V_{ce(Q1)} = V_{be(Q1)} + V_{ce(Q2)}$$
$$\cong 0.9 + 0.6 = 1.5 \text{ V}$$

At $V_{ce(Q1)}$ of 1.5 V, its losses will be small and yet drive currents of up to 1 A or more are available to the base of the series-pass element without the addition of a floating power supply as in Fig. 6–7B.

One further valuable feature of the circuits of Fig. 6–9 is that the base drive for the inverter amplifier Q2 is to a voltage point somewhere between the positive and negative terminals of the prime input power supply. Thus, in Fig. 6–9A the base drive to Q2 is a current source to a point lower than $+V1$ and in Fig. 6–9B it is a current source to a point above ground and less than $+V1$. The significance of this is that additional supply voltages above $+V1$ as are used in Fig. 6–7B are unnecessary.

Q2, the driver for Q1, could also be an npn emitter follower as in Fig. 6–10A (a current source into the base of Q1 is needed). But, in this case, the drive for the base of Q2 would have to come from a point at a potential which is somewhat more than two base emitter drops above V_o. This forces two undesirable choices: either increasing $V1$ so as to permit it to be the supply voltage source for the base of Q2 or adding a second floating supply as in Fig. 6–7B. The first alternative increases Q1 power dissipation; the second adds components and increases costs and required space.

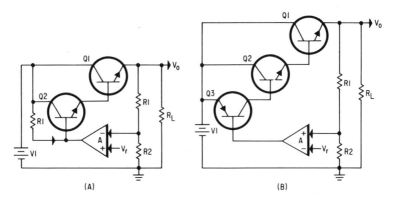

Fig. 6–10. (A) An npn emitter follower driving an npn emitter follower output stage requires current from a point above V_o and results in higher dissipation than Fig. 6–9A, since a higher input voltage is required. (B) A pnp driver feeding an npn emitter follower driver with an npn emitter follower output stage.

If an npn emitter follower drive for the main npn series-pass elements is dictated by other considerations, the best way to drive the base of the driver is with a pnp inverter as in Fig. 6–10B. This is the equivalent of Fig. 6–9A and has all its advantages. It still permits the voltage $V1$ to be as low as only 2.2 V above V_o. For

$$(V1 - V_o)_{min} = V_{be(Q1)} + V_{be(Q2)} + V_{ce(Q3)}$$
$$\cong 0.9 + 0.8 + 0.5 = 2.2 \text{ V}$$

6.5   Difference Amplifiers

As seen in Fig. 6–1, an essential element in the series-pass regulator is the difference amplifier. This circuit senses the difference between a standard reference voltage and a constant fraction of the output voltage and generates an error voltage proportional to this difference. This error voltage (after further amplification, if necessary) is used to control the drive to the series-pass element in such a direction as to make the sampled constant fraction of the output almost equal to the reference voltage.

With a very nearly constant reference voltage source (which can be achieved by proper selection of a zener diode and its circuitry), the stability of regulator against temperature, line voltage, and load-current changes depends almost entirely on the nature of the difference amplifier. Its output voltage must be dependent only on the difference in dc voltage level between the two inputs and must not be affected by temperature changes or absolute dc level of the two inputs.

Difference amplifiers can be designed in various ways. Thus, the base-emitter voltage characteristic of a transistor can be used as a difference amplifier. The reference voltage can be fed to the emitter and the sampled fraction of the output to the base. Changes in the voltage difference between these two inputs cause collector current changes proportional to the difference between the two inputs. But since the collector current versus base-emitter voltage characteristic varies with temperature, changes in temperature alone will cause output error signals indistinguishable from changes in the difference between the two input voltages.

A diode whose forward voltage characteristic matches that of the base-emitter diode of the transistor can be used in various ways to compensate for the drawback of the single-transistor difference amplifier, although this is a cumbersome and not completely effective solution. By use of a two-transistor difference amplifier (especially if the two transistors are on one chip as in an integrated circuit), variations in output error signal with temperature can largely be eliminated. Such two-transistor, emitter-coupled difference amplifiers are now almost universally used.

6.5.1 Two-Transistor, Emitter-Coupled Difference Amplifier

This circuit is shown in Fig. 6–11. The two transistors are of a similar type, preferably with matched V_{be}-I_c characteristics. Best results are achieved if the two are integrated transistors on the same chip, since they are then more

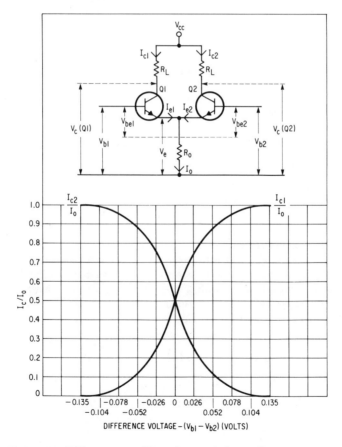

Fig. 6–11. Difference amplifier characteristics: collector currents versus difference in base voltages.

likely to have matched characteristics and remain better matched over a large temperature range.

The circuit is operated with as good a "constant-current" source in the common emitter as possible. This is achieved if the average voltage V_{b1} or V_{b2} is large compared to their average change (which will be about ±0.026 V) or the V_{be} change with temperature which can be as high as 0.2 V. Thus, making V_{b1}, V_{b2} anything greater than about 3 V results in a fairly good constant-current source. The current looking into the collector of an emitter follower with a properly designed base input voltage provides a better constant-current source and is often used. This was discussed in Sect. 1.6.3.

The difference amplifier circuit works as follows: If $V_{b1} = V_{b2}$, the current in R_o is $(V_{b1} - V_{be})/R_o \cong (V_{b1} - 0.7)/R_o$. Of this current, the emitters of Q1 and Q2 each supply half the total. If say V_{b2} is kept fixed and a small positive increment $+\Delta V_{b1}$ is applied to the Q1 base, the common emitter potential increases by $\Delta V_{b1}/2$. The base-emitter potential of Q1 has then increased by $\Delta V_{b1}/2$ and that of Q2 has decreased by $\Delta V_{b1}/2$. Since $\Delta V_{b1}/2$ is small compared to the initial value of V_{b1}, the current in R_o remains constant at I_o. Since the base-emitter potential of Q1 has increased by as much as that of Q2 has decreased, the current increase in Q1 is exactly equal to the current decrease in Q2. Similarly, if V_{b2} remains fixed and V_{b1} decreases by ΔV_{b1}, the common emitter decreases by $\Delta V_{b1}/2$. Then the base-emitter voltage change in Q1 is equal and opposite to that in Q2. Consequently, the decreases in Q1 current is exactly equal to the increase in Q2 current.

The circuit is used as a difference amplifier by inserting equal load resistors in the two collectors and sensing these current changes as voltage changes at the collectors. If the supply voltage V_{cc} and R_L are selected so that at the lowest collector potential the transistors are safely out of saturation, the potential at each collector with respect to ground or the potential between collectors is proportional to the difference $(V_{b1} - V_{b2})$. For changes in V_{b1} volts around the point where $V_{b1} = V_{b2}$, current changes in Q1 and Q2 or voltage changes at their collectors are very linear functions of $V_{b1} - V_{b2}$.

The voltage used to control the series-pass base drive may be taken as either the single-ended signal at one of the collectors or the voltage difference between the two collectors.

The dc voltage level with respect to ground at either collector is truly proportional to the voltage difference between base inputs. But it is also a function of V_{be}, which varies with temperature, and V_{cc} and, hence, variations in these parameters will produce "error" voltages in the signal, which supposedly is a measure of the base input voltage differences alone. This can be seen quantitatively as follows (see Fig. 6–11):

$$V_{c(Q1)} \text{ or } V_{c(Q2)} = V_{cc} - \frac{I_o R_L}{2}$$

$$= V_{cc} - \left(\frac{V_{b1} - V_{be(Q1)}}{2R_o}\right) R_L$$

And

$$\frac{\Delta V_{c(Q1)}}{\Delta T} = \left(\frac{R_L}{2R_o}\right)\left(\frac{\Delta V_{be(Q1)}}{\Delta T}\right)$$

But the base-emitter voltage $V_{be(Q1)}$ varies with the temperature at the rate of 2 mV/°C:

$$\frac{\Delta V_{c(Q1)}}{\Delta T} = \frac{R_L(2)}{2R_o} = \frac{R_L}{R_o} \quad \text{in millivolts per °C} \tag{6-21}$$

There are various means to compensate for the temperature dependence of the single-ended output voltage of a difference amplifier. These will be discussed in Sect. 6.6.1.

A preferable way of taking a measure of the voltage difference between the base input potentials is to use the voltage difference between collectors of Q1 and Q2. This voltage difference is far less a function of temperature than is the absolute voltage of either collector with respect to ground, for as temperature, say, increases, V_{be} decreases, I_o increases, and I_{c1} and I_{c2} both increase. Thus, although the absolute dc level at each collector falls, if the I_c–V_{be} curves of Q1 and Q2 both track with temperature and if both transistors are so located physically that their temperature changes are identical, then the voltage difference between the collectors will remain unchanged and will be a function of $V_{b1} - V_{b2}$ only.

If the voltage difference between collectors is used as a measure of $V_{b1} - V_{b2}$ somewhat later in the dc feedback amplifier, this double-ended control signal must be converted to a single-ended signal to drive the series-pass base. This is rather easily done and is usually preferable to using a single-ended collector output from the difference amplifier. This will be discussed further in Sect. 6.6.1.

The two-transistor difference amplifiers have the valuable feature that, whether a single- or double-ended output is used, since opposite polarity signals are available from each collector, it is always possible to choose the collector output connections in such a way as to provide an odd number of phase reversals around the closed loop to achieve negative feedback.

The design of the complete dc feedback amplifier must include means to translate the dc voltage level at the difference amplifier collectors to a level that is correct for driving the base of the series-pass elements. Such a design usually comprises various combinations of npn and pnp transistors and will be discussed in Sect. 6.7.

6.5.2 Transconductance and Gain in the Emitter-Coupled Difference Amplifier

A precise relationship between collector currents and base difference voltages can be obtained from the fundamental solid-state relationships in the transistor.

From the solid-state equations of the transistor, it can be shown that the emitter current is related to the base-emitter voltage and temperature by

$$I_e = I_s \{ \exp [V_{be}/(KT/Q)] - 1 \} \text{ amperes}$$

where I_e is the emitter current in amperes, I_s is a minimum "saturation" current of about 2×10^{-16} A, K is Boltzman's constant in joules per °K = 1.33×10^{-23} J/°K, Q is the charge on the electron in coulombs = 1.6×10^{-19}, T is in °K = 273 + temperature in °C, and V_{be} is the base-to-emitter voltage in volts. Then

$$\frac{KT}{Q} = \frac{(1.38 \times 10^{-23})(300)}{1.60 \times 10^{-19}} = 0.026 \text{ V for 27°C}$$

And $\qquad I_e = I_s [\exp(V_{be}/0.026) - 1]$

But for $V_{be} = 0.5$ to 0.8 V, the range of normal base-to-emitter potentials [$\exp(V_{be}/0.026) \gg 1$]; then

$$I_e \cong I_s[\exp(V_{be}/0.026)] \qquad (6\text{-}22)$$

And in the difference amplifier of Fig. 6-11

$$
\begin{aligned}
I_o &= I_{e1} + I_{e2} \\
&= I_{e1}(1 + I_{e2}/I_{e1}) \\
&= I_{e2}(1 + I_{e1}/I_{e2})
\end{aligned}
$$

or $\qquad I_{e1} = \dfrac{I_o}{1 + I_{e2}/I_{e1}} \qquad I_{e2} = \dfrac{I_o}{1 + I_{e1}/I_{e2}}$

And from Eq. 6-22

$$
\begin{aligned}
I_{e1}/I_{e2} &= \exp[(V_{be1} - V_{be2})/0.026] \\
I_{e2}/I_{e1} &= \exp[(V_{be2} - V_{be1})/0.026]
\end{aligned}
$$

Then for large values of β (current gain)

$$I_{c1} \cong I_{e1} \cong \frac{I_o}{1 + \exp[(V_{b2} - V_{b1})/0.026]} \qquad (6\text{-}23)$$

$$I_{c2} \cong I_{e2} = \frac{I_o}{1 + \exp[(V_{b1} - V_{b2})/0.026]} \qquad (6\text{-}24)$$

A plot of these currents as a function of base-emitter voltage is shown in Fig. 6-11. It is seen that over a range of ± 0.026 V about the point where $V_{b1} = V_{b2}$, currents are very linear functions of $V_{b1} - V_{b2}$. Now from Eqs. 6-23 and 6-24, at $V_{b1} = V_{b2}$, both currents are equal and are each one-half of the total demanded by R_o. For small variations of $V_{b1} - V_{b2}$ as the current in one transistor changes, that in the other changes by an equal and opposite amount.

The transconductance g_m, which is the collector current change per unit change in $V_{b1} - V_{b2}$ is given by the derivative of Eqs. 6-23 or 6-24. Thus

$$
\begin{aligned}
g_m &= \frac{\Delta I_c}{\Delta(V_{b1} - V_{b2})} \\
&= \left(\frac{I_o}{\{1 + \exp[(V_{b1} - V_{b2})/0.026]\}^2}\right)\left(\frac{\exp[(V_{b1} - V_{b2})/0.026]}{0.026}\right)
\end{aligned}
$$

And in the region where $V_{b1} - V_{b2} \cong 0$

$$g_m = \frac{\Delta I_c}{\Delta(V_{b1} - V_{b2})} = \frac{I_o}{0.104} \cong 10I_o \qquad (6\text{-}25)$$

where g_m is in amperes per volt for I_o in amperes, and voltage gain from base-to-collector output in Fig. 6-11 is

$$A = g_m R_L = \frac{I_o R_L}{0.104} \cong 10I_o R_L \qquad (6\text{-}26)$$

The transconductance given by Eq. 6-25 is used in Eqs. 6-5 and 6-8 in calculating line and load regulation. Or if the complete feedback amplifier of Fig. 6-1 consists of a voltage amplifier of open-loop gain A_2 from the collector of the difference amplifier to the output node, the total open-loop gain A_t is given by

$$A_t = AA_2 = g_m R_L A_2 = \frac{I_o R_L A_2}{0.104} = 10 I_o R_L A_2 \qquad (6\text{-}27)$$

From Eqs. 6-25 and 6-26, it is seen that transconductance or voltage gain is proportional to the total emitter current I_o. This is a valuable feature in that it offers a means of setting the open-loop voltage gain by simply selecting R_o to give the desired value of I_o.

Difference amplifiers of the type of Fig. 6-11 are usually operated in the region of $I_o = 1\text{-}3$ mA. Then at 3 mA, transconductance from Eq. 6-25 is $g_m = 10(0.003) = 0.03$ A/volt. And from Eq. 6-26 voltage gain with, say, 1,000-ohm load resistors is $0.03(1,000) = 30$.

6.5.3 Difference Amplifier Transconductance from a Circuits Viewpoint

The transconductance calculation of Sect. 6.5.2, although precise, fails to give a good picture of the factors involved from a circuits viewpoint. The circuit's behavior can be better appreciated from the following:

In Fig. 6-11, consider the base of Q2 fixed at a constant reference voltage and a small incremental voltage ΔV_{b1} applied to the base of Q1. Then at the common emitter, the equivalent circuit is as in Fig. 6-12. Looking from the common emitter back into the emitter of Q1, the source impedance R1 is that of a common base amplifier. Similarly, looking from the emitter of Q1 into the emitter of Q2, the load impedance seen is also that of a common base amplifier. The common emitter resistor R_o is large compared to these impedances and can be ignored. Thus, with the source and load impedances equal, a voltage change ΔV_{b1} at the base results in a voltage change $\Delta V_{b1}/2$ at the common emitters.

Then looking up into the emitter of Q2 when ΔV_{b1} is applied to the base of Q1, the equivalent circuit is that of a grounded base amplifier whose emitter is driven an amount $\Delta V_{b1}/2$. Its output current change is then

$$\Delta I_c = g_{mgb} \, \Delta V_{b1}/2$$

where g_{mgb} is the transconductance of a grounded base amplifier. This may be calculated from Eq. 6-22 as follows:

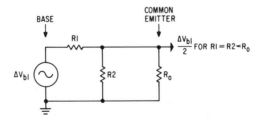

Fig. 6-12. In the difference amplifier of Fig. 6-11, because of equal source and load impedance. for ΔV_{b1} at one base, each base-emitter potential changes by an amount $\frac{1}{2}\Delta V_{b1}$.

$$g_{mgb} = \frac{\Delta I_c}{\Delta V_{eb}} \cong \frac{\Delta I_e}{\Delta V_{eb}} = \frac{I_s[\exp(V_{be}/0.026)]}{0.026} = \frac{I_e}{0.026}$$

But current in each emitter is half that in the common-emitter resistor or $I_o/2$, then

$$g_{mgb} = \frac{I_o}{2(0.026)}$$

and
$$\Delta I_c = g_{mgb}\left(\frac{\Delta V_{b1}}{2}\right) = \frac{I_o \Delta V_{b1}}{4(0.026)} = \frac{I_o \Delta V_{b1}}{0.104}$$

or
$$\Delta I_c/\Delta V_{b1} = I_o/0.104 \tag{6-28}$$

This is exactly the expression calculated in Eq. 6–25.

6.5.4 Alternative Difference Amplifiers

Other alternatives to the difference amplifier of Fig. 6–11 are shown in Fig. 6–13. Figure 6–13A is the double-ended pnp equivalent of Fig. 6–11. The pnp circuit is used when output voltages close to ground are needed for controlling a series-pass base through the base of an npn upward-level-shifting amplifier. The output voltages of the npn difference amplifier are at a dc level close to $+V_{cc}$ and, hence, may not be appropriate for driving the input of a series-pass element.

The forward voltage drop of diode D1 in Fig. 6–13A varies with temperature at a rate of -2 mV/°C. This cancels to a large extent the roughly equal Q1 and Q2 base-emitter voltage changes with temperature. Now if Z1 is a temperature-compensated zener diode (Fig. 1–13), this makes the absolute voltage at either collector with respect to ground independent of temperature and a function of (V_b-V_r) only. Thus, single-ended outputs may be taken from either collector and used to control the base of the series-pass elements. Without such a temperature-compensating diode, for a control signal independent of temperature, a double-ended signal – the voltage difference between the two collectors – must be used to control the input to the series-pass element.

Figure 6–13B shows the equivalent difference amplifier using npn transistors and diode D1 again making the absolute dc voltage level at each collector independent of temperature.

An alternative means for keeping the emitter current constant and independent of temperature is shown in Fig. 6–13C. Here, Q3 is used as an emitter follower whose emitter current is maintained constant and independent of temperature by combination of the zener Z1 and diode D1 at its base. Collector current in Q3 is

$$I_c = \left(\frac{\beta}{\beta+1}\right)\left(\frac{V_{Z1} + V_{D1} - V_{be(Q3)}}{R1}\right) \cong \frac{V_{Z1}}{R1}$$

and since $\Delta V_{be(Q3)}/\Delta T \cong \Delta V_{D1}/\Delta T$, the collector current of Q3 and, hence, the emitter currents in Q1 and Q2 are independent of temperature. Single-ended outputs can then be taken from either collector to control the input to the series-pass element. These collector voltages with respect to ground will depend on the Q1 and Q2 base voltage differences only and will not shift with temperature. Figures 6–13D and 6–13E show single-ended npn difference amplifiers. In both cases, diode D1 is used to compensate for the Q1 base-emitter voltage variation with temperature.

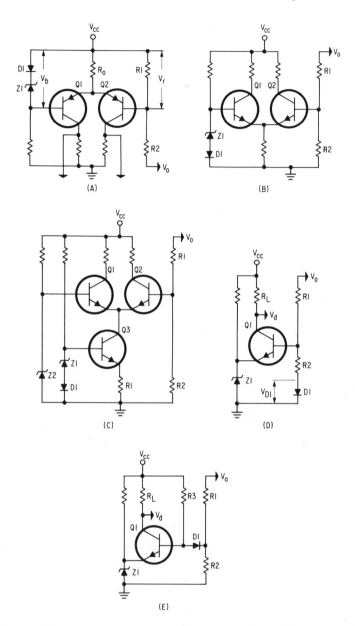

Fig. 6–13. Temperature-compensated difference amplifiers. (A) A pnp difference amplifier with diode D1 to cancel base-emitter voltage variation with temperature. (B) The equivalent temperature-compensated npn difference amplifier. (C) A temperature-compensated emitter follower constant-current emitter load for the difference amplifier. (D) A single-ended difference amplifier with temperature compensation by diode D1. (E) A single-ended difference amplifier with improved temperature compensation.

The circuit of Fig. 6-13D does not provide complete cancellation; it depends on the ratio R2/R1. This can be seen as follows: Assume the top end of R1 senses the voltage to be controlled and that there are neither load nor dc input voltage variations. Then, if temperature varies, the Q1 collector voltage, which is the control signal, must not vary. Since for constant current, the base-emitter voltage decreases at the rate of 2 mV/°C, the voltage applied to the emitter-base terminals of Q1 must decrease at the rate of 2 mV/°C. Now

$$V_{eb(Q1)} = -V_{Z1} + V_{D1} + (V_o - V_{D1})\left(\frac{R2}{R1 + R2}\right)$$

$$= -V_{Z1} + V_{D1}\left(\frac{R1}{R1 + R2}\right) + V_o\left(\frac{R2}{R1 + R2}\right)$$

And
$$\frac{\Delta V_{eb(Q1)}}{\Delta T} = \left(\frac{\Delta V_{D1}}{\Delta T}\right)\left(\frac{R1}{R1 + R2}\right)$$

And for the compensation to be complete R1/(R1 + R2) must be close to unity — which it generally is not.

The circuit of Fig. 6-12E provides better compensation. The output voltage V_o is sampled by R1 and R2. The potential at the junction of R1 and R2 is level-shifted upward one diode drop by D1. R3 is made large so that its current is small compared to that in R1 and R2. Thus, the voltage at the base of Q1 is primarily a function of R1 and R2 and fairly independent of current in R3. Thus, the downward-level shifts in the base emitter of Q1 is canceled by the upward-level shift in diode D1. Since these two semiconductor junction drops vary about equally with temperature, the applied base-emitter potential decreases at just the rate required to keep a constant collector current. Z1 is a temperature-compensated zener and is chosen for minimum drift (Sect. 1.5.5.).

6.6   Drift in Regulated Output Voltage

The output voltage drift in a regulated power supply is due primarily to temperature variation of the constant voltage reference source and temperature variation of the difference amplifier characteristics.

6.6.1 Single- and Double-Ended Difference Amplifier Drift

Both the double- (Fig. 6-11) and single- (Figs. 6-13D and 6-13E) ended difference amplifiers exhibit drift characteristics with temperature. This exhibits itself as a variation in collector current with temperature even with a constant voltage difference between the input terminals. Essentially, this comes about because the collector-current versus base-emitter voltage characteristic moves with temperature along the base-emitter voltage axis at the rate of 2 mV/°C.

The effect of this is as if a small battery or drift voltage source were placed in series with the base-emitter terminals. This "battery" has a voltage of about 0.6 V at 25°C and decreases with temperature at the rate of 2 mV/°C.

In the single-ended amplifier, the effect is canceled to a large extent by the use of diodes located (Figs. 6-13D and 6-13E) so that their drift with temperature of 2 mV/°C cancels the base-emitter voltage drift of roughly equal magnitude. With perfect matching of the diode and transistor's base-emitter characteristic, the single-ended circuit of Fig. 6–13D achieves close to zero output drift.

As discussed in Sect. 6.5.4, the circuit of Fig. 6–12D does not achieve zero drift even with perfect matching of the diode D1 and the base-emitter characteristic of Q1. The ratio $R1/(R1 + R2)$ also affects the magnitude of the resultant drift as discussed in the aforementioned section.

The drift of output current with temperature in the double-ended difference amplifier of Fig. 6–11 is generally less than with single-ended amplifiers. This can be seen from Fig. 6–11 by considering the current drifts as due (as pointed out above) to two small batteries in series with each base. The magnitude of the "battery voltage" is about 0.6 V, and it decreases at the rate of 2 mV/°C. Now if the two equivalent "battery voltages" have equal temperature coefficients (as can be achieved by using two integrated circuit transistors close together on the same chip), the difference in collector voltages (or currents) remains constant—there is no drift in the collector voltage difference with temperature.

But if the voltage proportional to the difference between base input voltages is taken as the voltage at a single collector with respect to ground, that voltage will drift even with temperature coefficient matched equivalent "battery voltages." This is a so-called "common mode effect," i.e., the voltage at a single collector with respect to ground also depends on the absolute dc level of the base input voltages—not only on their difference.

Thus, the potential at a collector with respect to ground is (Fig. 6–11)

$$V_{c(Q1)} = V_{cc} - I_{c1}(R_L)$$

and for $V_{b1} = V_{b2}$ and $V_{be1} = V_{be2}$,

$$I_{c1} = \frac{V_{b1} - V_{be1}}{2R_o}$$

assuming the I_o current is equally shared, and

$$V_{c(Q1)} = V_{cc} - \left(\frac{R_L}{2R_o}\right)(V_{b1} - V_{be1})$$

$$\frac{\Delta V_{c(Q1)}}{\Delta T} = \left(\frac{R_L}{2R_o}\right)\left(\frac{\Delta V_{be1}}{\Delta T}\right)$$

In the usual case, R_L will be two to five times R_o.

Then for $\Delta V_{be1}/\Delta T$ of 2 mV/°C, and, say, for $R_L = 2R_o$, $\Delta V_{c(Q1)}/\Delta T$ = 2 mV/°C.

This drift in potential of a single collector of the double-ended difference amplifier can be compensated by a diode in series with the reference voltage as in Figs. 6–13A and 6–13B. Or, as in Fig. 6–13C, the difference amplifier emitter current can be kept constant by the use of a temperature-compensated emitter follower constant load circuit. These compensation schemes are not always perfect, since they depend on exact matching of the temperature coefficients of two semiconductor junctions that may not be carrying the same current or that may be operating at different temperatures.

There is thus a certain amount of drift voltage that is never compensated out. If there were no negative feedback this output voltage drift would be the net remaining input voltage drift multiplied by the gain from the drift injection point to the output.

But with negative feedback, output drift voltage is not multiplied by the open-loop gain. It is rather multiplied by an amount depending on where this drift voltage arises in the feedback loop. This can be seen as follows.

Output Voltage Drift Dependence on Point in a Negative-Feedback Loop Where an Input Drift is Permitted

The magnitude of the resultant output drift and its relationship to where in the complete feedback loop the initial drift or error voltage is permitted to appear can be seen from the following:

In Fig. 6–14, assume an "error" or "drift" voltage V_d appears at the output of the difference amplifier, which has a gain of $A1$ from a base to its collector. This drift voltage can be the uncompensated change in absolute dc voltage at either collector when a single-ended output signal is used. This error as discussed above arises from changes in common emitter current due to the temperature dependence of V_{be} of the difference amplifier. Now assume following the difference amplifier output there are two amplifier stages of gain, $A2$ and $A3$, before the base of the emitter follower output stage, which has unity gain. Then the output change ΔV_o resulting from the drift voltage is

$$\Delta V_o = V_d A2 A3 - \left(\frac{R2}{R1 + R2}\right)\Delta V_o A1 A2 A3$$

or
$$\Delta V_o = \frac{V_d A2 A3}{[1 + R2/(R1 + R2)]A1 A2 A3}$$

and for $[R2/(R1 + R2)]A1 A2 A3 >> 1$

$$\Delta V_o \cong \left(\frac{V_d A2 A3}{A1 A2 A3}\right)\left(\frac{R1 + R2}{R2}\right)$$

$$\cong \left(\frac{V_d}{A1}\right)\left(\frac{R1 + R2}{R2}\right) \qquad (6-29)$$

Equation 6–29 is a general and valuable relation in feedback amplifiers. It states that any drift or error voltage appearing or inserted in the feedback loop is multiplied by the total forward gain between the point of insertion and the output ($A2 A3$) and divided (degenerated) by the total open-loop gain ($A1 A2 A3$). Thus, drift or error voltages are most serious when they are permitted to appear closest to the output of the difference amplifier as the forward gain in this case is highest before degeneration by the entire loop takes place. In the case of Fig.

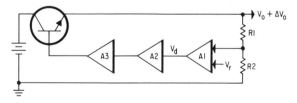

Fig. 6–14. Output drift for a drift signal inserted as shown is $\Delta V_o = (V_d/A1)[(R1 + R2)/R2]$.

6–13, if the same V_d were permitted to appear between $A2$ and $A3$, the resultant output change would be

$$\Delta V_o \cong \left(\frac{V_d A3}{A1 A2 A3} \right) \left(\frac{R1 + R2}{R2} \right)$$

$$\cong \left(\frac{V_d}{A1 A2} \right) \left(\frac{R1 + R2}{R2} \right) \tag{6–30}$$

which is $1/A2$ times as great as the output drift when the same V_d is permitted to appear earlier in the feedback loop (as in Eq. 6–29).

An appreciation of this effect is seen by the following numerical example. In Sect. 6.6.1, it was seen in a two-transistor difference amplifier with $R_L = 2R_o$ and $\Delta V_{be1}/\Delta T = 2$ mV/°C, the voltage with respect to ground of a single collector moves at the rate of 2 mV/°C. Then for a temperature change of 50°C, the output drift at one collector is 100 mV. Now assume in a feedback amplifier as in Fig. 6–14, $A1 = A2 = A3 = 20$ and $R1 = R2$. Thus, the drift at the output for a 100-mV drift at the output of the difference amplifier is from Eq. 6–29

$$\Delta V_o = \left(\frac{V_d}{A1} \right) \left(\frac{R1 + R2}{R2} \right) = \left(\frac{100}{20} \right)(2) = 10 \text{ mV}$$

But if in some manner, the 100-mV drift were to appear between $A2$ and $A3$ in Fig. 6–14, the output drift from Eq. 6–30 would be

$$\Delta V_o = \left(\frac{V_d}{A1 A2} \right) \left(\frac{R1 + R2}{R2} \right) = \left(\frac{100}{(20)(20)} \right) 2$$

$$= \left(\frac{100}{(20)(20)} \right) 2 = 0.5 \text{ mV}$$

It is for this reason (Eqs. 6–29 and 6–30) that in a difference amplifier it is preferable to use the difference in potential between collectors rather than the potential at one collector to ground as the error signal. This is shown in Fig. 6–15A, in which the output of the first difference amplifier is used to drive both bases of a second difference amplifier.

The difference in collector potentials of Q1 and Q2 is relatively independent of temperature despite the base-emitter voltages and common emitter current being temperature dependent. The difference amplifier Q3–Q4 converts the double-ended signal to a single-ended one to drive the base of the series-pass Darlington driver. But now the single-ended drift signal at the collector of Q3 is not so serious, for it is amplified only by the unity forward gain of emitter followers Q5 and Q6 but degenerated by the product of the gains of both difference amplifiers in accordance with Eq. 6–30. Thus, assume a drift voltage at the collector of Q3 of 100 mV because of the temperature-caused change in base-emitter voltage of Q3 and Q4. Now as above, assume gains of 20 from base to collector of each difference amplifier and $R1 = R2$. Then from Eq. 6–30, output voltage drift is $(100 \times 2)/(20 \times 20) = 0.5$ mV.

6.6.2 Difference Amplifier "Offset" Voltage Drift

Even with a double-ended output from the difference amplifier, this difference voltage between collectors will drift with temperature. This occurs because the base-emitter voltage versus collector-current characteristics of the two transistors are not exactly identical, and their relative characteristics change with temperature.

A measure of the similarity of the I_c versus V_{be} curves of the two transistors is the so-called "offset voltages." This is the small voltage difference that must exist between bases to bring the differences between collector potentials to zero. It is not important that a nonzero offset voltage exists, since this can be canceled by adjustment of the sampling resistor ratio R1/R2. But if the offset voltage is temperature dependent, even with the double-ended outputs from the

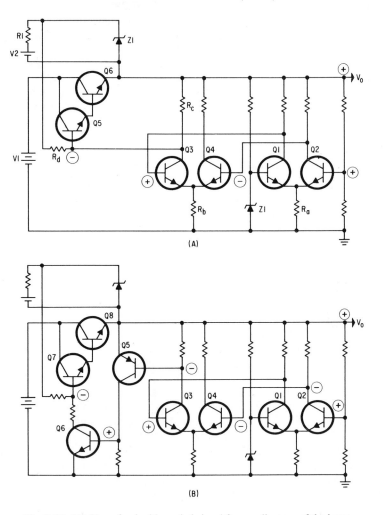

(A)

(B)

Fig. 6–15. (A) Use of a double-ended signal from collectors of the input difference amplifier. Output drift arises from its temperature-caused base-emitter voltage change. (B) The same difference amplifier with double-ended outputs but with additional open-loop gain provided by Q6 and dc level shifting by Q5. Polarities indicate an odd number of phase reversals (negative feedback) for an assumed ⊕ change at the output.

collectors, there will be an output drift. Thus, the most significant parameters in determining drift in a difference amplifier is the rate of change of "offset" voltage with temperature.

If the two transistors in the difference amplifier are integrated devices on the same chip their V_{be}-I_c characteristics and current gains are very closely matched and remain better matched with temperature changes. Offset (V_{off}) voltage acts much like a small voltage in series with one of the bases in the difference amplifier, or specifically like a voltage in a series with the voltage reference source. Thus, output voltage in Fig. 6–13 is

$$V_o = \left(\frac{R1 + R2}{R2}\right)(V_r + V_{off})$$

And by adjusting R1/R2 any desired output volts can be obtained at, say, room temperature for any value of V_{off}. But if V_{off} varies with temperature at a rate of $\Delta V_{off}/\Delta T$, then the output voltage varies at a rate of

$$\frac{\Delta V_o}{\Delta T} = \left(\frac{R1 + R2}{R2}\right)\left(\frac{\Delta V_{off}}{\Delta T}\right)$$

With integrated transistors on the same chip $\Delta V_{off}/T$ can be kept to 5–10 μV/°C.[1]

6.6.3 Difference Amplifier Offset Current Drift

If both transistors in the difference amplifier (Fig. 6–11) draw equal current and have equal current gain, β, then their base current is $I_o/2\beta$. Now either unequal source impedances seen by the two bases or poor tracking of β in the two transistors will generate an error voltage between the two bases. The voltage actually seen at each base is $V_{oc} - I_o R_s/2\beta$, where V_{oc} is the open circuit source voltage and R_s is the source impedance looking back from each base.

Clearly, the smaller the value R_s, the less is the base voltage affected by β and its variation with temperature. Source impedance seen looking back from the base to the resistor sampling network (Fig. 6–13B) is the parallel impedance of R1 and R2. These are generally made sufficiently small so that the current through them is 50–100 times the current demanded by the base ($I_o/2\beta$).

Generally, the impedance looking into the sampling resistor network is larger than that looking back into the zener reference. These are usually equalized by adding a resistor in series between the top of the zener and the base that senses it. With both transistors on the same chip, variation in β with temperature and the consequent voltage change because of the equal and minimized source impedances will result in relatively small error voltage changes with temperature. Usually, power supply output drift due to the temperature coefficient of offset voltage and current combined can be kept under 20 μV/°C with an integrated circuit difference amplifier and equalized source impedance looking back from the bases.

6.6.4 Reference Voltage Drift

Zener reference voltage sources have previously been discussed at length in Sect. 1.5. Conventional zener diodes have temperature coefficients

---

[1] RCA Linear Integrated Circuits, pp. 43–72.

ranging from $-0.06\%/°C$ for a 3.3-V zener to $+0.060\%/°C$ for a 12-V zener (Fig. 1–10F).

But these temperature coefficients hold only at a fixed operating current unique to a given voltage rating. Thus, as can be seen in Fig. 1–10F a 4.7-V zener (1N750) crosses the zero temperature coefficient axis at about 4 mA, a 5.1-V unit (1N751) at about 8 mA and a 5.6-V unit (1N752) at about 30 mA. Thus, if the zener current can be kept constant at these zero temperature coefficient points, fairly good drift-free operation is possible. Zener current can be kept constant, either by feeding the zener current-limiting resistor from the regulated output of the power supply or by use of a double zener regulator as shown in Fig. 1–11.

But even at the optimum current setting, a conventional zener's temperature coefficient remains low only over a limited temperature range. When maximum zener stability over a large temperature range is required, better results are achieved with temperature-compensated zeners (Fig. 1–13). Such zeners are characterized by maximum guaranteed voltage changes over a range of temperatures usually -55 to $+100°C$. This defines the device more precisely than a temperature coefficient that varies with temperature and, hence, is only quoted as an average. Thus, it is seen in Fig. 1–13 that the 1N829A has an average temperature coefficient of $0.0005\%/°C$ and is guaranteed to have an output voltage change of only 5 mV over the range of -55 to $+100°C$ if operated at its optimum current of 7.5 mA.

6.7   Feedback Amplifier Configurations

The dc voltage level at the collectors of the difference amplifier (Fig. 6–11) is generally not at the correct value to permit it to drive the base of the series-pass element or the base of the series-pass base drivers (Figs. 6–6 to 6–10). Either for this dc voltage level incompatibility or to increase the total open-loop gain, usually additional transistor amplifiers are required between the output of the difference amplifier and the input to the series-pass element or its drivers.

There is vast variety of npn–pnp transistor combinations possible between the series-pass element input and difference amplifier output. The configuration chosen depends on the nature of the series-pass element npn or pnp, emitter follower or inverter (Fig. 6–6). It depends to some extent on the nature of the base drive circuit, which may be any of the configurations of Figs. 6–7 to 6–10. And it depends, of course, on the nature of the difference amplifier output node or nodes, which may be any of the versions of Figs. 6–13 and 6–15. Some of the possible feedback amplifier configurations used with the frequently occurring series-pass combinations are shown in Figs. 6–15 to 6–17.

6.7.1 Feedback Amplifiers with Double-Ended Difference Amplifier Output

Figures 6–15 and 6–16, respectively, show npn emitter followers and npn inverters as series-pass elements. In both figures, a double-ended output is taken from the difference amplifier and is further amplified by a two-transistor difference amplifier before conversion to a single-ended signal for driving the input of the series-pass element.

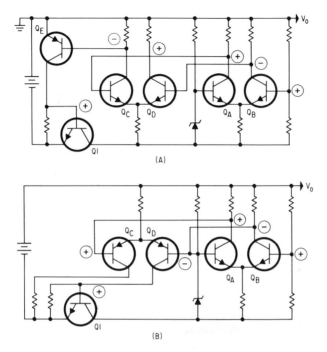

Fig. 6–16. Feedback amplifier configurations for npn inverter series-pass elements.

Figure 6–15A shows a single-ended output from one collector of the second difference amplifier driving the base of the Darlington driver. The base drive for Q5 comes from a constant-current source formed from floating power supply V2, zener Z1, and resistor R1. Resistor R_d must be able to supply somewhat more than the maximum current demanded by Q5 when β in Q5 and Q6 are at their minimum and output load current is a maximum. For maximum beta in Q5 and Q6 and minimum load current, R_d supplies more current than is required by the base of Q5. The excess R_d current is drained off by Q3, and R_b must be sufficiently low so that Q3 can absorb this excess current. The current demanded by R_b should be large (at least five times the excess current from R_d) so that the currents in Q3 and Q4 remain roughly equal, no matter what current is demanded by the base of Q5. For large currents in Q5, a second Darlington driver for its base may be needed.

Figure 6–15B shows a two-stage amplifier between the collector of the second stage and the series-pass base input point. This provides more open-loop gain and makes the collector current changes in Q3 and Q4 negligible, thus contributing to output voltage stability.

Figure 6–16 shows some possible configurations for driving the base of collector-loaded npn series-pass elements. For large current variations in Q1, a Darlington driver for its base may be necessary.

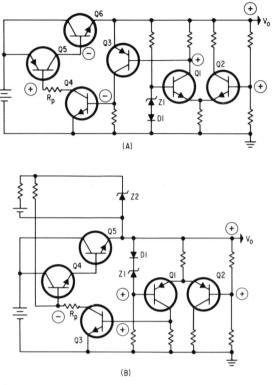

Fig. 6–17. Complete feedback amplifier configurations with single-ended outputs from a two-transistor difference amplifier and npn emitter follower series-pass element. Polarity symbols show an odd number of phase reversals (negative feedback) around the loop.

6.7.2 Feedback Amplifiers with Single-Ended Difference Amplifier Output

As discussed in Sect. 6.6.1, when somewhat greater output drift with temperature is acceptable, single-ended outputs from a difference amplifier can be taken as shown in Fig. 6–17 for npn emitter follower series-pass elements. The configurations show temperature-compensating zener diodes that give output drifts with temperature almost as low as with double-ended outputs from difference amplifiers. Some of the series-pass base drive schemes of Figs. 6–7 and 6–8 are shown in Fig. 6–17 along with a number of "current sink" amplifiers for driving them.

6.8   Protection Circuits

Most present-day power-supply specifications require protection against two common potentially disastrous faults: accidental shorts to ground or overload currents, which can destroy the series-pass element, or output over-voltage, which can destroy voltage-sensitive loads.

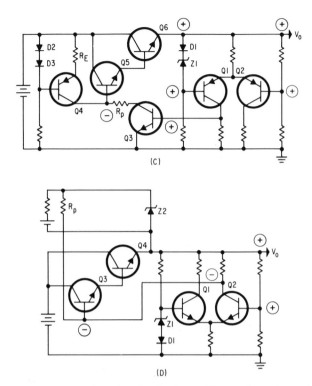

Fig. 6–17. (*Cont'd.*) Complete feedback amplifier configurations with single-ended outputs from a two-transistor difference amplifier and npn emitter follower series-pass element. Polarity symbols show an odd number of phase reversals (negative feedback) around the loop.

6.8.1 Overcurrent Protection

Overcurrent protection is primarily intended to protect against over-dissipating the series-pass elements when the output node is shorted to ground. A shorted output node is a common failure mode, since it can be brought about by shorted loads, the output bus being accidentally shorted to ground in its long path to pick up all its loads, or most probably by accidental momentary shorts during testing.

A persistent short at the loads makes an entire system inoperative, of course, but it is a very desirable feature that the load short does not also cause a power-supply failure and the system is operative on removal of the load short alone. Further, some shorts will burn themselves out in a short time, and it is desirable that in the short time they exist they do not also damage the power supply. Voltmeter or oscilloscope probes accidentally slipping and shorting to ground during system testing is a very frequent occurrence, and it is unacceptable that each such accident result in a power-supply failure.

Now, although the prime reason for overcurrent protection is to protect against a dead short at an output, it is also useful in the protection against smaller and limited overcurrents above the maximum specified load current. The current level at which protective action sets in is generally kept at 40–80% above the maximum specified load current. With greater complexity in circuit design, it is generally possible to set the threshold at which protective action sets in to be only 10–20% above the maximum load current—but this is not usually necessary.

There are two generally used modes of overcurrent protection: constant current and current foldback shown in Figs. 6–18A and 6–18B, respectively.

6.8.2 Constant-Current Overcurrent/Short-Circuit Protection

In constant-current protection (Fig. 6–18A), as output current is increased beyond I_{ms} (the maximum specified load current) the output voltage remains constant and within its load regulation specifications. At some critical current level I_c, output current can no longer be increased, and, as the external load impedance decreases, the output voltage falls along the vertical line (I_c-V_o). Actual operating point of the supply in voltage and current is at the intersection of the volt–ampere characteristic described above with a load line whose slope $\Delta V/\Delta I$ is equal to the external resistance. Thus, in Fig. 6–18A, three different external resistors R1, R2, and R3 are shown together with their intersections P1, P2, and P3. These yield output voltages $V1$, $V2$, and $V3$.

It should be noted that, although the maximum current that can be drawn through the supply is limited to I_c, the dissipation in the series-pass element is a maximum for a dead short at the output $(R_L = \Delta V/\Delta I = 0)$. For at a dead short, the current throughout the series-pass element is still I_c, but the voltage across it is a maximum. This maximum voltage is equal to the full maximum dc input voltage to the series-pass regulator at high ac line input voltage. This voltage is considerably greater than that existing across the series-pass element in normal operation, for it will be recalled (Sect. 6.3) that the dc input voltage was chosen so that at low ac line input, the rectified dc input to the series-pass element was minimized to $V_o + 2 + V_{\text{ripple}}/2$ and the voltage across the series-pass element was $2 + V_{\text{ripple}}/2$ volts.

Then for an output short occurring when the ac line input is high, assuming ±10% ac line voltage tolerances, the dissipation across the series-pass element is $(1.1)(1.1)(V_o + 2 + V_{\text{ripple}}/2)I_c$.

This compares to a series-pass dissipation (nonshorted) at high ac line input voltage and maximum specified load current, I_{ms}, of

$$[(1.1)(1.1)(V_o + 2 + V_{\text{ripple}}/2) - V_o]I_{ms}$$

It is obvious that, even with I_c, not much more than I_{ms} (25% above it), at high output voltages the series-pass dissipation under shorted conditions can be far greater than 25% above the nonshorted dissipation.

Thus, although constant-current limiting puts an upper limit on the output current, there must be a large enough number of series-pass elements in parallel so that their junction temperatures calculated as in Sect. 4.3 remain safely below their maximum specified value.

6.8.3 Current Foldback Overcurrent Protection

It was pointed out in the previous section that constant-current overcurrent protection results in maximum series-pass element power dissipation in the shorted condition, and this dissipation can be many times greater than in the nonshorted condition.

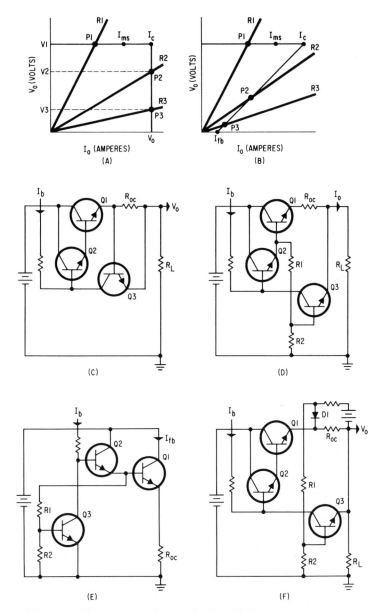

Fig. 6–18. Overcurrent protection circuits. (A) Constant-current over-current protection. (B) Foldback-current overcurrent protection. (C) Constant-current overcurrent circuit configuration. (D) Foldback-current overcurrent circuit implementation. (E) Foldback circuit with output shorted. (F) Compensating the V_{be} drop of Q3 with an auxiliary diode D1 rather than with the base-emitter drop of Q1.

In a relatively simple way, the lower dissipation "foldback" characteristic of Fig. 6–18B can be obtained. In this mode, output voltage remains constant and within specification limits up to a critical current I_c, which is some factor (40–60%) greater than the maximum specified value I_{ms}. Beyond I_c, the output voltage and current start falling along the "foldback" line (I_c-I_{fb}).

The foldback line (I_c-I_{fb}) is not necessarily a straight line. Its exact shape depends on circuit details and generally, just after the turnaround point at I_c, it will have an upward concavity. It is important to note that along I_c-I_{fb}, the impedance at the output node is a negative resistance. For moving along I_c-I_{fb}, as the current drawn from the node increases, the output voltage also increases, i.e., the definition of negative resistance. Because of this negative resistance, once the point I_c is rounded by a decreasing load line, output voltage rapidly jumps down the I_c-I_{fb} to a stable intersecting point such as P2 or P3.

Now the advantage of the current foldback scheme is that on a dead short the output current is I_{fb}, which can be a small fraction of I_c. Thus, series-pass dissipation is greatly decreased below that in the constant-current scheme and significantly fewer series-pass elements are required to maintain safe junction temperatures under prolonged short-circuit conditions. Current foldback circuits are somewhat trickier to design and require more components than constant-current circuits, but the advantage of far lower dissipation under shorted condition makes them preferable.

As the output load impedance is decreased beyond the I_c intersection, operation will be at the intersection of the resistive load line and the foldback current characteristics. This is seen in Fig. 6–18B, in which three successively lower impedances R1, R2, and R3 are shown along with their intersections P1, P2, and P3 with the current foldback characteristics. These intersections are stable operating points and care must be taken that under odd operating conditions (usually at power supply turnon) a nonlinear load corresponding to R2 or R3 is not presented to the supply even momentarily, for this can cause the output voltages to "latch up" at intersection points P2 or P3 and voltage will never come up to its full value. "Latch up" is a frequent problem with foldback circuits and will be considered in more detail in Sect. 6.8.8.

6.8.4 Constant-Current Circuit Implementation

Circuit implementation for constant-current overcurrent protection is shown in Fig. 6–18C. A current-sensing resistor R_{oc} is inserted in series in the output load. A transistor Q3, which is normally off, is used to divert the series-pass base drive (I_b) when the threshold current I_c is reached. The base-emitter terminals of Q3 are bridged across R_{oc} to sense its voltage which is proportional to output current. The resistor R_{oc} is selected so that at the highest specified output current I_m, Q3 is safely biased off by an adequately low forward bias V_{off}. At the critical current limit I_c, the increased drop across R_{oc} reaches V_{on}, the turn-on potential for Q3.

Now Q3 turns on, diverting just enough of the base drive of Darlington driver Q2 to keep the Q1 output current at a level I_c such that $I_c R_{oc} = V_{on}$. Transistors Q1, Q2, and Q3 form a local negative-feedback loop which has taken over from the main voltage-regulating feedback loop. The output current remains constant at I_c and the output voltage is fixed by the output load impedance R_L at a value $V_o = I_c R_L$ (the intersection of an R_L load line with the vertical I_c

curve). For a dead short at the output ($R_L = 0$), $V_c = 0$. The governing relationships are thus

$$V_{off} = I_{ms}R_{oc} = Q3 \text{ base potential}$$

to ensure Q3 is off at any temperature at $I = I_{ms}$, and

$$V_{on} = I_c R_{oc} = Q3 \text{ base potential}$$

to ensure Q3 is on at I_c at any temperature. Or

$$I_c = I_{ms}(V_{on}/V_{off})$$

Now if V_{off} and V_{on} were sharply defined, were almost equal in magnitude, and had little production spread, the current limit point I_c could be kept just slightly above I_m. Since output voltage starts falling at I_c when Q3 turns on, it must be ensured that the lowest value of I_c is greater than I_m, the maximum load current at which the output voltage is to remain constant.

Since there are production spreads in the I_c–V_{be} characteristic, R_{oc} must be chosen small enough so that $I_{ms}R_{oc}$ is less than the minimum value of $V_{on(min)}$, i.e., the most easily turned on Q3 is safely kept off at a forward bias of $I_{ms}R_{oc}$. For low-level transistors like Q3, forward bias of 0.40 V is still low enough to keep all transistors safely off up to about 75°C. Then for $R_{oc} = 0.4/I_{ms}$, the current limit point I_c will have a spread determined by the production spread in V_{on}. The maximum value of the current limit point $I_{c(max)}$ is given by the above relation by $I_{c(max)} = V_{on(max)}/R_{oc}$.

Now for most transistors like Q3, production spread can make $V_{on(max)}$ as large as 0.65 V. Thus

$$I_{c(max)} = I_{ms}\left(\frac{V_{on}}{V_{off}}\right) = I_{ms}\left(\frac{0.65}{0.40}\right) = 1.63I_{ms}$$

Thus, with constant-current limiting, for an output short, the series-pass elements can be subjected to a total maximum dissipation as great as $P_{max} = 1.63I_{ms}V_{in(max)}$. Enough series-pass elements in parallel must be used so that each element's dissipation is within safe junction temperature limits.

It should be noted that the nominal current-limiting point is temperature sensitive as it is fixed by the base turn-on voltage V_{be}, which is nominally about 0.60 V and varies about 2 mV/°C. Thus, the current limit point varies about $(0.002/0.65)(100)$ or 0.3%/°C.

6.8.5 Current Foldback Circuit Implementation

The current foldback characteristic of Fig. 6–18B can be implemented as in Fig. 6–18D. As discussed in Sect. 6.8.3, it has the advantage that for a dead short at the output, series-pass current is equal to I_{fb}, which may be a small fraction of I_{ms}. Power dissipation in the series-pass element is thus considerably less than for the constant-current circuit and fewer series-pass elements in parallel are necessary.

There is yet a further advantage in the foldback circuit of Fig. 6–18D in that I_c, the critical current at which protective action commences, is relatively independent of temperature. For in Fig. 6–18D as temperature, say, rises, the base-emitter voltage required to turn on Q3 decreases, but the control voltage used to turn on Q3 is taken from the base of Q1 whose base-emitter potential decreases with temperature at roughly the same rate. And since $R2/(R1+R2) \cong 1$, the turn-on point for Q3 will depend only on the IR drop in R_{oc} and the divider ratios $R2/(R1 + R2)$ and will be relatively uninfluenced by temperature.

A qualitative understanding of why the circuit of Fig. 6–18D yields the current foldback characteristic of Fig. 6–18B can be seen as follows. Transistor Q3 serves the same purpose as in Fig. 6–18C. It is normally off, up to the maximum specified output current I_{ms}. Its base-emitter potential is the sum of the IR rise in R_{oc}, the rise in V_{be} of the Q1 base and the IR drop in R1. R_{oc} and the ratio $R2/(R1 + R2)$ are selected so that when V_o is high (at $I = I_{ms}$), Q3 is biased partly on to just below the conduction level or to about +0.4 V. To initially turn on Q3 (at I_c) the voltage rise in R_{oc} must increase to overcome the downward drop in R1. But the drop in R1 is significant only if V_o is high enough to cause a bias current to flow in R1. When V_o is shorted, the bias current in R1 is lost and the voltage rise in R_{oc} required to keep Q3 on is considerably less. The current flowing through R_{oc} required to keep Q3 on in the shorted condition is thus much less than is required to turn it on initially when V_o is high and is providing bias current in R1.

6.8.6 Quantitative Relations in the Current Foldback Overcurrent Protection Circuit

Significant parameters in the circuit of Fig. 6–18D can be calculated as follows:

$$V_{be(Q3)} = I_o R_{oc} + V_{be(Q1)} - V_{R1}$$

$$= I_o R_{oc} + V_{be(Q1)} - (V_o + I_o R_{oc} + V_{be(Q1)})\left(\frac{R1}{R1 + R2}\right)$$

or
$$V_{be(Q3)} = \left(1 - \frac{R1}{R1 + R2}\right)(I_o R_{oc} + V_{be(Q1)}) - V_o(R1 + R2) \quad (6\text{-}31)$$

Now choose R_{oc} and the ratio $R1/(R1 + R2)$ so that, at the maximum specified output current, Q3 is so biased that the most easily turned-on transistor is still safely off. Let this be a forward bias of 0.35 V or 0.3 V below the forward voltage required (0.65 V) to turn on the hardest-to-turn-on transistor. Now from Eq. 6–31

$$\frac{\Delta V_{be(Q3)}}{\Delta I_o} = \left(1 - \frac{R1}{R1 + R2}\right)R_{oc}$$

And generally $R1/(R1 + R2) \ll 1$ for $V_o > 5$ V. Then

$$\frac{\Delta V_{be(Q3)}}{\Delta I_o} \cong R_{oc}$$

And if the Q3 bias at $I_o = I_{ms}$ is set at 0.3 V below what is required to turn it on, choose R_{oc} so that at a current of $I_o = I_c$, which is to be no more than $1.5I_{ms}$, Q3 picks up the additional 0.3 V of forward bias and does turn on. Then

$$\Delta V_{be} = 0.3 = R_{oc}\Delta I_o$$
$$= R_{oc}(I_c - I_{ms})$$
$$= R_{oc}(1.5I_{ms} - I_{ms})$$
$$= 0.5R_{oc}I_{ms}$$

Or
$$R_{oc} = \frac{\Delta V_{be}}{0.5 I_{ms}} = \frac{0.3}{0.5 I_{ms}} = \frac{0.6}{I_{ms}} \qquad (6\text{-}32)$$

Similarly, for overcurrent tripping at $I_o = 1.3 I_{ms}$,

$$\Delta V_{be} = 0.3 = R_{oc} \Delta I_o = R_{oc}(1.3 I_{ms} - I_{ms}) = 0.3 R_{oc} I_{ms}$$

and
$$R_{oc} = 1.0/I_{ms} \qquad (6\text{-}32A)$$

Now from Eq. 6-31, since $V_{be(Q3)}$ is to be 0.35 V at $I_o = I_{ms}$,

$$V_{be(Q3)} = 0.35 = \left(1 - \frac{R1}{R1 + R2}\right)[I_{ms}R_{oc} + V_{be(Q1)}] - V_o\left(\frac{R1}{R1 + R2}\right)$$

Now for overcurrent tripping at $1.5 I_{ms}$, $I_{ms} R_{oc} = 0.6$ V from Eq. 6-32 and since $V_{be(Q1)} = 0.8$ V typically for power transistors, then

$$0.35 = \left(1 - \frac{R1}{R1 + R2}\right)(0.6 + 0.8) - V_o\left(\frac{R1}{R1 + R2}\right)$$

or
$$R1/(R1 + R2) = 1.05/(1.4 + V_o) \qquad (6\text{-}33)$$

And similarly for overcurrent tripping at $1.3 I_{ms}$, since from Eq. 6-32A, $I_{ms} R_{oc} = 1.0$,

$$0.35 = \left(1 - \frac{R1}{R1 + R2}\right)(1.0 + 0.8) - V_o\left(\frac{R1}{R1 + R2}\right)$$

or
$$R1/(R1 + R2) = 1.45/(1.8 + V_o) \qquad (6\text{-}33A)$$

Equations 6-32 and 6-33 are plotted in Figs. 6-19 and 6-20 for some common output currents and voltages. In most instances, R2 would be a fixed resistor in series with a trimming potentiometer to permit setting the forward bias on Q3 at +0.35 V at maximum specified output current.

Somewhat better stability in the overcurrent trip point (I_c) can be achieved by taking the top of R1 from a point one diode drop above the emitter of Q1 in Fig. 6-18D. This is shown in Fig. 6-18F. It was noted above that the temperature variation of V_{be} of Q3 is being canceled by the base-emitter drop of power transistor Q1. But this cancellation is rather imperfect, for Q1 is a power transistor which in the first place has larger spreads in V_{be} than a lower power transistor like Q3. Further, Q1 operates at a higher temperature than Q3, since it supplies all the output power. It is also located on a heat sink rather than on a printed circuit board as is Q3. And finally V_{be} of Q1 depends on output current and it is desirable to have all the current-sensing characteristics in a fixed, stable, and passive element—the sensing resistor R_{oc} itself.

Thus, if a voltage fixed with respect to V_o is available, it can be used to supply a constant current into a diode D1 as in Fig. 6-18F. Now with D1 physically close to Q3, tracking of V_{D1} and V_{be} of Q3 with temperature will be considerably better than V_{be} of Q1 and V_{be} of Q3. Further, the voltage rise in the diode is independent of output current and current sensing is a function of the passive element R_{oc} alone. But it should be noted a relatively constant current must be available to generate the diode bias voltage. Otherwise, current variations in the diode will change its bias voltage and, hence, the overcurrent trip point. If the supply voltage for the diode bias current is taken from the collector of the

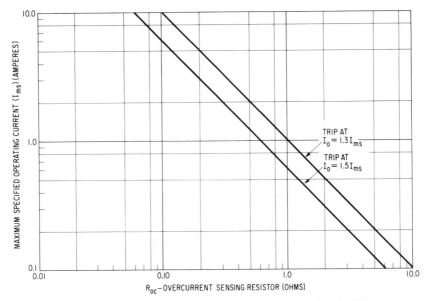

Fig. 6–19. Foldback-current overcurrent protection circuit (Fig. 6–18D). Current-sensing resistor versus maximum specified operating current (I_{ms}) for current limiting at $I_o = 1.3I_{ms}$ and $1.5I_{ms}$. (From Eqs. 6–32 and 6–32A)

series-pass element, this varies with input ac line voltage. Diode operating current should be sufficiently high above the low current knee so that its forward voltage drop is relatively independent of current.

6.8.7 Magnitude of Short-Circuit Foldback Current (I_{fb} of Fig. 6–18D)

In Fig. 6–18D, if the output is shorted to ground, the circuit is as shown in Fig. 6–18E. The magnitude of the foldback current (see Fig. 6–18B) is given by

$$I_{fb} = \frac{V_{be(Q3)} + V_{R1} - V_{be(Q1)}}{R_{oc}}$$

Now to a close approximation, $V_{be(Q1)} = V_{be(Q3)}$ even though Q3 is a low-power TO5 type and Q1 is a TO3 power transistor. This is so as the base current in Q1 is quite small. At most $V_{be(Q1)} = 0.7$, $V_{be(Q3)} = 0.6$. But as an approximation assume the voltages equal. Then

$$I_{fb} = \frac{V_{R1}}{R_{oc}}$$

$$I_{R1} \cong \frac{V_{be(Q3)}}{R2} + \frac{I_b}{\beta_{Q3}}$$

since most of the current I_b will drain away into the collector of Q3. Then

$$V_{R1} = R1\left(\frac{V_{be(Q3)}}{R2} + \frac{I_b}{\beta_{Q3}}\right)$$

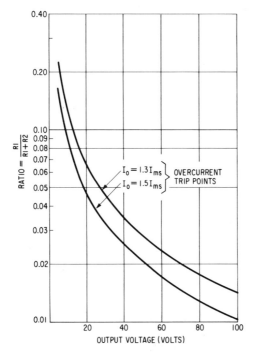

Fig. 6–20. Foldback-current overcurrent protection circuit (Fig. 6–18D). Resistance ratio R1/(R1 + R2) versus output voltage for current limit trip points at $I_o = 1.3 I_{ms}$ and $I_o = 1.5 I_{ms}$. (From Eqs. 6–33 and 6–33A)

And
$$I_{fb} = \frac{V_{R1}}{R_{oc}}$$

$$\cong \left(\frac{R1}{R_{oc}}\right)\left(\frac{0.6}{R2} + \frac{I_b}{\beta_{Q3}}\right) \tag{6–34}$$

It can be seen from Eq. 6–34 that, for the foldback current to be relatively constant and independent of production spread and temperature variations of current gain β of Q3, the term $0.6/R2$ should be greater than I_b/β_{Q3}. This is always possible since Eq. 6–33 fixes only the ratio of R1/R2, not their absolute value. Thus, R2 can be chosen small enough so that variations in Q3 gain do not significantly affect the magnitude of the foldback current.

In general, foldback current I_{fb} should be made small enough so that $V_{\text{collector input voltage (max)}} (I_{fb})$ does not overdissipate the series-pass elements. But making I_{fb} too small can lead to a variety of problems: "latch-up" or the failure of the supply to come up to full voltage under odd load conditions. This is discussed in the following section. A common value for I_{fb} is one-fifth of the maximum specified current.

6.8.8 Latch-Up in Overcurrent Protection Circuits

A serious failure mode referred to as "voltage latch-up" can occur with either constant-current or foldback circuits. This phenomenon, which occurs at power supply turnon, is the failure of the output voltage to come up to its full value. Instead, it "hangs" or "latches" up at some voltage between zero and its full output value. Besides not generating its correct output, the supply can possibly hang up at such a voltage current point that it can overdissipate the series-pass elements and destroy them.

The explanation of the "latch-up" phenomenon is obvious from Figs. 6–18A and 6–18B. Actual operating point in voltage and current in either the constant-current or foldback mode is at the intersection of the output load line with the supply's volt–ampere characteristics. Thus, in the load lines in Figs. 6–18A and 6–18B, crossing the volt–ampere characteristic beyond I_c such as at R2 or R3 will cause the output voltages to latch up at points P2 and P3. Such load lines can exist during turnon even if they do not exist during normal operation. One such troublesome load line exists when the load is primarily an incandescent lamp load. A lamp when cold has low impedance and does not come up to normal impedance unless sufficient voltage is applied to it to heat it up. Thus, when a supply with the overcurrent-protect feature is switched on to a lamp load, the initial inrush of current may drive the output beyond I_c and voltage will fall as the points P2 or P3 (Figs. 6–18A and 6–18B) slide down the load line. Unless the lamp at the low voltage beyond I_c is subjected to enough power dissipation to heat it up and raise its resistance, then there will be an equilibrium point in the lamp's resistance such that a stable intersection point with the supply's volt–ampere characteristic is found at a lower than normal voltage.

A second type of load that can cause latch-up is a load requiring both positive and negative supply voltages. Depending on the exact circuit configuration of such a load, the current drawn out of the positive output node can be greater than normal if the negative portion is not up to its full value. Frequently, a negative supply furnishes a bias to transistors in the positive portion, and when the negative bias source is momentarily not present, load current in the positive output node increases. Hence, at turnon, if the positive voltage source comes up to its full value only a short time before the negative voltage, its momentarily larger output current drives it over the edge of I_c and positive output voltage starts sliding down the foldback characteristic of Fig. 6–18B to a lower output voltage. Now, if at the lower voltage, the negative supply (because it may derive some of its voltages from the positive supply) cannot supply proper bias current for the positive supply, the positive supply continues to draw a larger than normal current. The larger current represents a load line that has a flatter slope than normal and may intersect the foldback characteristic at some point at P2 or P3 of Fig. 6–18B. The effect is that the positive supply remains permanently latched up at lower voltages corresponding to the P2 and P3 intersections of Fig. 6–18B.

This is a regenerative action and whether or not both supplies come up to full value is determined by circuit details and the time races as to which supply comes up first. Generally, difficulties in such cases arise if critical resistors are bridged directly between the positive and negative rails. Resistors, transistors, or ICs should preferably be bridged between either the positive or negative rail and the common ground.

This type of latch-up is only one of many other subtle ones that can occur with loads bridged between positive and negative rails. Another frequently occurring one exists with too small a foldback current. Thus, a load bridged between a positive and negative rail draws a certain current out of the positive rail. Depending on the nature of the load circuit, this current does not fall to zero if the positive rail is at ground and the negative rail is at its full negative value.

Thus, at initial turnon, if this current demanded by the on-turning negative source is greater than that available from the positive source (at $V = 0$) as it tries to come on (i.e., is greater than the positive rail foldback current I_{fb}) the positive source output node is pulled below ground. As the negative source rises toward its full value, it demands even more current out of the positive source and pulls it even further below ground. Thus, the positive source can never rise up along the foldback characteristic of Fig. 6–18B. Latch-up can occur either at a small voltage below or above ground.

The exact latch-up point is the intersection of the positive source's foldback characteristic with a load line corresponding to the negative source's current demand. This load line, drawn from a point at $I = 0$, $V = -V$ (negative source) obviously has an intersection with the positive source's foldback characteristic somewhere close to the zero voltage axis.

Latch-up problems are generally very subtle. They depend on time races — the order in which positive and negative voltages rise to full value. They depend on the magnitude of the load currents demanded out of either positive or negative voltage rails at dc voltage less than full value. These load currents are functions of instantaneous relative voltage and perhaps temperature.

Complete certainty that no latch-up problems exist can only be guaranteed by testing the supply with the exact operational loads with their odd nonlinear characteristics. Testing should include repeated switch on and switch offs to verify all voltages come fully on.

Such testing, of course, is not usually practical in the initial power supply design stages when even the nature of the loads and their nonlinearities are not known. But sufficient assurance that no latch-up is possible is generally obtainable by keeping the foldback current as high as possible. Foldback current should be designed so that it is no less than that which yields maximum permissible junction temperature (105°C or 135–150°C as discussed in Sect. 4.2) at maximum input voltage and with the output shorted.

Care should also be taken that the overcurrent trip point (I_c in Fig. 6–18B) is not too close to the maximum specified dc load currents, for some systems may have time-varying load currents, and short duration current peaks can drive the power supply over I_c and down along the foldback characteristic if these current peak durations are too long to be supplied from the output filter capacity. Although the supply recovers to normal voltage without latching up after the high-peak current goes away, the dip in output voltage as I_c is exceeded is, of course, not acceptable.

6.9 Overvoltage Protection

Most semiconductor loads are voltage sensitive and even momentary overvoltage conditions could be economically disastrous if an entire load system is wiped out by a high-voltage condition that may last only microseconds.

Most often, supplies are protected for overvoltage by a "crowbar" circuit (Fig. 6–21). This consists of a threshold device that senses for output

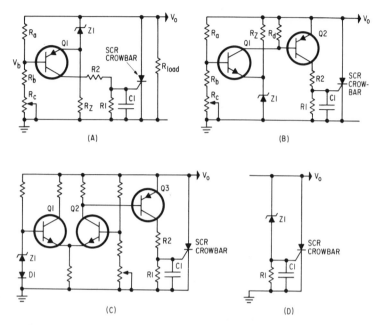

Fig. 6–21. Various overvoltage protecting crowbar circuits. (A) Single-transistor crowbar amplifier. (B) More precise double-transistor crow-bar amplifier. (C) Differential amplifier overvoltage-sensing comparator with temperature-compensated reference source. (D) An inexpensive but imprecise crowbar circuit.

overvoltages, and if it occurs, throws a fast-acting short circuit (crowbar) across the output terminals.

The "short" circuit is a silicon-controlled rectifier (SCR) that is normally off (high impedance between its anode and cathode). A voltage or current impulse between its gate and cathode fires the SCR to its "on" state, in which its anode-to-cathode potential remains at about 1 V at current levels up to maximum rating, which ranges from under 1 A up to 100 A or more for various SCR types. The SCR turn-on time after application of a trigger pulse is about 1 μsec — fast enough to ensure survival of semiconductor loads subjected to a rapidly rising input voltage.

Once fired, the SCR remains "on" until its anode voltage is removed, decreased below its 1-V "on" level or until anode current falls below a minimum "holding" current. A power supply that has been thrown into "crowbar" must have its input power momentarily removed to extinguish the "on" SCR. The firing signal to the SCR can be either a current or voltage impulse that can be as short as 10 down to 0.5 μsec in width. Because of the ease with which SCRs are turned on by narrow pulses, the gate-to-cathode terminals should be paralleled by a "low" impedance RC combination to integrate out narrow noise spikes. The amplitudes of the voltage and current impulses required to fire the SCR is given in each type's data sheets but are not very precise parameters. The gate-firing voltage ranges from about 0.2 to 2.0 or even 3.0 V for some types with a typical value of about 1 V. If firing is done from a current source, current is the critical firing parameter. Gate-firing currents range from a few tenths of a milliampere up to 50–100 mA.

Because of the impreciseness of voltages and currents required to fire the SCR gate, the firing circuit usually consists of two basic parts. First, there is a temperature-stable voltage comparator that senses the difference between the output (or a fixed fraction of it) and a stable voltage reference. The voltage comparator is followed by a high-gain amplifier for driving the SCR gate. Sufficient gain is designed into the amplifier to ensure firing the hardest-to-fire SCR.

The voltage comparison and gain functions may be incorporated in a single element – using the base-emitter terminal of a transistor for voltage comparison, with its output current providing the gain (Fig. 6–21A). A second transistor amplifier can also provide the gain (Fig. 6–21B). This usually makes the voltage comparison more precise. In "cheap" designs (Fig. 6–21D) in which economy of parts is paramount, a single zener interposed between the output voltage and the SCR gate provides both the voltage comparison and "gain." This last scheme, although often used, is a poor design approach. Because of tolerances in the zener diode's breakdown voltage, its "soft knee" at low-current levels, and wide tolerances in the SCR gate firing current and voltage, there is a wide variation in output voltage at which crowbarring can occur. It can occur at prematurely low voltages, shutting the supply down unnecessarily, or at excessively high voltages and thus be ineffective in protecting the loads.

6.9.1 Overvoltage Protection Circuits

Details of some of the usual overvoltage protection circuits are shown in Fig. 6–21. The main objective in any such design is to achieve a stable threshold at which crowbarring occurs. The voltage threshold at which the comparator fires the SCR has a finite width. When component tolerances and temperature shift in one direction, crowbarring may occur at too low a voltage and falsely shut the supply down. When components and temperature shift in the opposite direction, crowbarring may not occur until the output reaches a high and potentially dangerous voltage level for some of the output loads.

Premature crowbarring at too low an output voltage is a rather common failure mode. It occurs when temperature effect, component tolerances, and the effect of noise voltages on the output line have not been thoroughly analyzed. A worst-case calculation of the upper and lower limits of the crowbarring voltage resulting from the above effects is essential for a trouble-free crowbarring circuit.

Single-Transistor SCR Crowbar Driver

Figure 6–21A shows a single pnp transistor used as a voltage comparator and amplifier. The reference voltage is at the pnp emitter and R_c is set so that at normal output voltages Q1 is off. Now when V_o moves upward an amount ΔV_o, V_b moves up a lesser amount ΔV_b where

$$\Delta V_b = \left(\frac{R_b + R_c}{R_a + R_b + R_c} \right) \Delta V_o$$

Thus, the emitter-to-base voltage increases an amount

$$\Delta V_{eb} = \Delta V_o - \frac{(R_b + R_c)\Delta V_o}{R_a + R_b + R_c}$$

$$= \Delta V_o \left(\frac{R_a}{R_a + R_b + R_c} \right) \tag{6-35}$$

Now if it is desired that an output voltage change ΔV_{o1} fires the SCR, then the resultant ΔV_{eb} for firing is $\Delta V_{eb1} = \Delta V_{o1} R_a/(R_a + R_b + R_c)$. Thus, the value of R_c must be set so that at normal output voltage, the base-emitter voltage of Q1 is ΔV_{eb} less than is required to turn on Q1.

This can be seen more clearly with specific values. Suppose $R_a/(R_a + R_b + R_c) = 0.5$ and an output change of 1 V above normal is desired to turn on Q1 and fire the SCR. Then $\Delta V_{eb1} = 0.5$ V and if the base-emitter firing voltage of Q1 is 0.6 V, then R_c must be set so that Q1 has a forward bias of 0.1 V at normal output voltage. Now a 1-V increase in output voltage will raise the Q1 emitter of 1 V but its base only by 0.5 V. With the added 0.5 V of base-emitter voltage above its initial value of 0.1 V, Q1 turns on and fires the SCR.

It should be noted that the smaller the ratio V_z/V_o is, the smaller the ratio $R_a/(R_a + R_b + R_c)$ is, and the smaller is the base-emitter voltage change for a given output voltage change (Eq. 6-35). This requires the forward bias on Q1 prior to crowbarring to be closer to the turn-on level for a given ΔV_o for crowbarring and makes the circuit more sensitive to component tolerances and noise. Or if a safer bias further away from the turn-on level of Q1 is desired, the ΔV_o required to turn Q1 on is larger, and it must be examined whether the highest output at which crowbarring occurs is still safe for the load.

Thus, if a 1-V ΔV_o is desired to cause crowbarring, practical values of V_z/V_o cannot be smaller than about 0.25 V. Then a 1-V output voltage change causes a 0.25-V base-emitter change in Q1. Then the forward bias on Q1 prior to crowbarring (at normal output voltage) is the turn-on bias of 0.6 V less 0.25 or +0.35 V. A nominal forward bias greater than +0.35 V cannot safely keep Q1 off when tolerances are considered, but it is generally true that for larger V_o and for a fixed V_z (of say the usual 6.2 V) when the ratio V_z/V_o becomes less than 0.25, larger ΔV_o values than 1 V for crowbarring can be tolerated.

Precaution in Use of Single-Transistor Crowbar Amplifier

The single-transistor amplifier of Fig. 6–21A is often used, but some precautions in its design must be observed.

Since the firing current for the SCR gate comes through the zener Z1, Z1 must be operated at a current level at which output voltage changes with current are small (from Fig. 1–10 this is above 10 mA). For otherwise, as Q1 started conducting, V_{Z1} would increase and the Q1 emitter would be back biased.

The effect would thus be that the threshold voltage at which the SCR would be fired would depend on the current required (from Q1) to fire the gate. SCRs with higher gate-firing current would fire at higher output voltage. Crowbarring voltage would also decrease as temperature increased because required gate-firing current decreases as temperature increases.

A further precaution to be observed is in the selection of the reference zener diode D1. Since the base-emitter voltage of the transistor decreases at the rate of 2 mV/°C, for the Q1 turn-on point to be independent of temperature, the Q1 emitter potential must move below V_o at the same 2 mV/°C. Thus, the zener must have a positive temperature coefficient of 2 mV/°C. From Fig. 1–10F it is seen that a 6.2-V zener diode (1N753 from Fig. 1–12A) operated at a 10-mA current level has a positive temperature coefficient of 0.03%/°C or (0.003)(6.2) = 1.9 mV/°C. Thus, the 1N753 operated at a 10-mA current level (by selection of R_z in Fig. 6–21A) would give least crowbarring voltage change with temperature.

And still a further precaution to be observed is in the selection of current level in the resistor chain R_a–R_b–R_c. This should be high enough so that, as emitter current in Q1 turns on, the resulting base current I_e/β_{Q1} does not appreciably change the reference potential at the base of Q4. For an SCR firing current I_f, the potential change at the base of Q1 is $R_{th}(I_f/\beta_{Q1})$, where R_{th} is the Thevenized [R_a and ($R_b + R_c$) in parallel] impedance looking out from the base. Another way of stating this is that for small values of R_{th}, current level in the R_a–R_b–R_c chain must be high.

This can be seen more clearly from a numerical example. Assume a gate-firing current of $I_f = 10$ mA. Then if β_{Q1} is, say, 50, the Q1 base voltage change is $R_{th}(0.01/50)$, and for the base voltage change to be no more than 0.25 V, $R_{th} = (0.25/0.01)(50) = 1,250$ ohms. And for, say, $R_a = R_b + R_c$, then R_a and $R_b + R_c$ can be no greater than 2,500 ohms.

Multiple-Transistor Crowbar Driver

The circuit of Fig. 6–21B provides more of a precise crowbarring voltage level. Since the SCR gate-firing current comes from Q2, current changes in the zener reference are small. Thus, its output voltage is more unique for different values of gate-firing current. Further, since Q1 collector-current changes are smaller, the base voltage changes, $R_{th}\Delta I_{c(Q1)}$, are smaller, and the crowbarring voltage changes less with current gain in Q1 and SCR gate-firing current.

For temperature tracking, Z1 in Fig. 6–21B should be a 6.3-V zener at a 10-mA operating current level, as discussed above.

The two-stage crowbarring amplifier of Fig. 6–21B can be used with a rheostat R_c as shown to set the crowbarring voltage throughout the entire range of values of the zener voltage V_Z within its tolerance limits. But often it is desired to dispense with R_c and use only two precise resistors R_a and R_b to give the desired crowbarring voltages at any value of V_Z within its production spread. If this is done, the maximum and minimum values of crowbarring voltages should be calculated for tolerances in R_a, R_b, and V_Z. These values can be calculated as follows.

First, assume that current in the R_a–R_b chain is sufficiently large that base current in Q1 does not change its base potential. Then at 25°C, for 0.60 ± 0.05 V base-to-emitter turn-on potential for Q1, and assuming ±1% resistors R_a and R_b, ±5% tolerance in the zener voltage, V_{Z1}, the nominal crowbarring voltage is

$$V_{\text{crowbar nom}} = (V_Z + 0.6)\left(\frac{R_a + R_b}{R_b}\right) \tag{6–36}$$

Minimum voltage at which crowbar can occur is

$$V_{\text{crowbar min}} = (0.95V_Z + 0.55)\left(\frac{0.99R_a + 1.01R_b}{1.01R_b}\right) \tag{6–37}$$

Maximum voltage at which crowbar can occur is

$$V_{\text{crowbar max}} = (1.05V_Z + 0.65)\left(\frac{1.01R_a + 0.99R_b}{0.99R_b}\right)$$

And if V_{Z1} is a 6.2-V zener operating at about a 10-mA current level, it has a positive temperature coefficient equal to the negative temperature coefficient of the base-emitter junction of Q1, and the above crowbarring voltages will be insensitive to temperature changes.

A more precise voltage comparator is shown in Fig. 6–21C. The combination of Z1, a 6.2-V zener, and D1 provides the usual temperature-compensated reference voltage source. They may be replaced by a temperature-compensated reference source such as the 1N825 series of Fig. 1–13.

Noise Sensitivity of Crowbar Circuits

Since the SCR will fire and remain turned on for noise spikes as narrow as 0.5–1.0 μsec, it is important that system noise be kept out of the SCR gate and the input of the voltage comparator circuit. High-frequency, high-energy noise spikes are almost always present on output buses and long wires in systems having switching regulators or dc/dc converters.

Noise spikes can couple directly into the SCR gate by passing the voltage comparator input terminals. Since it requires only about 1 V of gate-to-cathode voltage to fire the SCR, noise pickup on the usually long lead from the output of the current amplifier Q2 (Fig. 6–21B) to the SCR gate terminal can be troublesome. An integrating capacitor of 0.1–0.5 μF is usually placed directly across the gate-cathode leads of the SCR to reduce its high-frequency noise sensitivity. Also a low resistance R1 of 100 ohms is usually placed in parallel with C1. This reduces lower-frequency noise pickup, which would not be attenuated sufficiently by C1 alone. The 100-ohm gate-to-cathode resistance also ensures dc leakage current from Q2 will not fire the SCR.

Noise pickup at the input terminals of the voltage comparators of Fig. 6–21 is probably more troublesome than noise picked up on the SCR gate wire itself. It was noted in the previous section that the voltage comparator may be operating forward biased to within 0.25 V of its turn-on level. If noise turns on Q1 in Fig. 6–21, since a large current source is generally available from the output of the current amplifier, the SCR can easily be fired, since the gate must move up only 1 V for firing. Since there is generally always some noise on the output wires (V_o), which the sampling resistor chain R_a–R_b senses, a certain fraction of that noise is always coupled into the input of the high-gain voltage comparator. The size of the integrating capacitor C1 of Fig. 6–21B may be calculated for noise pickup that turns on Q1.

Generally, noise pickup from switches and dc/dc converters will be no wider than 1 μsec. But for safety's sake, assume the widest noise pickup turning Q1 on is 5 μsec. Now choose R2 and C1 so that if Q2 is on for 5 μsec, the gate potential of the SCR just barely charges up to the 1-V firing level and fires the SCR.

This means any noise spike turning on Q1 for anything less than 5 μsec will not fire the SCR. Also, under normal crowbarring, the SCR will not fire until 5 μsec after the voltage comparator senses an overvoltage condition. This 5-μsec delay is not likely to harm any of the loads.

Now choose R2 so that, when Q1 is turned on, it supplies 50 mA to the SCR gate. This is sufficient to fire the hardest-to-fire SCR of almost any type that would be used in a crowbarring application. Now since R1 was selected as 100 ohms to provide a low gate-to-cathode impedance, if R1 is a source of 60 mA, R1 drains away $\frac{1}{100}$ or 10 mA when the gate has risen to its firing level of 1 V. Thus, to a close approximation, there is available 60 − 10 or 50 mA to charge the capacitor C1 to the 1-V gate-firing level.

Then, since the 50 mA is very closely a constant current of that magnitude, the value of C1 may be chosen to rise only 1 V in the specified 5 μsec. Thus,

$$c = \frac{I\Delta t}{\Delta V} = \frac{0.050(5 \times 10^{-6})}{1}$$
$$= 0.25 \ \mu F$$

SCR Anode Protection

Figure 6–21 shows the SCR bridged directly across the output terminals it is protecting. Usually, there is no current-limiting resistor used, since this would slow up the output filter capacitor discharge time. When the SCR is fired, its initial spike of current is limited only by the ESR (equivalent series resistor) of the output filter capacity and the wiring inductance. Although the current spike is large in amplitude, it is short in duration and cannot harm the usually selected SCR crowbar type.

But if the value of I^2t for the discharge pulse is anywhere near the maximum specified value for the selected SCR type, a small series current-limiting resistor should be placed in series with the SCR anode. This is rarely necessary—except in cases in which the output filter capacitance is large (1,000 μF or more), the output voltage is high, and there is thus a large amount of energy stored in the capacitor.

6.9.2 Overvoltage Protection Situations

In designing a crowbar overvoltage protection system, thought must be given to the cause of the original overvoltage, how the fired SCR at the output achieves its protection, and whether it alone is enough.

Overvoltage can be caused by a shorted series-pass element, a narrow single or multiple or frequently occurring noise spike at the output, a momentary short to a higher voltage, or a failure in the feedback amplifier opening the feedback loop and saturating the series-pass element.

The failure mode causing most difficulty is a shorted series-pass element. If this occurs, output voltage goes high, fires the SCR crowbar, and puts a short at the output. But with an output short and a series-pass element shorted, the raw dc input ahead of the series-pass element is shorted and passes high currents through these two shorted elements.

Now if the series-pass element burns out due to the high current, there is no problem—the output loads are saved. But it is not predictable whether the series-pass element or the SCR crowbar (or a small current-limiting resistor in series with it) will burn out first. If either of the latter two burn out first, the short to ground is lost, the output rises, and, through the shorted series-pass elements, overvoltage is applied to the now unprotected loads, thereby destroying them. To protect against a shorted series-pass element (probably the most likely cause of overvoltage), the supply must be fused in the transformer primary or secondary or the SCR crowbar must be such a high-current device that in the event of a shorted series-pass element, it, rather than the SCR, will burn out open first.

All other failure modes generating an output overvoltage are taken care of by the SCR crowbar. A momentary overvoltage (either noise spike, accidentally shorting the higher voltage, or a turn-on overshoot) will energize the threshold detector and fire the SCR crowbar. The output will short to ground (actually to the 1-V anode-to-cathode "on" potential of the SCR) and go into current limit. If current foldback overcurrent protection is used, current will fall to the foldback current value (Eq. 6–24) and will remain there. The series-pass elements will be subjected to a dissipation of $I_{cf}(V_{in(max)} - 1)$ W, which they have been designed to withstand by their thermal design.

If the overcurrent protection circuit is "constant" current, the series-pass element dissipation is $I_c(V_{in(max)} - 1)$ W. From Sect. 6.8.4, I_c can be as high as 1.63 I_{max} and from Sect. 6.8.7, I_{cf} is about $I_m/5$. Thus, even a momentary overvoltage will cause crowbarring which will cause overcurrent limiting with the output shorted. But with a constant-current overprotection circuit, the series-pass dissipation is 1.63/0.2 or 8.15 times as great as in a current foldback circuit, and there must be enough paralleled series-pass elements to take this higher power dissipation.

6.10   Thermal Calculations

The most frequent failure mode in series-pass power supplies is over-dissipating the series-pass element and exceeding its maximum rated junction temperature.

No power supply design is complete unless the thermal calculations described in Chap. 4 are made. Maximum series-pass dissipation must first be calculated. This occurs at maximum series-pass input voltage and zero output voltage at I_c in the constant current overprotection circuit (Fig. 6–18A). For the foldback circuit, it occurs at $V_{in(max)} - V_{o(min)}$ and at a current I_c (Fig. 6–18B). It should be assumed that, although the maximum specified normal output current is I_{ms} (Sect. 6.8.6), some fault condition can put the circuit at $I \cong I_c$ (Fig. 6–18B) just inside the turnaround current threshold. The dissipation under foldback condition, $V_{in(max)}I_{cc}$, is generally smaller than dissipation just below the start of foldback.

But one further precaution should be observed. For high output voltages, under foldback, even though power dissipation is low, it should be checked that the operating point at maximum input voltage and maximum foldback current is not outside the forward-biased safe area limits of the series-pass elements.

From the worst-case dissipations, series-pass junction temperatures are calculated as in Chap. 4. If parallel series-pass elements are used, current sharing in the parallel elements is usually ensured by using small resistors in series with each of the paralleled emitters. Nevertheless, in calculating series-pass dissipation, it should not be assumed each paralleled series-pass element takes equal current because of production spread in base-emitter potentials. As a guide, current in any one of the group of n-paralleled series-pass elements should be taken as about 20% more than the value it would have if all paralleled elements shared current equally.

Maximum permissible junction temperatures should be derated below the manufacturer's specified maximum values. Guidelines as to usual industry derating factors for maximum transistor junction temperatures are presented in Sect. 4.1.

PROBLEMS

6.1 A battery supplies prime power to an electronic system at $+30$ V $\pm 10\%$. Assume a simple series-pass regulator drops this down to a regulated 10 V at 3 A output. What are the minimum, nominal, and maximum efficiencies of such a regulator? What are the internal dissipations at low-, nominal-, and high-input voltages?

6.2 A series-pass power supply uses for its series-pass element a single 2N3055 to supply $+15$ V at 4 A. Its input is from the rectifier–filter at the secondary of a power transformer. If the filter capacitance is limited to a value yielding 10 V peak-to-peak ripple output, what must the open-loop gain (including that of the sampling resistor network of Fig. 6–1) be to limit output ripple to 10 mV peak to peak?

6.3 Assume a series-pass regulator with an output of $+15$ V draws a quiescent current of 3 A. It has an open-loop gain of 500 (including that of the sampling resistor network). What is its output voltage change for a current change of 1 A?

6.4 The raw dc input to a series-pass power supply is the rectified secondary voltage of a power-line transformer. Assume the secondary voltage has been so selected that, at the bottom of the ripple triangle at low ac line voltage, the input is still 3 V above the output. Assume the ac line voltage tolerance is $\pm 10\%$, the output filter capacitor has been selected to yield 4 V peak-to-peak ripple, and the output voltage is 10 V. What is the regulator efficiency at maximum ac input voltage with a 1-V drop across the rectifier diodes? At 2 A of output current, what is the internal dissipation?

What would be the minimum efficiency and internal dissipation at that efficiency for 2 A output current assuming a battery input source with no ripple and a nominal input voltage of 14 V with a $\pm 10\%$ tolerance?

6.5 Assume a series-pass regulator with $+15$ V output has the rectified secondary output of a power transformer as a supply source. What is the required rms secondary voltage, assuming ac line voltage tolerance of $\pm 10\%$, a filter capacitor chosen to give 4 V peak-to-peak ripple, and a voltage at the bottom of the ripple triangle that is 3 V above the regulated output?

6.6 In a difference amplifier such as in Fig. 6–11, assume a reference voltage of 6.2 V at the base of Q2 and an input signal at the base of Q1.

For a common-emitter resistor R_o of 2,000 ohms and collector-load resistors of 6,000 ohms, what is the collector-current change per unit voltage change at the base of Q1? What is the voltage gain from base to collector of Q1 to collector of Q2?

6.7 Assume a series-pass regulator with output voltage of $+15$ V has been designed so that at the bottom of the input ripple triangle (which is 4 V peak to peak in amplitude), at low ac line voltage, the voltage across the series pass element is 2 V. Assume a ±10% ac line voltage tolerance and a maximum output current of 1 A with constant-current short-circuit protection at a current level of 1.3 A.

What is the maximum series-pass dissipation at high ac line input at maximum output current with the output not shorted? With the output shorted?

6.8 In a current-foldback overcurrent protection circuit as in Fig. 6–18D, what is the required value of overcurrent sense resistor R_{oc} in a supply whose maximum output current is 2 A if overcurrent tripping is to occur at 50% above the maximum output current?

6.9 In Prob. 6.8, for the current-foldback circuit of Fig. 6–18D, for R1 = 500 ohms, what is the required value of R2 for the overcurrent trip point 50% above the maximum specified output current?

6.10 In Prob. 6.9, what is the value of the folded-back current (Fig. 6–18D), assuming base current to Q3 is small compared to the current in the R1–R2 resistance divider in the folded-back condition?

6.11 In an overvoltage protection circuit as in Fig. 6–21B, for a zener voltage of 6.2 V ±5%, an output voltage of +30 V, and R_b = 1,000 ohms and R_c = 0, what is the required value of R_a for a nominal crowbarring voltage of + 32 V?

What are the minimum and maximum crowbarring voltages for ±1% resistor tolerances?

7

Integrated-Circuit Voltage Regulators

7.0   Introduction

A number of the major semiconductor vendors offer integrated-circuit voltage regulators on a single chip packaged either in a 14-pin DIP package, $\frac{1}{4} \times \frac{1}{4}$ in. flat pack, or a low-profile TO5 can.

These integrated-circuit voltage regulators contain most of the essential parts and perform most of the low-power control functions required of a series-pass regulator (Fig. 6–1).

They also contain the series-pass element that permits using them (without external current amplification) at output currents up to 150–250 mA or even up to 600 mA for some vendors' devices. They can generate output voltages ranging from about 2 to 45 V in the above current ranges. Most units have an internal power dissipation capability of 0.5–0.8 W and in some packages up to 3 W.

These regulators are almost completely self-contained units. To function as a regulator, in the above current–voltage range, they require relatively few additional external elements—about a half dozen or so low-power resistors, the raw dc input source, and possibly an output filter capacitor.

The raw dc input source, if supplied from the ac line, is composed of the input transformer (or an additional properly specified secondary winding, if a transformer already exists in the system), the rectifier diodes, and filter capacitor (selected from Eq. 5–3).

With the addition of external series-pass current amplifiers, the integrated circuit regulator, used as a control and driver element, can supply output currents up to tens of amperes. Step-down switching regulators (Sect. 1.2) can be built from the integrated regulator by the addition of the usual LC filter (Fig. 1–4).

The basic elements contained in the integrated regulators are the constant-voltage zener reference source, the high-gain difference amplifier, the low-current series-pass element, and the major components of the short-circuit protect scheme. It can be seen from Fig. 6–1 that, aside from the dc input source, overvoltage protection elements, and output filter capacitors, these are most of the components of a voltage regulator.

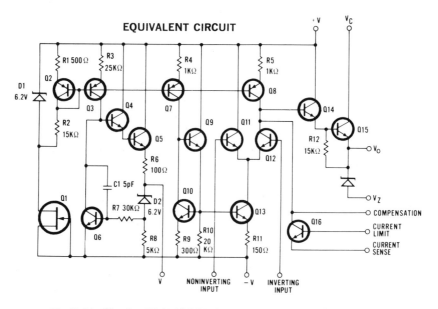

Fig. 7–1A. Circuit of Fairchild 723 integrated-circuit voltage regulator. (*Courtesy* Fairchild Semiconductor)

Application notes for building a large variety of voltage regulators based on the integrated unit as a control device are presented in the vendors' data sheets. Highlights of the internal circuit design and various application possibilities for some of the more frequently used integrated regulators will be covered in this chapter.

New integrated voltage regulators with greater capabilities are becoming available at a phenomenal rate. But their essential characteristics are much the same as the few basic original types considered in this chapter, and the following study of the original types provides guidance in the understanding and applications of the newer types.

7.1   Fairchild 723 Integrated-Circuit Voltage Regulator[1]

The detailed circuit diagram of this regulator is shown in Fig. 7–1A and in block diagram in Fig. 7–1B. It can be used as a regulator without additional series-pass elements as shown in Figs. 7–2A and 7–2B and with various npn or pnp external series-pass elements as shown in Fig. 7–3 to boost its output-current capability.

In Fig. 7–1A, the raw, unregulated dc (any voltage between 9.5 and 40 V) is applied between $+V$ and $-V$. The series-pass element is Q15 and Q14 is its driver. Output can be taken at the emitter of Q15 and if $+V_c$ is tied to $+V$, Q14 functions as a Darlington driver. Output current up to 150 mA (or limited by the

---

[1] Data presented here on the 723 are by courtesy of Fairchild Semiconductor.

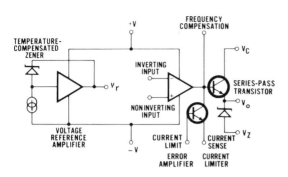

Fig. 7–1B. Block diagram of Fairchild 723 integrated-circuit voltage regulator. (*Courtesy* Fairchild Semiconductor)

800-mW internal dissipation specification) can be taken directly off the emitter of Q15 (V_o terminal).

The emitter of Q15 can drive the base of an external npn emitter-loaded amplifier as shown in Fig. 7–3B for higher output currents, or a reverse-polarity control signal can be taken from the collector of Q15 by inserting a collector load resistor between $+V$ and V_c and using the collector signal at V_c to drive the base of an external pnp current boost amplifier as shown in Fig. 7–3C.

For still higher output currents, the external current-boosting amplifier can be an npn Darlington driver feeding an npn emitter-loaded output stage as in Fig. 6–10A. In this case, the 723 control signal is still most conveniently taken from the emitter of Q15 (V_o) as in Fig. 7–3B, since a current source is required for the base of an npn transistor. If the compound external boost amplifier is a pnp inverter driving an npn emitter-loaded amplifier (Fig. 6–10B), the pnp base drive, which must be a current sink, is taken from the collector of Q15 as in Fig. 7–3C.

7.1.1 Internal Circuit Details

Returning to the detailed schematic of Fig. 7–1A, Q11 and Q12 make up the difference amplifier used to compare a fraction of the output to a constant reference voltage. The constant reference voltage of $+7.15 \pm 0.2$ V is generated internally by zener diode D2 and is available at the output terminal "V_r," at a stability of 0.015%/°C. The reference voltage is wired externally either directly as in Fig. 7–2B or through a voltage divider as in Fig. 7–2A to the noninverting input (N.I.) of the error amplifier. The sampled fraction of the output voltage is delivered to the inverting input (Inv) terminal of the error amplifier as in Fig. 7–2A or 7–2B.

A number of interesting circuit tricks are used to achieve good reference voltage stability and high open-loop voltage gain without requiring additional voltage amplification after the output of the difference amplifier. These are discussed below.

Constant Error Amplifier Current

Thus, in Fig. 7–1A, emitter follower Q13 is used as a constant-current device to provide a constant emitter current for the common emitters of the difference amplifier, Q11–Q12. As discussed in Sect. 6.5.4, this decreases the drift in Q12 collector output voltage resulting from temperature variation of the base-

BASIC LOW VOLTAGE REGULATOR
(V₀ = 2 to 7 V)

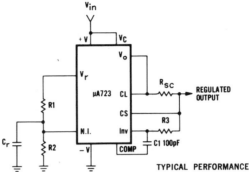

TYPICAL PERFORMANCE

Regulated Output Voltage   5 V
Line Regulation (ΔV_{in} = 3 V) 0.5 mV
Load Regulation (ΔI_L=50 mA) 1.5 mV

Note: $R3 = \dfrac{R1\ R2}{R1 + R2}$ for minimum temperature drift.

(A)

BASIC HIGH VOLTAGE REGULATOR
(V₀ = 7 to 37 V)

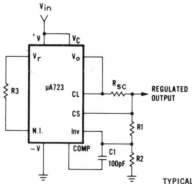

TYPICAL PERFORMANCE

Regulated Output Voltage   15 V
Line Regulation (ΔV_{in} = 3 V) 1.5 mV
Load Regulation (ΔI_L=50 mA) 4.5 mV

Note: $R3 = \dfrac{R1\ R2}{R1 + R2}$ for minimum temperature drift.

R3 may be eliminated for minimum component count.

(B)

Fig. 7–2. Basic low-current applications of the Fairchild 723 integrated-circuit voltage regulator. (A) A fraction R2/(R1 + R2) of the internal 7.15-V reference source is fed to the noninverting input of the error amplifier. The regulated output is fed to the inverting input and the negative-feedback circuit forces V_o to equal [R2/(R1 + R2)]7.15 V. (B) Here a fraction of the output voltage, V_o[R2/(R1 + R2)], is fed to the inverting input of the error amplifier and forced by the negative-feedback circuit to be equal to the 7.15-V reference source connected to the noninverting terminal. V_o = [(R1 + R2)/R2]7.15 V. For higher currents, external series-pass current boosters may be added as in Figs. 7–3B and 7–3C. (*Courtesy* Fairchild Semiconductor)

emitter voltage of Q11–Q12. To compensate for the temperature variation of the Q13 base-emitter voltage (which would change Q13 collector current and, hence, output voltage), the base of Q13 is fed from the base of Q10. The network composed of zener diode D1 and R1, R2, Q2, Q7, and R4 provides a constant current for the collector of Q10 and, hence, for R9. Thus, the base of Q13 is above ground $(-V)$ by $V_{R9} + V_{be(Q10)}$. Now if the base of Q13 were fixed in potential with respect to $-V$, as temperature say increased, V_{be} of Q13 would decrease and the current in Q13 would, hence, decrease. But the base of Q13 is not fixed with respect to ground; rather, it decreases with temperature as V_{be} of Q10 decreases with temperature at the same rate as V_{be} of Q13. The effect is thus a constant potential at the top of R11 and, hence, a constant emitter current for the common emitters of Q11 and Q12.

Voltage Reference Circuit

The voltage reference circuit is made up of zener diode D2 and Q4, Q5, Q6, R6, R7, and R8 arranged in a local negative-feedback loop. Zener D2, being a 6.2-V unit, has a positive temperature coefficient (Fig. 1–10F). This is compensated for by the negative temperature coefficient of the base-emitter junction of Q6. The output reference potential at V_r is equal to $V_{D2} + V_{R8}$. V_{R8} is controlled by the local negative-feedback loop to assume such a potential that the base of Q6 is at the proper level so that its collector can carry away most of the constant current supplied from the collector of Q3.

The circuit consisting of zener D1 and R1, R2, Q2, and Q3 supplies a constant current from the collector of Q3. Most of this current must be carried away by the collector of Q6, since the base current of Q4 is small by comparison. Thus, the top of R8 is at a level sufficiently higher than the Q6 base, that the base current supplied via R7, multiplied by the β of Q6 is equal to the current supplied from the collector of Q3. Since the base-emitter potential of Q6 decreases 2 mV/°C, the potential at the top of R8 must decrease at the same rate so that Q6 can always carry away the same current supplied from the collector of Q3. Selection of the magnitude of R8 fixes the dc operating point in current for zener D2 and, hence, fixes its temperature coefficient. This temperature coefficient is set so that $V_{D2} + V_{R8}$ is constant to 0.015%/°C. The negative-feedback loop around zener D2 results in low-output impedance at the output terminal V_r and makes its potential independent of load current drawn by the base of Q11 to which it is usually connected externally directly or via a resistance voltage divider as in Fig. 7–2A.

Constant-Current Supply Network (Fig. 7–1A)

This is composed of three constant-current sources: First, Q3 supplies a constant current to Q6, which, as described in the previous section, improves the constancy of the reference voltage output. Second, Q7 provides a constant current to the collector of Q10, which thus permits making Q13 a constant-current source for the common emitters of Q11 and Q12. Third, Q8 supplies a constant current (high impedance) to the collector of Q12 and thus permits very high gain (gain = $g_m R_L$ from Sect. 6.5.2) between input and output for the Q11–Q12 difference amplifier. This obviates the need for a second stage of voltage amplification.

NEGATIVE VOLTAGE REGULATOR

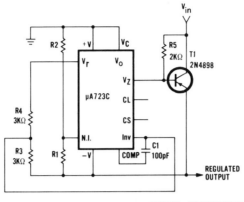

TYPICAL PERFORMANCE

Regulated Output Voltage   −15 V
Line Regulation ($\Delta V_{in} = 3$ V)   1 mV
Load Regulation ($\Delta I_L = 100$ mA) 2 mV

(A)

Fig. 7–3. Some applications for the Fairchild 723 integrated-circuit voltage regulator. (*Courtesy* Fairchild Semiconductor)

The scheme for generating these three constant current sources includes zener diode D1, n-channel field-effect transistor (FET) Q1, resistor divider chain R1–R2, temperature-compensating base-emitter source Q2, and emitter followers Q3, Q7, and Q8. These elements generate constant current from the collectors of emitter followers Q3, Q7, and Q8 by keeping the voltage across the emitter resistors R3, R4, and R5 constant and independent of supply voltage ($V+$) and temperature. This can be seen as follows:

$$I_{R3} = \frac{V + - (V_{b(Q3)} + V_{be(Q3)})}{R3}$$

But $$V_{b(Q3)} = (V+) - [R1(I_{R1}) + V_{be(Q2)}]$$

Then $$I_{R3} = \frac{(V+) - (V+) + R1(I_{R1}) - V_{be(Q2)} + V_{be(Q3)}}{R3}$$

$$= \frac{R1(I_{R1}) - V_{be(Q2)} + V_{be(Q3)}}{R3}$$

And since $V_{be(Q2)} \cong V_{be(Q3)}$ and tracks it with temperature,

$$I_{R3} = \frac{R1(I_{R1})}{R3} = \left(\frac{500}{25,000}\right)\left(\frac{V_{D1} - V_{be(Q2)}}{R1 + R2}\right)$$

$$= \left(\frac{500}{25,000}\right)\left(\frac{6.2 - 0.6}{500 + 15,000}\right)$$

$$= (500/25,000)(360) = 7.2 \ \mu A$$

POSITIVE VOLTAGE REGULATOR
(External NPN Pass Transistor)

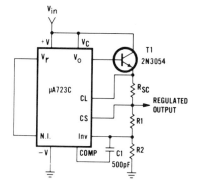

TYPICAL PERFORMANCE

Regulated Output Voltage $+15$ V
Line Regulation ($\Delta V_{in} = 3$ V) 1.5 mV
Load Regulation ($\Delta I_L = 1$ A)   15 mV

(B)

POSITIVE VOLTAGE REGULATOR
(External PNP Pass Transistor)

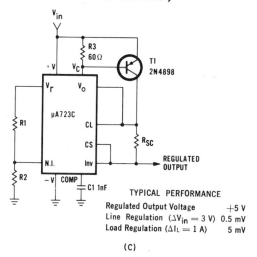

TYPICAL PERFORMANCE

Regulated Output Voltage $+5$ V
Line Regulation ($\Delta V_{in} = 3$ V) 0.5 mV
Load Regulation ($\Delta I_L = 1$ A)   5 mV

(C)

Fig. 7–3. (*Cont'd.*) Some applications for the Fairchild 723 integrated-circuit voltage regulator. (*Courtesy* Fairchild Semiconductor)

Similarly, $$I_{R4} = \left(\frac{R1}{R4}\right)(I_{R1}) = \left(\frac{500}{1,000}\right)(360) = 180 \ \mu A$$

$$I_{R5} = \left(\frac{R1}{R5}\right)(I_{R1}) = \left(\frac{500}{1,000}\right)(360) = 180 \ \mu A$$

FOLDBACK CURRENT LIMITING

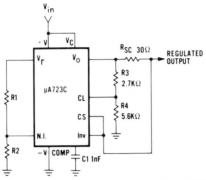

TYPICAL PERFORMANCE

Regulated Output Voltage	$+5$ V
Line Regulation ($\Delta V_{in} = 3$ V)	0.5 mV
Load Regulation ($\Delta I_L = 10$ mA)	1 mV
Short Circuit Current	20 mA

(D)

POSITIVE FLOATING REGULATOR

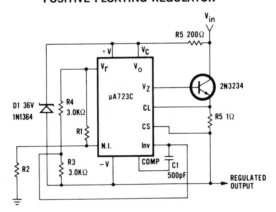

TYPICAL PERFORMANCE

Regulated Output Voltage	$+50$ V
Line Regulation ($\Delta V_{in} = 20$ V)	15 mV
Load Regulation ($\Delta I_L = 50$ mA)	20 mV

(E)

Fig. 7–3. (*Cont'd.*) Some applications for the Fairchild 723 integrated-circuit voltage regulator. (*Courtesy* Fairchild Semiconductor)

NEGATIVE FLOATING REGULATOR

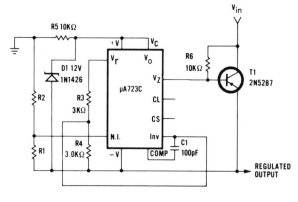

TYPICAL PERFORMANCE

Regulated Output Voltage — -100 V
Line Regulation ($\Delta V_{in} = 20$ V)   30 mV
Load Regulation ($\Delta I_L = 100$ mA)   20 mV

(F)

Fig. 7-3. (*Cont'd.*) Some applications for the Fairchild 723 integrated-circuit voltage regulator. (*Courtesy* Fairchild Semiconductor)

Diffused, integrated resistors have temperature coefficients ranging between 0.05% and 0.2%/°C.[2] However, the above currents are proportional to resistor ratios, and, since these resistors are on the same chip, their temperatures and temperature coefficients are very nearly equal and the resistor ratios are independent of temperature. Thus, the percentage variation of currents I_{R3}, I_{R4}, and I_{R5} with temperature is identical to that of I_{R1} alone. Then

$$I_{R1} = \frac{V_{D1} - V_{be(Q2)}}{R1 + R2} = \left(\frac{V_{D1}}{R1 + R2}\right)\left(1 - \frac{V_{be(Q2)}}{V_{D1}}\right)$$

$$I_{R1} \cong \frac{V_{D1}}{R1 + R2} \qquad \text{since } V_{D1} \gg V_{be(Q2)}$$

and

$$\frac{1}{\Delta T}\left(\frac{\Delta I_{R1}}{I_{R1}}\right) = \frac{1}{\Delta T}\left(\frac{\Delta V_{D1}}{V_{D1}}\right) - \frac{1}{\Delta T}\left(\frac{\Delta(R1 + R2)}{R1 + R2}\right)$$

Or, the percentage change of I_{R1} per °C is equal to the percentage change of V_{D1} less the percentage change of R1 + R2. The zener voltage V_{D1} changes roughly -2 mV/°C or $-0.002/6.2 = -0.03\%$/°C. Temperature coefficient of R1 + R2 depends on the semiconductor impurity concentration or "ohms per square." As cited in the aforementioned references, it ranges from $+0.05\%$ to $+0.2\%$/°C. At an average value of $+0.1\%$/°C for the resistor sensitivity, the temperature sensitivity of I_{R1} is $-0.03 - 0.10 = -0.13\%$/°C. This is a sufficiently low temperature sensitivity to satisfy the constancy requirements of I_{R3}, I_{R4}, and I_{R5}.

---

[2] R. M. Warner and J. M. Fordemwait, Motorola Inc., "Integrated Circuit Design Principles."

Error Amplifier Gain

It has been shown in Sect. 6.5.2 that the gain from base to collector of a difference amplifier such as Q11–Q12 is $A = g_m R_{eff}$ (Eq. 6–26), where R_{eff} is the effective collector load impedance and g_m is the transconductance. Thus, very large gains are achievable even with modest values of g_m, if R_{eff} is sufficiently large.

Now the impedance seen by the collector of Q12 is that looking into the collector of emitter follower Q8. It can be shown (from Eq. 1–11) that the effective impedance looking into the collector of an emitter follower is

$$R_{eff} = R_t(1 + R_L/R_t + g_m R_L)$$

where R_L is the emitter load resistor, R_t is the slope of the V_c–I_c curve, and g_m is the transconductance at the operating point. For a low current transistor like Q8 operating at 0.18 mA, R_t is approximately 150,000 ohms. Now from Eq. 6–22, the emitter current (= collector current) of a transistor is

$$I_e \cong I_c \cong I_s \exp (V_{be}/0.026)$$

Then the transconductance is

$$g_m = \frac{dI_c}{dV_{be}} = \frac{I_s \exp (V_{be}/0.026)}{0.026} = \frac{I_c}{0.026} = \frac{0.18}{0.026} = 6.9 \text{ mA/volt}$$

Then

$$\begin{aligned} R_{eff} &= R_t(1 + R_L/R_t + g_m R_L) \\ &= 150,000[1 + 1,000/150,000 + (0.0069)(1,000)] \\ &= (150,000)(7.9) = 1.18 \times 10^{+6} \text{ ohms} \end{aligned}$$

And since the sum of the Q11 and Q12 currents is 0.36 mA, the transconductance from either Q11 or Q12 base to the Q12 collector is from Eq. 6–26: $g_m = 10I_o$ $= 10(0.36) = 3.6$ mA/volt. Hence, gain from the base of Q11 or Q12 to the Q12

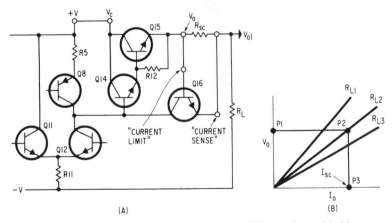

(A)   (B)

Fig. 7–4. (A) Constant-current limiting in the 723 regulator. Limiting occurs when the Q16 turns on at a current of $I_{cl} = 0.65/R_{sc}$. Current from Q8 is diverted into Q16 and starves out Q14. (B) Output voltage for various load resistors in the 723 is at the intersection of the load line with the P1, P2, and P3 characteristics. Beyond I_{sc}, output falls along the vertical P2–P3 line. Inside of I_{sc}, output remains constant.

collector is $A = g_m R_{eff} = (0.0036)(1.18 \times 10^{+6}) = 4,248$. This compares quite well with gain measurements running in the range of 4,000–6,000.

Current-Limiting and Short-Circuit Protection

This feature is discussed in general in Sect. 6.8.4 and is implemented in the 723 by Q16 (Fig. 7–1A) and a small resistor in series between the V_o terminal and the load. This can be seen more clearly in Figs. 7–2A, 7–2B, 7–3B, 7–3C, and 7–3D.

The circuit works as follows (Fig. 7–4A). Normally, Q16 is turned off. Its base-emitter terminals are bridged across the output-current-sensing-resistor R_{sc}, which is in series with the output load. The value of R_{sc} is chosen so that Q16 turns (at $V_{be} = 0.65$ V at 25°C) at the current, I_{sc}, at which current limiting is intended to commence. Then, R_{sc} is chosen as

$$R_{sc} = 0.65/I_{sc} \tag{7-1}$$

Now it can be seen in Fig. 7–1A that the collector of Q16 is connected to the collector of Q8. When Q16 turns on, its collector robs most of the current coming down from the collector of Q8. Only enough current is allowed to flow into the base of Q14 so that, multiplied by β of Q14 and Q15, the Q15 emitter current is I_{sc}.

In current limiting, Q14, Q15, and Q16 form a local negative-feedback loop that takes over from the main voltage control loop and maintains constant current in Q15. This can be seen more clearly in Fig. 7–4. Assume that $V_{be(Q16)}$ at the "on" potential is approximately 0.65 V. The collector potential of Q16 with respect to its emitter is

$$V_{R_{sc}} + V_{be(Q14)} + V_{be(Q15)} = 0.65 + 0.70 + 0.70$$
$$= 2.05 \text{ V}$$

The circuit remains locked keeping I_{sc} flowing into R_{sc}. If I_{sc} for some reason tries to rise, it turns on Q16 harder. This robs more of the collector current from Q8, reduces the current into the Q14 base, and brings the emitter current from Q15 down, i.e., Q14, Q15, and Q16 form a negative-feedback loop.

Output potential after R_{sc} ($= V_{o1}$) follows the curve shown in Fig. 7–4B. At currents below I_{sc}, output remains constant at the value fixed by the sampling resistor chain and the zener reference (Fig. 7–2). At I_{sc}, current no longer increases as the load impedance is lowered. Instead, voltage starts falling along a vertical line as shown in Fig. 7–4B. Output voltage is $I_{sc}R_L$. It can be more easily visualized in Fig. 7–4B as the intersection of an R_L load line (drawn from the origin) with the vertical I_{sc} line.

Power Dissipation and Temperature Considerations

It should be noted that it is possible to overdissipate the regulator when operating in "current limit," for the series-pass dissipation (in Q15) is $(V_{in} - R_L I_{sc})I_{sc}$. This dissipation is a maximum at short circuit and is $V_{in(max)}I_{sc}$. It will usually be arranged that the unregulated input voltage at its minimum is 3 V above the desired regulated output. Then, for ±10% raw dc regulation, the maximum dc input is $1.1(1.1)(V_o + 3) = 1.21(V_o + 3)$. And the dc dissipation under short-circuit conditions is

$$PD = 1.21(V_o + 3)I_{sc}$$

Power dissipation under short-circuit conditions should be calculated, since this is the worst case. Maximum power dissipation at 25°C is specified by the vendor as 800 mW for the TO5 package and 900 mW for the dual-in-line (DIP) packaged regulator.

Total internal dissipation is the sum of the dissipation across the series-pass element plus the internal dissipation due to the maximum standby current (which flows from V_{in} directly to ground). The former is

$$(V_{in(max)} - V_{o(min)})I_{o(max)} = V_{in(max)}I_{sc}$$

Maximum standby current is specified as 3.5 mA at 30 V V_{in} but is relatively independent of input voltage. Hence, dissipation due to standby current is $V_{in(max)}(0.0035)$ W. Thus, total internal dissipation, which is a maximum under short-circuit conditions, is

$$PD_{max} = V_{in(max)}(I_{sc} + 0.0035) \tag{7-2}$$

Now the maximum internal dissipation as specified by the vendor is that dissipation that brings the transistor chip junctions to their maximum of 150°C when operated in an ambient of 25°C without a heat sink. Thus, a better way to specify the device is to convert this maximum dissipation to thermal resistance in °C per watt. Then, if lower junction temperatures are desired to provide a margin of safety, any internal dissipation can be converted to a junction temperature rise above ambient.

Since 800 mW of dissipation in a 25°C ambient brings the internal junctions to 150°C, the junction-to-ambient thermal resistance for the TO5 can device is

$$\Delta T/\Delta P = (150 - 25)/0.8 = 156°C/watt$$

And if the maximum junction temperature is to be derated to 105°C for safety, then in a 65°C ambient, the maximum permissible internal dissipation, PD_{max} is given by

$$T_{j(max)} = T_{ambient(max)} + PD(156) \quad \text{or}$$
$$105 = 65 + 156PD$$
$$PD_{max} = (105 - 65)/156 = 256 \text{ mW}$$

For 105°C maximum junction temperature, it is this dissipation that should be used in Eq. 7-2 to calculate I_{sc} for a given maximum input voltage.

Current-foldback techniques as discussed in Sects. 6.8.3, 6.8.5, and 6.8.6 can be used to decrease the internal dissipation under short-circuit conditions. This permits higher output current, since under short-circuit conditions the folded-back current I_{fb} can be as low as one-fifth of the maximum output current (Sect. 6.8.5).

Input–Output Differential and Voltage Ranges

In addition to the internal dissipation, there are precautions to be taken in the ranges of input–output voltage differentials and input and output voltages.

The input–output voltage differential is specified by the vendor as 3 V minimum, 38 V maximum. The 3-V minimum limit is set by the necessity (Fig. 7-1A) to maintain base-emitter voltages of about 0.7 V for Q14 and Q15 and an adequate drop from base of Q14 to $+V$. This drop is $V_{R5} + V_{ec(Q8)}$. For $I_{R5} = 0.18$ mA (see the constant-current supply network section earlier in this chapter), this totals to $(1,000)(0.00018) + 0.70 = 0.98$ V. Then the total minimum input–output differential is

$$0.98 + V_{be(Q14)} + V_{be(Q15)} = 0.98 + 0.70 + 0.70 = 2.38 \text{ V}$$

which is rounded off to 3.0 V for safety.

Maximum input–output voltage differential of 38 V is set by the voltage breakdown ratings of the transistor junctions on the integrated circuit chip.

Input voltage range of 9.5–40 V is specified by the vendor. The 9.5-V lower limit is fixed by the 6.2-V zener diode D2 and the sum of the required voltages across the base emitters of Q4 and Q5 (2×0.7 or 1.4 V) and the drop from $V+$ to the collector of Q3 ($= V_{R3} + V_{ec(Q8)}$) $= 0.18 + 0.70$ or 0.98 V. Thus, total minimum input voltage is $6.2 + 1.4 + 0.98 = 8.58$ V. With tolerances on the zener drop, this rounds off to a required minimum of 9.5 V.

The maximum input and output voltage specifications of $+40$ and $+37$ V, respectively, are fixed by transistor junction breakdown ratings.

7.1.2 Integrated Regulator Applications Using the 723

Many of the possible circuit configurations with external pass transistors are shown in the vendors' data sheets, and some are reproduced in Figs. 7–2 and 7–3. The 723 is a versatile, flexible device, and many other configurations limited only by the designer's imagination are possible.

But basically most configurations are similar to or outgrowths of Figs. 7–3B and 7–3C. The general rules to be followed are:

1. If the external series-pass base requires outward-directed current from the 723 (such as an npn base with emitter loads or an npn Darlington driver base whose emitter drives an npn emitter-loaded power stage), then output is most conveniently taken from the "V_o" terminal or the emitter of Q15 output stage as in Fig. 7–3B.

2. If the external series-pass elements require a current sink (current directed inward into the 723), such as pnp bases, the 723 output terminal to be used is the collector of Q15 or V, which is then connected via a collector load resistor to $+V$ as in Fig. 7–3C. This connection is used whether the pnp collector drives the load directly or the base of an npn emitter-loaded output stage as in Fig. 6–9A.

3. Whatever the configuration, there must, of course, be an odd number of phase reversals in the loop for negative feedback.

Thus, if sampled input is to the inverting terminal and output is from V_o, there is one phase reversal in Q12. Then, external to the 723, there must be either no phase reversals (npn emitter follower or npn Darlington emitter follower driving an npn emitter follower output stage as in Q4 and Q5 of Fig. 6–16B). Or there must be two external phase reversals as the npn inverter–pnp inverter–npn emitter follower combination of Q4, Q5, and Q6 in Fig. 6–17A.

When sampled input is to the inverting terminal and output is from the Q15 collector, there are two phase reversals internal to the 723. There must then be an odd number of phase reversals externally (pnp inverter as in Fig. 7–3C or pnp inverter driving npn emitter follower as in Q2 and Q1 of Fig. 6–9A).

Switching Regulators with the 723

The 723 can be used as the control element in switching regulators of the type described in Sect. 1.2 and Figs. 1–4 and 1–5. These latter regulators consist of a transistor switch and an LC filter network. The switch is externally driven and is forced closed with essentially zero voltage drop for a time T_c out of T units of time. For an input voltage, V_{in}, the output voltage after the filter is $V_o = V_{in}(T_c/T)$. Regulation is achieved by varying the ratio T_c/T. The great advantage of such regulators is their high efficiency, which results because the switch transistor operates at about 1 V across it when its current is high and at zero current when the voltage across it is high. This is discussed in detail in Sect. 1.2.1, in which it was shown its efficiency is $E = V_o/(V_o + 2)$.

Design details of switching regulators are taken up in Chap. 9. The major design points are selection of the operating frequency, calculation of the required values of L and C in the L–C filter and design of the T_c/T ratio control circuitry. All these points are discussed fully in Chap. 9 and are essential to an understanding of the application of the 723 in switching regulators.

Design of 723 controlled switching regulators is well covered in vendors' application notes[3] and will not be taken up in detail here. Discussion here will be limited to the unique feature of the usual 723 controlled switching regulator— its operation in a self-oscillating rather than an externally driven switching mode.

The basic operation of the self-oscillating switching regulator can be seen from Fig. 7–5. It consists of the switch transistor Q1, the L1–C1 filter, and "free-wheeling" diode D1. In the driven switching regulator of Fig. 1–5, an external pulse of fixed period and variable width or fixed width and variable period is used to switch the transistor on and off. In contrast, in the self-oscillating switching regulator of Fig. 7–5, no external pulse generator is used. The interesting circuit "trick" shown in Fig. 7–5 provides the variable-width pulse drive by use of only a dc difference amplifier and does not require pulse-generating and width- or period-modulating circuits.

The circuit of Fig. 7–5 works as follows. The dc difference amplifier A senses the difference between a fraction of the output voltage and the voltage at P1. The voltage at P1 is the sum of a dc reference voltage, V_r, and a small fraction of the voltage between V_r and P2.

Now if the switch Q1 is closed, P2 is essentially at the potential of V_{in} and P1 is slightly above V_r or

$$V_{P1} = V_r + \left(\frac{R1}{R1 + R2}\right)(V_{in} - V_r)$$

The output is substantially at V_o and a potential $(V_{in} - V_o)$ exists across L1 and the current in it ramps up linearly at a rate $dI/dT = (V_{in} - V_o)/L1$. This current flows into the load and into C1 to replenish any charge it lost when Q1 was open. Now as the voltage at C1 (V_o) rises, that at P3 rises proportionately. As long as Q1 remains closed, P3 continues rising. As it reaches equality with the potential at P1, it overshoots slightly and the output of the high-gain dc difference amplifier goes negative and opens switch transistor Q1.

---
[3] M. J. English, Fairchild Semiconductor, "Switching Regulators Using the 723 Integrated Voltage Regulator."

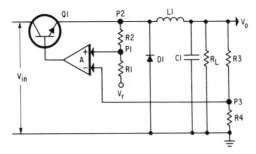

Fig. 7–5. A self-driven switching regulator requiring no external variable-width pulse-generating circuitry.

Now with Q1 open, the inductive impulse at the input end to L1 drives it negative. It falls toward ground and is caught and clamped to one diode drop (of about 0.8 V) below ground by free-wheeling diode D1. Now P1 is slightly below V_r at a potential of $V_{P1} = V_r - [R1/(R1 + R2]V_r$. It is also below V_{P3}. With this reversed polarity at the input to the difference amplifier, its output is at the correct polarity to hold Q1 off.

With Q1 off, and the input end of L1 at -0.8, the current that had been flowing in L1 when Q1 was on continues to flow, but now through the load and up through free-wheeling diode D1. Now a constant voltage of reversed polarity (input end of L1 negative relative to the end connected to C1) exists across L1. The magnitude of the voltage across L1 when Q1 is off is $(V_o + 0.8)$. Now the current in L1 ramps downward linearly at a rate of $dI/dT = (V_o + 0.8)/L1$. The load current is supplied partly from this decreasing ramp of current from L1 and partly from C1. As current flows out of C1, its potential falls linearly and so proportionately does P3. As P3 falls toward P1, it overshoots slightly and the high-gain difference amplifier reverses polarity, turning Q1 on again.

Now again P1 is positive relative to P3, C1 starts charging positive again moving P3 up with it. When P3 overshoots P1, Q1 turns off again. This process continues cyclically with P3 always racing after P1. As it catches up on the way up, Q1 opens and P1 turns around going below P3. P3 starts falling down toward P1, overshoots it, Q1 closes, driving P1 up again, and P3 turns around to chase it up.

The circuit must, therefore, operate with a small amplitude square wave of ripple at P1. This ripple voltage goes positive and negative relative to the dc reference voltage V_r. Since the voltage at P3 continues to chase P1 and switches high-gain amplifier A when P3 has caught up to P1 (and overshoots it by a few millivolts), the ripple amplitude at P3 is essentially equal to that at P1. Then the ripple output at V_o is simply $(R3 + R4)/R4$ times as great as that at P1 and is triangular in waveform.

The circuit thus generates its own switching waveforms in attempting to keep output centered about a dc voltage of $V_o = [(R3 + R4)/R4](V_r)$. The time to reach the switching thresholds of A as P3 races either up or down depends on ripple amplitude at P3, which fixes the ripple amplitude at V_o. But the ripple frequency at V_o depends on the magnitude of C1 and the dc load current.

In Chap. 9, magnitudes of L1 and C1 are calculated for a driven switching regulator. Equation 9–14 gives the required value for L1 in terms of the dc load current, V_{in}, V_o, and the switching periods T. In the self-oscillating switching regulator, L1 is calculated from the same expression. Equation 9–15 gives the required value of C1 as a function of L1, V_{in}, V_o, switching period, and the permissible peak-to-peak ripple, $V_{p/p}$.

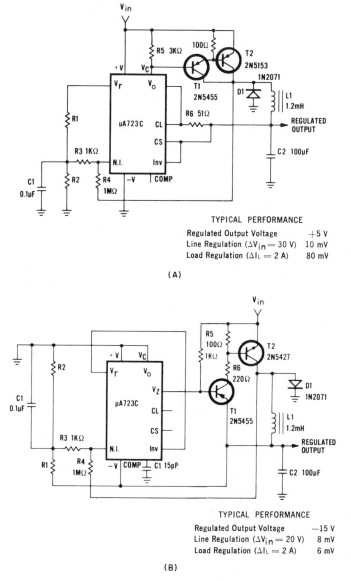

TYPICAL PERFORMANCE

Regulated Output Voltage	+5 V
Line Regulation ($\Delta V_{in} = 30$ V)	10 mV
Load Regulation ($\Delta I_L = 2$ A)	80 mV

(A)

TYPICAL PERFORMANCE

Regulated Output Voltage	−15 V
Line Regulation ($\Delta V_{in} = 20$ V)	8 mV
Load Regulation ($\Delta I_L = 2$ A)	6 mV

(B)

Fig. 7–6. Use of the 723 in the positive (A) and negative (B) switching regulators. (*Courtesy* Fairchild Semiconductor)

In the self-oscillating regulator, the ripple at P1 (and hence at P3) is chosen by selection of R1, R2 to be such that multiplied by (R3 + R4)/R4, it yields the permissible ripple at V_o.

Now, since the ripple at P1 is small compared to $V_{in} - V_r$ or to V_r, R2 can be designed most easily as a constant-current source supplying current to small resistor R1. When Q1 is closed, the current from R2 is $(V_{in} - V_r)/R2$ and P1 is above V_r by $(V_{in} - V_r)R1/R2$. When Q1 is open, P1 is below V_r by $(V_r/R2)R1$. Thus, the peak-to-peak ripple at P1 is

$$V_{p/p} \text{ [at P1]} = \left(\frac{R1}{R2}\right)(V_{in} - V_r + V_r) = \left(\frac{R1}{R2}\right)V_{in}$$

Then
$$V_{p/p} \text{ [at } V_o\text{]} = \left(\frac{R3 + R4}{R4}\right)V_{p/p} \text{ [at P1]}$$

$$= \left(\frac{R3 + R4}{R4}\right)\left(\frac{R1}{R2}\right)V_{in} \qquad (7\text{-}3)$$

And with fixed V_r and V_o, (R3 + R4)/R4 is fixed. Then with a known V_{in} and specified output ripple, R1/R2 is given by Eq. 7-3. Generally, R1 is taken as a small resistor in the range of 100–500 ohms.

The self-oscillating switching regulator is very economical in components. The 723 is convenient to use in building it, since it has the built-in dc difference amplifier, voltage reference source, and low-power output driver, which can be used to control an external high-current switch. Typical applications are shown in Figs. 7–6A and 7–6B, and further details are given in the aforementioned vendor's application notes.

It should be noted that, although the self-oscillating switching regulator is economical in parts, the fact that its operating frequency depends on dc load current and magnitude of the output filter capacitance is often objectionable.

7.2   National Semiconductor Integrated Voltage Regulators[4]

7.2.1 LM105 Integrated-Circuit Voltage Regulator[5]

This regulator is shown in Fig. 7–7. It has the same basic components as the 723: a reference source, an error amplifier, and an npn series-pass emitter follower output fed from an npn Darlington driver. The current-limiting feature is provided and it can be operated either in the constant-current or current-foldback mode (Sects. 6.8.2 and 6.8.3).

Output voltage range is 4.5–40 V, input voltage range is 8.5–50 V, and output input differential is 3–30 V. Output current capability is limited by the maximum allowable chip junction temperature, which is specified at 150°C but should be derated for a safe worst-case design. Allowable output current thus depends on input voltage, short-circuit current limit (I_{sc}), and thermal design. This will be taken up subsequently.

The regulator can be used with external pnp or npn current-boosting transistors to provide output current up to ten or even tens of amperes.

---

[4] Information on these devices is by courtesy of National Semiconductor Corp.
[5] R. J. Widlar, National Semiconductor Corp., "The LM105 – An Improved Positive Voltage Regulator."

Circuit Details

The detailed schematic is shown in Fig. 7–7A. Although the functions it performs are much like the 723, the proprietary "circuit tricks" it uses to achieve good reference voltage stability, high-error amplifier gain, and constant-current sources for low drift and temperature stability are different.

In Fig. 7–7A, Q2 and Q3 make up the error amplifier whose load impedance is R6 in the Q2 collector. Gain to the bottom of R6 is 20, and output from the bottom of R6 is further amplified by the difference amplifier pair Q4 and Q5. Load impedance in the collector of Q5 is the constant-current source consisting of one of the multiple collector outputs from Q12. Because of the high impedance

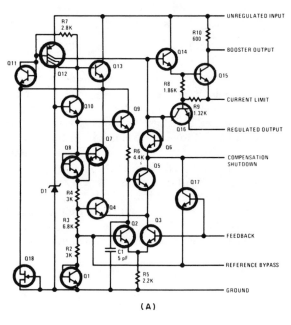

(A)

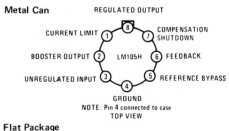

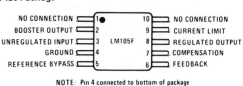

Fig. 7–7. National Semiconductor LM105 regulator. (A) Circuit schematic. (B) Available packages. (*Courtesy* National Semiconductor Corp.)

(B)

10A Regulator with Foldback Current Limiting

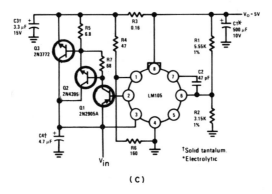

(C)

1.0A Regulator with Protective Diodes

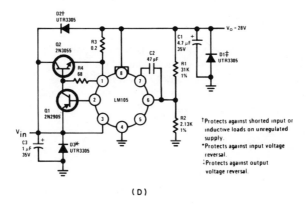

(D)

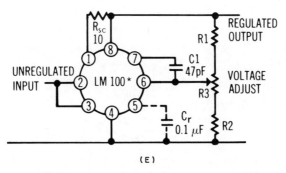

(E)

Fig. 7–7. (*Cont'd.*) Some applications of the National Semiconductor LM105 regulator. (C) With external pnp-npn-npn current booster and current foldback. (D) With pnp-npn current booster and current foldback. (E) Basic regulator with no external current-boosting constant-current mode with $I_{sc} = 0.65/R_{sc} = 0.65/10 = 65$ mA. (*Courtesy* National Semiconductor Corp.)

of this source as seen looking out of the collector of Q5, the gain of the second difference amplifier is 1,500. Output from the second difference amplifier is at the base of Q14 (level shifted upward by the base-emitter drop of Q6).

Q14 and Q15 make up an npn Darlington emitter follower output stage when collector load resistor R10 is shorted out. When no external current-boosting transistors are used, R10 is shorted out externally and output current is taken at the emitter of Q15. Open-loop voltage gain in this configuration is the product of the two difference amplifier pairs discussed above or $(20 \times 1,500 = 30,000$.

When external npn emitter follower or npn emitter follower driver–npn emitter follower power stage boosters are used, the LM105 output must be a current source and is taken from the emitter of Q15 with R16 shorted externally.

With a compound npn emitter follower output stage, the minimum input–output differential voltage across the power output transistor must be increased to accommodate the 4-V minimum input–output differential in the LM105 plus the two base-emitter drops or about $(2)(0.8) = 1.6$ V of the external transistors.

A preferable external boosting amplifier consists of a pnp inverter–npn emitter follower configuration as in Figs. 7–7C and 7–7D. In this case, the unregulated input can be as little as 2–$3V_{be}$ or about 2 V maximum above the regulated output, and the consequent dissipation across the external series-pass elements is minimized. When the external load is the base of a pnp driver, the LM105 must be used as a current sink, and its output is taken from the bottom end of R10, the collector load resistor for Q15. The emitter of Q15 must then be moved down to a lower potential as shown in Fig. 7–7C. There it is moved down to the junction of R4, R6 to permit carrying away the base current from the external pnp(Q1) plus the current from R10 inside the regulator.

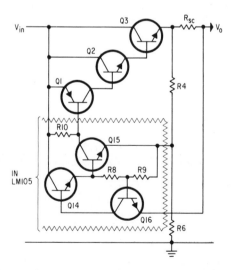

Fig. 7–8. LM105 integrated voltage regulator driving an external pnp–npn compound current-boosting amplifier. When the first transistor in the external chain (Q1) is a pnp type, the minimum V_{in} voltage can be as close as $3V_{be} = V_{be(Q1)} + V_{be(Q2)} + V_{be(Q3)}$ above the output. This minimizes power dissipation in Q3.

The advantage of a compound pnp–npn–npn external boosting amplifier can be seen more clearly in Fig. 7–8.

Q16 is the current-limiting transistor. It is normally off and when the drop across its base-emitter terminals rises to 0.65 V, it turns on and diverts current away from the base of Q14. The configuration of Fig. 7–7C or 7–8 offers foldback-current limiting because of R4 and R6. This was discussed in detail in Sect. 6.8.3. Briefly, current foldback operates in Fig. 7–8 because of the canceling effect of the downward drop in R4 on the voltage rise in R_{sc}. When V_o is high, R6 draws a significant current through R4, and the resultant voltage drop opposes the voltage rise in R_{sc}, which tends to turn Q16 on. But when V_o is low, the current drained by R6 is low, and there is less of a drop across R4. Hence, the current through R_{sc} required to generate the 0.65-V turn-on potential is lower. The result is the characteristic foldback curve shown in Fig. 6–18B.

Power Dissipation and Maximum Output Current

The LM105 comes in a low-profile TO5 package and $\frac{1}{4} \times \frac{1}{4}$ in. flatpack version. The TO5 can version has a maximum chip junction temperature of 150°C and junction-to-ambient thermal resistance (θ_{ja}) of 150°C/watt and junction-to-case thermal resistance (θ_{jc}) of 45°C/watt.

Maximum internal dissipation and, hence, maximum output current depends on the maximum permissible junction temperature. Although rated at 150°C, this should be derated for a safe worst-case design. Assume a maximum junction temperature of 105°C. Then for a 65°C ambient temperature and no heat sink,

$$T_j = T_{\text{ambient}} + PD(\theta_{ja})$$

or
$$PD = \frac{T_j - T_{\text{ambient}}}{\theta_{ja}} = \frac{105 - 65}{150} = 266 \text{ mW}$$

Now for constant-current overcurrent protection, maximum dissipation occurs at maximum input voltage and is equal to $PD_{\text{max}} = V_{in(\text{max})} I_{sc(\text{max})}$

And assuming $I_{sc(\text{max})}$ is 30% above the normal maximum operating current (to ensure we do not go prematurely into current limit at high dynamic load currents), then

$$0.226 = 1.3 I_{\text{max}} V_{in(\text{max})}$$

For $V_{in(\text{max})}$ of 10, 20, 30, and 40 V, this gives maximum output currents of 17.3, 8.6, 5.3, and 4.3 mA, respectively.

These currents can be increased by going to current-foldback overcurrent protection, since the internal dissipation in the nonshorted case is $(V_{in(\text{max})} - V_o)1.3 I_{\text{max}}$. And for foldback to $I_{\text{max}}/5$ (which is easily possible), the available output current increases by a factor of 5 before the circuit becomes dissipation limited.

Circuit Applications

Just as the 723, the LM105 can be used by itself as in Fig. 7–7E at low-current levels or with external current-boosting transistors as in Fig. 7–7C and 7–7D at higher-current levels. It can also be used as a switching regulator with or without external boosting transistors. A large variety of circuit configura-

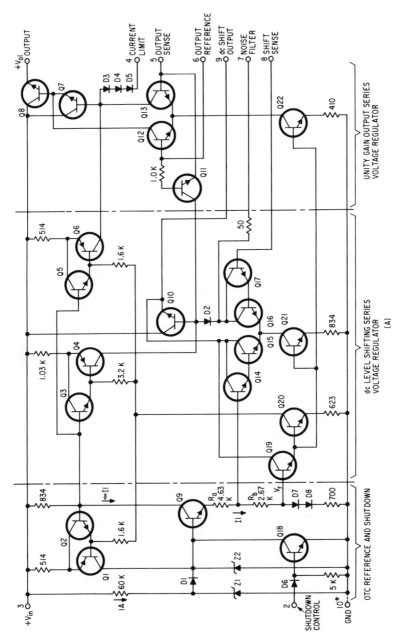

Fig. 7–9A. Circuit schematic of the Motorola MC1560/1561 integrated-circuit voltage regulator. (*Courtesy* Motorola, Inc.)

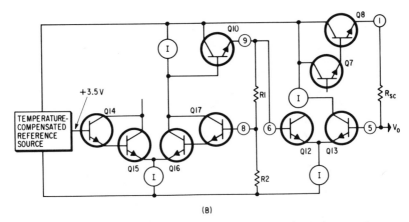

(B)

Fig. 7-9B. Block diagram of the Motorola MC1560/1561 integrated-circuit voltage regulator. (*Courtesy* Motorola, Inc.)

tions are shown in the vendors' application notes[6] and will not be taken up here. They are basically small variations on those shown in Figs. 7-7C and 7-7D.

7.3 Motorola Integrated Voltage Regulators[7]

7.3.1 MC1561 Integrated-Circuit Voltage Regulator

The circuit schematic of this regulator is shown in Fig. 7-9A and its block diagram in Fig. 7-9B. It has all the elements that the Fairchild 723 or National Semiconductor LM105 has but circuitizes them in its proprietary and rather unique way. It has the temperature-compensated constant-voltage reference source, an error amplifier, and an npn–npn Darlington emitter follower output stage.

It is packed in a low-profile TO5 (G package) at a maximum power dissipation rating of 680 mW at 25°C ambient. In a TO66 (R package), it has a dissipation rating of 3 W. It can be used at output currents limited only by thermal considerations. Current ratings are a function of internal dissipation and thermal resistances. The TO5 version has a thermal resistance of 184°C/watt from junction to air and 69°C/watt from junction to case. The TO66 version has a 42°C/watt junction-to-air thermal resistance and 7.2°C/watt junction to case. From these thermal resistances, maximum current ratings at various dc input voltages can be calculated as in the previous section.

Input voltage range of the MC1561 is 8.5–40 V, output range is 2.5–37 V, and input–output differential is a minimum of 2.7 V. With these voltage limits, it is much like the 723 and LM105.

---

[6] R. J. Widlar, National Semiconductor Corp.: "The LM105 – An Improved Positive Regulator"; "A Versatile, Monolithic Voltage Regulator"; "New Uses For the LM105 Regulator"; "Designing Switching Regulators."

[7] Information presented here courtesy of Motorola, Inc.

Circuit Details

The circuit schematic of Fig. 7–9A shows the MC1561 to have a rather unique configuration. It consists of a regulator within a regulator as can be seen more clearly in Fig. 7–9B.

The error amplifier Q14, Q15, Q16, and Q17 together with Q10 form a local internal series-pass regulator. The reference source supplies a constant temperature-compensated 3.5 V to the base of Q14. The output of the error amplifier feeds the series-pass emitter follower output stage Q10. The emitter of Q10 generates an output voltage fixed by the external resistors R1 and R2. The output at the emitter of Q10 (pin 9) is [(R1 + R2)/R2]3.5 V. This voltage is made equal to the desired output voltage and serves as a stable, temperature-compensated reference source for a second error amplifier, Q12–Q13.

This error amplifier and series-pass transistors Q7 and Q8 form a unity-gain voltage regulator. Thus, when pin 1 is connected to pin 5, through the current-limiting resistor R_{sc} as in Fig. 7–9B, the output voltage at pin 5 is forced to be equal to the voltage at pin 6, i.e., [(R1 + R2)/R2]3.5 V.

In actual operation, the R1 + R2 network is forced to carry 0.56 mA and R1 and R2 are calculated to give the desired output voltage. Thus, in Fig. 7–10A, it is seen that the junction of R1 and R2 is connected to pin 8. Potential at pin 8 is +3.5 V, since the negative-feedback loop forces pin 8 to be at the same potential as the base of Q14, which is the 3.5-V output of the reference source. Thus, I_{R2} = 3.5/6,800 = 0.56 mA. Now since 0.56 mA flows through R2, it also flows through R1. Then the level-shifted reference voltage at pin 9 is

$$V_o = V \text{ [pin 8]} + 0.56 \text{ R1}$$

Then for a desired output voltage V_o, R1 is selected as

$$R1 = \frac{V_o - 3.5}{0.00056} = (1,785 V_o - 6,250) \text{ ohms}$$

This is a somewhat smaller resistance than shown in Fig. 7–10A (R1 = 2,000 V_o − 7,000 ohms). The discrepancy arises because the reference source is not exactly 3.5 V.

When output lower than 3.5 V is required, connections are as in Fig. 7–10C. Here, pins 8 and 9 are connected together, and it can be seen from Fig. 7–9B that this forces output at pin 9 to be equal to 3.5 V. Now 3.5 V is divided down by R1 and R2 and their junction is fed to pin 6. The negative-feedback loop around the output regulator (Q12, Q13, Q7, and Q8) then forces potential at pin 5 (pin 1 through the current-limiting resistor R_{sc}) to equal that at pin 6. Thus, output voltage is [R2/(R1 + R2)]3.5 V.

Now R1 and R2 are forced to carry 0.50 mA, since potential at pins 8 and 9 is 3.5 V. Since R1 and R2 are chosen to equal 7,000 ohms, current through them is 3.5/7,000 = 0.5 mA. Then potential at the top of R2 will be the potential at pin 6 and, hence, also at pin 5. The output voltage at pin 5 (Fig. 7–10C) will be V_o = 0.0005(R2) volts. Thus, for a desired output V_o, R2 = 2,000 V_o as shown in Fig. 7–10C.

Fig. 7–10. Various applications of the Motorola MC1561. (A and B) Connection for $V_o \geq +3.5$ V. (C) Connections for $V_o \leq +3.5$ V. (*Courtesy Motorola, Inc.*)

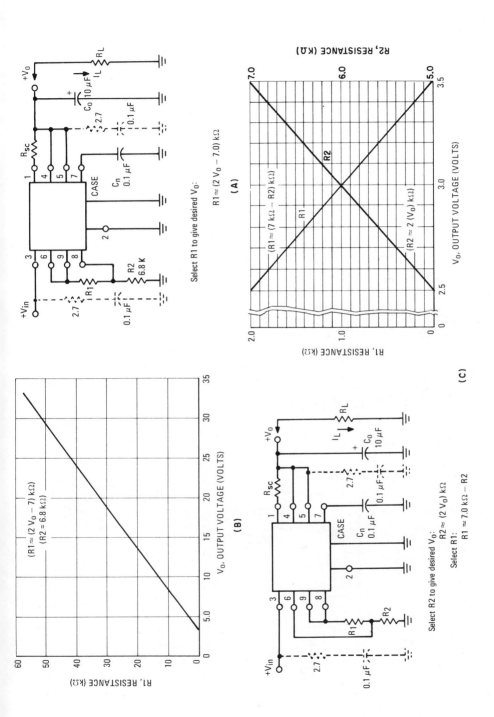

Select R1 to give desired V_O:

$R1 \approx (2 V_O - 7.0) k\Omega$

(A)

R2, RESISTANCE (kΩ)

$(R1 \approx (7 k\Omega - R2) k\Omega)$

$(R2 \approx 2 (V_O) k\Omega)$

V_O, OUTPUT VOLTAGE (VOLTS)

R1, RESISTANCE (kΩ)

(C)

$(R1 \approx (2 V_O - 7) k\Omega)$
$(R2 = 6.8 k\Omega)$

(B)

V_O, OUTPUT VOLTAGE (VOLTS)

R1, RESISTANCE (kΩ)

Select R2 to give desired V_O:

$R2 \approx (2 V_O) k\Omega$

Select R1:

$R1 \approx 7.0 k\Omega - R2$

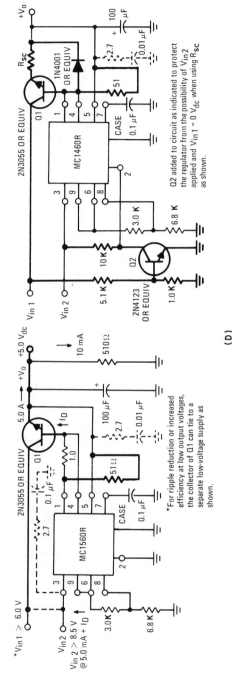

Fig. 7-10. (*Cont'd.*) Various applications of the Motorola MC1561. (D) npn current-boosting circuits. (*Courtesy* Motorola, Inc.)

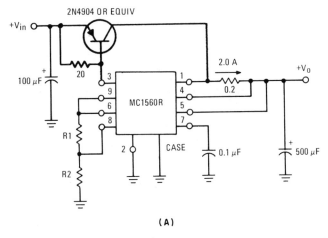

(A)

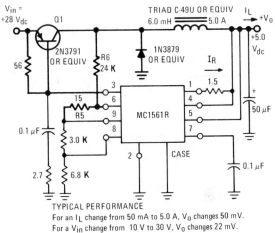

TYPICAL PERFORMANCE
For an I_L change from 50 mA to 5.0 A, V_0 changes 50 mV.
For a V_{in} change from 10 V to 30 V, V_0 changes 22 mV.
Ripple $< 60\ mV_{p/p}$

(B)

Fig. 7-11. Additional applications of the Motorola MC1561 regulator. (A) A pnp current-boosting circuit. (B) A switching regulator. (*Courtesy* Motorola, Inc.)

Current-Boosting Circuit Configurations

Figure 7-10D shows npn current boosters, and Fig. 7-11 shows pnp boosters. The MC1561 has no load collector resistor for the series-pass stage, neither internal as the LM105 nor external as for the 723. Thus, when a pnp booster is used, the "current sink" to absorb pnp base current is the $+V_{in}$ terminal itself, pin 3 as shown in Fig. 7-11A. The MC1561 can be used in a variety of switching applications. Further details on these and other applications and design information are available in the vendor's application notes.[8]

---

[8] T. M. Frideriksen, Motorola, Inc., AN473, "MC1561—A Monolithic High Power Series Voltage Regulator." E. Renschler and D. Schrock, Motorola, Inc., AN500,·"Development, Analyses, Operation of the MC1561 Monolithic Voltage Regulator." M. Gienger and D. Kesner, Motorola, Inc., AN498, "Voltage and Current Boost Techniques Using the MC1561."

8

DC/DC Square-Wave
Converter Design

8.0   Introduction

In Chap. 2, the elements of square-wave dc/dc converters were presented. Their merits were pointed out, and the general design equations and design details were discussed with emphasis on component selection for reliable designs. Chapter 3 showed in block diagram form how square-wave converters are used in combination with series-pass and switching regulators to build complex, multivoltage power supplies.

In this chapter, specific design examples for converters of various output-current and voltage levels will be taken up. Transformer core selection will be taken up in more detail, and design of the transformer windings will be presented. Frequently occurring circuit problems will be discussed, and circuit configurations to minimize the problems will be shown.

8.1   Transformer Core Geometry, Hysteresis Loss, and Peak Flux Density

Most present-day power (above 50 W) converters operate in the range of 10–50 kHz. In that range, as pointed out in Sect. 2.1.8, ferrite cores are preferable to metallic-tape cores. Ferrite cores are inexpensive and come in a variety of shapes that lend themselves easily to different packaging requirements. Some of the various-shaped ferrite cores are shown in Figs. 8–1 to 8–6.

The U–U and toroidal cores are generally used for higher-output powers of 300 W or more. They have the advantage that output powers greater than obtainable for a single core can be achieved by stacking two cores side by side and threading windings through both. Cup and E–E cores of Figs. 8–2 to 8–6 come with bobbins, making coil winding easier and less expensive.

In driven converters, unlike the square-wave oscillators of Sect. 2.4, core geometry and number of primary turns are so chosen as to keep the core safely below saturation flux density. This avoids the high-current spike (Fig. 2–19) at the end of each half cycle, characteristic of a square-wave power oscillator. Since core losses increase rapidly with peak flux density, the driven converter operating at a controlled peak flux level safely below saturation keeps core dissipation low.

ELECTRICAL CHARACTERISTICS

CONFIGURATION	U-U
A_L mH per 1000 turns ±25%	3800
μ_e ref.	2550
A_L mH per 1000 turns at 3000 G, 100°C	≥1550 (μ_A ≥1050 ref.)

MECHANICAL CHARACTERISTICS

CORE SET		U-U
MAGNETIC PATH LENGTH	ℓ_e	6.77 in. 17.2 cm
CORE CONSTANT	$\Sigma \frac{\ell_e}{A_e}$	21.42 in.$^{-1}$ 8.431 cm^{-1}
EFFECTIVE CORE AREA	A_e	.316 in.^{2} 2.04 cm^2
EFFECTIVE CORE VOLUME	V_e	2.14 in.^{3} 35.1 cm^3
WINDING AREA	A_c	1.500 in.^{2} 9.675 cm^2
WEIGHT		5.6 oz. 160 g

(A)

MECHANICAL CHARACTERISTICS

MAGNETIC PATH LENGTH	ℓ_e	6.7 in. 17.1 cm
CORE CONSTANT	$\Sigma \frac{\ell_e}{A_e}$	19.66 in.$^{-1}$ 7.72 cm^{-1}
EFFECTIVE CORE AREA	A_e	.342 in.^{2} 2.21 cm^2
EFFECTIVE CORE VOLUME	V_e	2.306 in.^{3} 37.95 cm^3
WEIGHT		7.21 oz. 206 g

(B)

CORE PART NUMBER	CORE MAT'L TYPE	A_L mH PER 1000 TURNS (±20%)	μ_o (REF.)	A_L (mH PER 1000 TURNS) AT 3000G, 100°C
144T500	3C8	4350	2700	≥1690 (μ_a ≥1050 REF.)

(C)

All dimensions are in inches and are nominal.

NOMINAL DIMENSIONS IN INCHES

DIMENSION	SINGLE U CORE	U-U
A	2.625	2.625
B	.562	.562
C	.562	.562
D	.500	1.00
E	1.06	2.12
F	1.50	1.50
G	.563	.563

Fig. 8-1. (A) Mechanical and electrical characteristics and dimensions of the type 1F10U–U ferrite core. (B) Mechanical characteristics and dimensions and (C) electrical characteristics of the type 144T500 toroidal core. (*Courtesy* Ferroxcube Corp.)

MECHANICAL CHARACTERISTICS

NOTE: Values given apply to a core set.

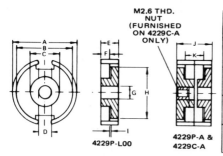

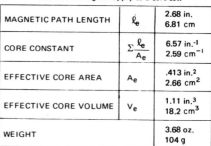

4229P-L00

4229P-A & 4229C-A

MAGNETIC PATH LENGTH	ℓ_e	2.68 in.	6.81 cm
CORE CONSTANT	$\Sigma \dfrac{\ell_e}{A_e}$	6.57 in.$^{-1}$	2.59 cm^{-1}
EFFECTIVE CORE AREA	A_e	.413 in.^{2}	2.66 cm^2
EFFECTIVE CORE VOLUME	V_e	1.11 in.^{3}	18.2 cm^3
WEIGHT		3.68 oz.	104 g

NOTE: MINIMUM CORE AREA 2.05 cm^2

POT CORE DIMENSIONS

All dimensions are in inches.

	MIN.	MAX.		MIN.	MAX.		MIN.	MAX.
A	1.641	1.697	E	.577	.587	I	.038	.048
B	1.402	1.456	F	.400	.408	J	1.154	1.174
C	.673	.697	G	.213	.221	K	.800	.816
D	.177	.225	H	1.232	1.288			

(A)

UNGAPPED POT CORES

CORE PART NUMBER*	CORE MATERIAL	A_L[†] mH PER 1000 TURNS (±25%)	μ_e[†] (REF.)
4229P-L00-3C8	3C8	11,500	2350
4229P-L00-3B7	3B7	10,300	2100

*Part number for a core half. † Per pair of cores.

(B)

DIMENSIONS: All dimensions in inches, except as indicated.

Part No.	A max.	B max.	C min.	D ref.	E min.	Mean Length of Turn	Winding Area
4229F1D	.780	1.394	.709	.701	.197	3.39 in. 8.6 cm	.217 in.^{2} 1.40 cm^2
4229F2L				.333			.195 in.^{2} 1.26 cm^2

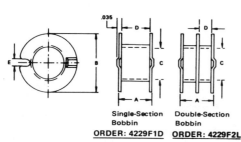

Single-Section Bobbin
ORDER: 4229F1D

Double-Section Bobbin
ORDER: 4229F2L

MATERIAL: DELRIN & LEXAN
MAX. OPERATING TEMP.: 130°C.

NOTE: All dimensions on this page are in inches, and are nominal, unless otherwise indicated.

(C)

TURNS PER BOBBIN

NUMBER OF TURNS vs A.W.G. WIRE SIZE

(4229F1D, 4229F2L)

Fig. 8–2. Mechanical characteristics and dimensions (A), electrical characteristics (B), and standard bobbins for the type 4229 cup core (C). (*Courtesy* Ferroxcube Corp.)

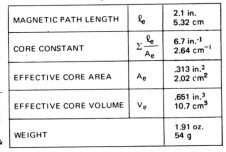

MECHANICAL CHARACTERISTICS

NOTE: Values given apply to a core **set**.

MAGNETIC PATH LENGTH	ℓ_e		2.1 in. 5.32 cm
CORE CONSTANT	$\Sigma \dfrac{\ell_e}{A_e}$		6.7 in.$^{-1}$ 2.64 cm^{-1}
EFFECTIVE CORE AREA	A_e		.313 in.^{2} 2.02 cm^2
EFFECTIVE CORE VOLUME	V_e		.651 in.^{3} 10.7 cm^3
WEIGHT			1.91 oz. 54 g

NOTE: MINIMUM CORE AREA 1.66 cm^2

3622P-L00

3622P-A &
3622C-A

POT CORE DIMENSIONS

All dimensions are in inches.

	MINIMUM	MAXIMUM		MINIMUM	MAXIMUM
A	1.378	1.418	G	.213	.221
B	1.177	1.217	H	1.007	1.055
C	.614	.630	I	.019	.029
D	.169	.217	J	.844	.866
E	.422	.433	K	.574	.590
F	.287	.295			

(A)

CORE PART NUMBER *	CORE MATERIAL	A_L † (mH PER 1000 TURNS) (±25%)	μ_e † (REF.)
3622P-L00-3C8	3C8	10,800	2250
3622P-L00-3B7	3B7	9660	2000
3622P-L00-3B9	3B9	7050	1440

*Part number for a core half.   †Per pair of cores.

(B)

Fig. 8–3. Mechanical characteristics and dimensions (A) and electrical characteristics (B) of the type 3622 cup core. (*Courtesy* Ferroxcube Corp.)

DIMENSIONS: All dimensions in inches, except as indicated.

Part No.	A max.	B max.	C min.	D ref.	E min.	Mean Length of Turn	Winding Area
3622F1D				.509			.116 in.² .748 cm²
3622F2D	.568	1.172	.645	.242	.113	2.92 in. 7.4 cm	.110 in.² .729 cm²
3622F3D				.186			.102 in.² .710 cm²

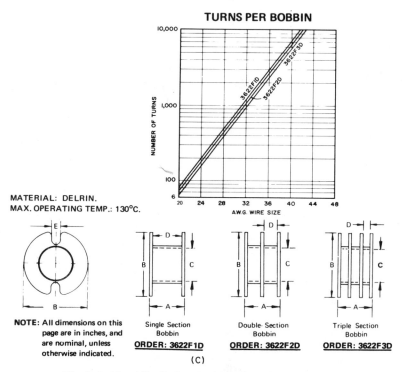

TURNS PER BOBBIN

MATERIAL: DELRIN.
MAX. OPERATING TEMP.: 130°C.

NOTE: All dimensions on this
page are in inches, and
are nominal, unless
otherwise indicated.

Single Section Bobbin
ORDER: 3622F1D

Double-Section Bobbin
ORDER: 3622F2D

Triple Section Bobbin
ORDER: 3622F3D

(C)

Fig. 8–3. (*Cont'd.*) (C) Standard bobbins for the type 3622
cup core. (*Courtesy* Ferroxcube Corp.)

From Fig. 8–7A, it is seen that ferrite material 3C8,[1] a typical ferrite
having low losses at high frequency, is still safely below saturation at 2,000 G.
From Fig. 2–6, it is seen that at 20 kHz, 2,000-G peak flux density, 3C8 has
losses of only 55 mW/cc. Thus, U–U core 1F10 of Fig. 8–1 is seen to have a
volume of 35.1 cu cm and will have losses of $0.055(35.1) = 1.93$ W at these
operating points.

---

[1] Proprietary material available from Ferroxcube Corp., Saugerties, N.Y. Somewhat similar materials are available from Magnetics, Inc., Butler, Pa. — material
types "F," "H," and "J"; Stackpole Carbon Co., St. Mary's Pa. — material
type CERAMAG 24B; Allen Bradley, Milwaukee, Wisc. — material types
WO3 and WO4; Indiana General, Keasbey, N. J. — SR15000 ferrites.

It can also be seen from Fig. 2–6 that there are no core loss limitations to operating at 50 kHz. Thus, at 50 kHz, 2,000-G peak flux density, core losses are still only 180 mW/cc, and total core losses for the 1F10 are $0.18(35.1) = 6.3$ W. This is not prohibitive if the thermal design of the transformer is adequate, but a preferable lower-loss design for 50 kHz would be to go to about 1,300 G, at which Fig. 2–6 shows the losses to be at 60 mW/cc. This yields total core losses of $0.06(35.1) = 2.1$ W for a 1F10 core.

Permeability versus frequency relationship for 3C8 is shown in Fig. 8–7B. It is seen permeability starts falling off significantly only beyond 1 MHz. This is considerably above the point where transistor switching time parameters have already become the frequency-limiting factors.

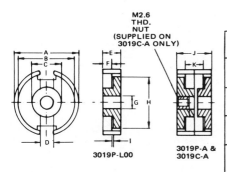

MECHANICAL CHARACTERISTICS

NOTE: Values given apply to a core set.

MAGNETIC PATH LENGTH	ℓ_e	1.78 in. 4.52 cm
CORE CONSTANT	$\Sigma \dfrac{\ell_e}{A_e}$	8.3 in.$^{-1}$ 3.30 cm^{-1}
EFFECTIVE CORE AREA	A_e	.214 in.^{2} 1.38 cm^2
EFFECTIVE CORE VOLUME	V_e	.376 in.^{3} 6.19 cm^3
WEIGHT		1.20 oz. 34 g

NOTE: MINIMUM CORE AREA 1.10 cm^2

POT CORE DIMENSIONS

All dimensions in inches.

	MINIMUM	MAXIMUM		MINIMUM	MAXIMUM
A	1.161	1.201	G	.213	.221
B	.984	1.016	H	.787	.827
C	.516	.532	I	.019	.029
D	.145	.193	J	.732	.748
E	.366	.374	K	.512	.528
F	.256	.264			

(A)

CORE PART NUMBER*	CORE MATERIAL	A_L[†] (mH PER 1000 TURNS) (±25%)	μ_e[†] (REF.)
3019P-L00-3C8	3C8	8300	2180
3019P-L00-3B7	3B7	7580	2020
3019P-L00-3B9	3B9	5750	1480

*Part number for a core half.   †Per pair of cores.

(B)

Fig. 8–4. Mechanical characteristics and dimensions (A) and electrical characteristics (B) for the type 3019 cup core. (*Courtesy* Ferroxcube Corp.)

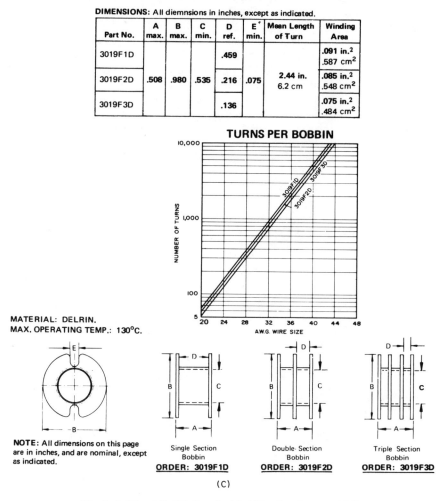

DIMENSIONS: All diemnsions in inches, except as indicated.

Part No.	A max.	B max.	C min.	D ref.	E* min.	Mean Length of Turn	Winding Area
3019F1D				.459			.091 in.² .587 cm²
3019F2D	.508	.980	.535	.216	.075	2.44 in. 6.2 cm	.085 in.² .548 cm²
3019F3D				.136			.075 in.² .484 cm²

TURNS PER BOBBIN

MATERIAL: DELRIN.
MAX. OPERATING TEMP.: 130°C.

NOTE: All dimensions on this page are in inches, and are nominal, except as indicated.

Single Section Bobbin
ORDER: 3019F1D

Double- Section Bobbin
ORDER: 3019F2D

Triple Section Bobbin
ORDER: 3019F3D

(C)

Fig. 8–4. (*Cont'd.*) (C) Standard bobbins for the type 3019 cup core. (*Courtesy* Ferroxcube Corp.)

Detailed design to set the peak flux density at any level dictated by the permissible core losses or core saturation will be taken up in Sect. 8.8.1. The first consideration in a transformer design is the selection of the specific core for the required output power level.

8.2   Transformer Core Selection: Core Geometry Versus Power-Handling Relationships

Guidance in the selection of a transformer core for a given output power is provided by the following quantitative relations. It should be kept in mind, however, that these relations are only guidelines. Often, by juggling parameters and operating points in current densities in windings and peak flux density, a smaller core than indicated can be used for a given output power.

The fundamental magnetic relationship in the transformer is

$$e = NA_e\left(\frac{dB}{dt}\right)10^{-8} \tag{8-1}$$

where e is the instantaneous voltage across a winding in volts, N is the number of turns in that winding, A_e is the transformer core area in sq cm, and dB/dt is the

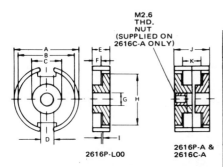

MECHANICAL CHARACTERISTICS

NOTE: Values given apply to a core set.

MAGNETIC PATH LENGTH	ℓ_e	1.48 in. 3.76 cm
CORE CONSTANT	$\Sigma \dfrac{\ell_e}{A_e}$	10.19 in.$^{-1}$ 4.00 cm^{-1}
EFFECTIVE CORE AREA	A_e	.147 in.^{2} .948 cm^2
EFFECTIVE CORE VOLUME	V_e	.215 in.^{3} 3.53 cm^3
WEIGHT		0.707 oz. 20.0 g

NOTE: MINIMUM CORE AREA .720 cm^2

POT CORE DIMENSIONS

All dimensions are in inches.

	MINIMUM	MAXIMUM		MINIMUM	MAXIMUM
A	.984	1.024	G	.213	.221
B	.834	.866	H	.693	.725
C	.437	.453	I	.019	.029
D	.126	.174	J	.626	.642
E	.313	.321	K	.432	.448
F	.216	.224			

(A)

CORE PART NUMBER *	CORE MATERIAL	A_L † (mH PER 1000 TURNS) (±25%)	μ_e † (REF.)
2616P-L00-3C8	3C8	6700	2100
2616P-L00-3B7	3B7	6000	1880
2616P-L00-3B9	3B9	4390	1380
2616P-L00-3D3	3D3	2340	735
2616P-L00-4C4	4C4	390	120

*Part number for a core half.   †Per pair of cores.

(B)

Fig. 8–5. Mechanical characteristics and dimensions (A) and electrical characteristics (B) for the type 2616 cup core. (*Courtesy* Ferroxcube Corp.)

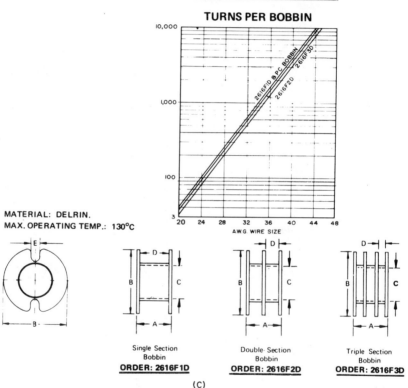

STANDARD BOBBIN DIMENSIONS
All dimensions in inches except as noted.

Part No.	A max.	B max.	C min.	D ref.	E min.	Mean Length of Turn	Winding Area
2616F1D				.380			.063 in.² .406 cm²
2616F2D	.429	.832	.457	.180	.075	2.08 in. 5.3 cm	.059 in.² .381 cm²
2616F3D				.113			.056 in.² .361 cm²

TURNS PER BOBBIN

MATERIAL: DELRIN.
MAX. OPERATING TEMP.: 130°C

Single Section Bobbin
ORDER: 2616F1D

Double Section Bobbin
ORDER: 2616F2D

Triple Section Bobbin
ORDER: 2616F3D

(C)

Fig. 8–5. (*Cont'd.*) (C) Standard bobbins for the type 2616 cup core. (*Courtesy* Ferroxcube Corp.)

instantaneous rate of change of flux density in gauss per second. A more useful form of Eq. 8–1 is

$$\Delta B \left[\text{over a time } \frac{T}{2} \right] = \frac{10^{+8}}{NA_e} \int_0^{T/2} e \, dt \qquad (8-2)$$

where T is the operating period in seconds.

In the converter of Fig. 2–1, the entire primary winding is wound around the core in the same direction and supply voltage E_{dc} is fed in at the center tap. Thus, for instance, when Q1 is on and in saturation, $\int e \, dt$ has a positive volt second area and ΔB is a positive increment. During the next half cycle when Q2 is on, the polarity across the driving winding is reversed, $\int e \, dt$ has a negative volt second area, and ΔB is a negative flux change equal and opposite to that occurring in the previous half cycle.

In the square-wave converter, when any transistor is on, it is in saturation at about 1 V and the voltage across a half primary (N_p turns) is $\simeq E_{dc} - 1$ $\simeq E_{dc}$ since usually $E_{dc} \gg 1$. Then

$$\Delta B = \frac{10^{-8}}{N_p A_e} \int_0^{T/2} e \, dt$$

$$= \frac{10^{-8} E_{dc}(T/2)}{N_p A_e} = 2B_{max}$$

ELECTRICAL CHARACTERISTICS

CORE MATERIAL	3C8	3E2A	CONFIG.
A_L mH per 1000 turns ±25%	5900	8000	E-E
μ_e ref.	2585	3500	E-E
A_L mH per 1000 turns at 3000g., 100°C	≥2450 (μ_a ≥ 1050 ref.)	---	E-E

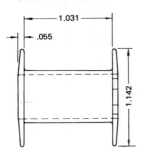

NOMINAL DIMENSIONS IN INCHES

DIMENSION	SINGLE E CORE	E-E
A	.466	.466
B	1.653	1.653
C	.592	.592
D	.234	.234
E	.597	1.194
F	.823	1.646
G	.359	.359
H	.226	.226

ORDER PART NO. 990-030-09

MATERIAL: REINFORCED NYLON
MAX. OPERATING TEMP.: 120°C
WINDING AREA: .276 in.^{2} (1.78 cm^2)
MEAN LENGTH OF TURN: 3.66 in. (9.3 cm)

MECHANICAL CHARACTERISTICS

CORE SET		E-E
MAGNETIC PATH LENGTH	ℓ_e	3.82 in. 9.70 cm
CORE CONSTANT	$\Sigma \dfrac{\ell_e}{A_e}$	13.97 in.$^{-1}$ 5.5 cm^{-1}
EFFECTIVE CORE AREA	A_e	.274 in.^{2} 1.77 cm^2
EFFECTIVE CORE VOLUME	V_e	1.05 in.^{3} 17.20 cm^3
WINDING AREA	A_c	.429 in.^{2} 2.77 cm^2
WEIGHT		2.7 oz. 77 g

STANDARD BOBBIN

All dimensions in inches (nominal)

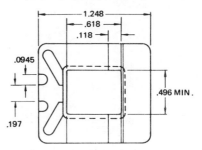

Fig. 8–6. Characteristics and dimensions of the type 783 E608 E–E core. (*Courtesy* Ferroxcube Corp.)

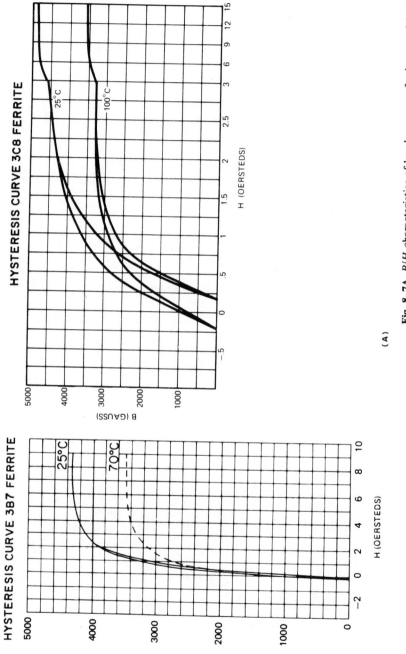

Fig. 8-7A. B/H characteristics of low-loss power ferrite materials 3B7 and 3C8. (*Courtesy* Ferroxcube Corp.)

(A)

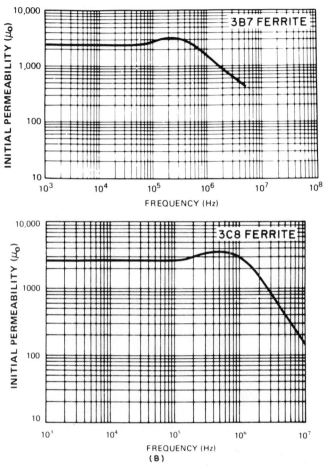

Fig.8–7B. Permeability of low-loss power ferrite materials 3B7 and 3C8. (*Courtesy* Ferroxcube Corp.)

where $B_{\max}$ is the maximum excursion in flux density around the zero flux density axis. Then

$$A_e = \frac{E_{\mathrm{dc}} T (10^{+8})}{4 N_p B_{\max}} = \frac{E_{\mathrm{dc}} (10^{+8})}{4 f N_p B_{\max}} \qquad (8\text{--}3)$$

Note that in calculating the required number of turns for any transformer, the exact primary voltage should be used in Eq. 8–3. Assuming a $V_{ce(\mathrm{sat})}$ of 1 V, the number of primary turns is

$$N_p = \frac{(E_{\mathrm{dc}} - 1) 10^{+8}}{4 f A_e B_{\max}} \qquad (8\text{--}3A)$$

In the above relations A_e is the core area in square centimeters, T is operating period in seconds, N_p is primary turns (either side of center tap), $B_{\max}$ is peak flux excursion in gauss, E_{dc} is supply voltage in volts, and f is operating frequency in cycles per second (or hertz).

Now let A_c be the total winding area in square inches for the given core (= A_c of Figs. 8–1 to 8–6), A_{ps} the total winding area (in square inches) allotted for the all windings together, and SF the winding "space factor" $= A_{ps}/A_c$. The goal is usually to make SF as close to 1.0 as possible so as to fill up as much as possible of the winding window. Values of SF generally average about 0.75. Then let A_p be the winding area (in square inches) allotted to the primary alone. Usually primary and secondary windings occupy equal area or $A_p = 0.5\,A_{ps}$. Then

$$A_p = 0.5A_{ps}$$
$$= 0.5(SF)A_c$$
$$= 0.5(0.75)A_c$$
$$= 0.375A_c$$

Further, let A_t be the area (in square inches) per single primary turn, I_p the primary current (amperes = peak), d the current density in the primary winding in peak amperes per square inch $= I_p/A_t$, and N_p the number of primary turns (either side of center tap). Then

$$A_c = \frac{A_p}{0.375}$$
$$= \frac{2N_pA_t}{0.375}$$
$$= \frac{2N_pI_p}{0.375d}$$

Or
$$A_c = \frac{5.33N_pI_p}{d}$$

where A_c is in square inches, d in amperes per square inch, and

$$A_c(\text{sq cm}) = 6.45A_c(\text{sq in.}) = 34.4N_pI_p/d \qquad (8\text{–}4)$$

Then, multiplying Eqs. 8–3 and 8–4,

$$A_eA_c = \left(\frac{E_{dc}(10^{+8})}{4N_pB_{\max}}\right)\left(\frac{34.4N_pI_p}{d}\right)$$
$$= \left(\frac{8.6 \times 10^{+8}}{B_{\max}fd}\right)(E_{dc}I_{dc}) = \left(\frac{8.6 \times 10^{+8}}{B_{\max}fd}\right)P_o \qquad (8\text{–}5)$$

where P_o is power input to the primary in watts and A_c and A_e are in square centimeters. Then

$$P_o = 1.16B_{\max}fd(A_eA_c)10^{-9} \qquad (8\text{–}6)$$

Current density is often expressed in terms of circular mils[2] per ampere (D_{cma}). It can be shown that this is related to current density in amperes per square inch (d) by

---

[2] A circular mil is the area of a circle 1 mil in diameter. Then area (sq in.) $= (\pi/4)$ (10^{-6}) [area in circular mils].

$$d = \frac{1.27 \times 10^{+6}}{D_{cma}}$$

Then
$$P_o = \frac{1.16(1.27)B_{max}fA_eA_c \times 10^{-3}}{D_{cma}}$$

$$= \frac{1.47B_{max}fA_eA_c \times 10^{-3}}{D_{cma}} \qquad (8-7)$$

where P_o is the power-handling capability in watts, B_{max} is the peak operating flux density in gauss, f is the operating frequency in hertz, A_e is the core area in square centimeters, A_c is the core (or bobbin if used) winding area in square centimeters, and D_{cma} is the coil current density expressed in circular mils per ampere.

Equations 8–6 and 8–7 are valuable guides in the initial selection of a transformer core for a given power level. They show that power-handling capability is proportional to the product of the core area (A_e) and the window winding area (A_c). These parameters are usually given in the core vendor's data sheets (Figs. 8–1 to 8–6). Power-handling capability is also seen to be directly proportional to B_{max} and f and inversely proportional to the circular mils per ampere (D_{cma}) operating point for the windings.

Generally, B_{max} will have been chosen as above for acceptable core losses. Operating frequency (f) will have been preselected by system requirements for an operating frequency some submultiple of the system clock frequency. This makes power supply noise synchronous with clock frequency and, hence, easier to cope with; or, possibly, operating frequency may have been selected to minimize component size, since the size of inductors and capacitors decreases with increasing frequency. Operating current density in circular mils (D_{cma}) is selected either on the basis of load regulation (minimizing output voltage change for a given load current change) or on the basis of minimizing copper losses. Generally, D_{cma} will be chosen somewhere in the range of 200–1,000 circular mils/ampere, depending on the thermal design of the transformer and its heat sink.

Thus, all variables in Eqs. 8–6 and 8–7 but P_o and the A_cA_e product are predetermined. Since power input, P_o, is fixed by system requirements (output load power plus known rectifier and low-level control amplifier losses), the core product A_cA_e is dictated and a core with the required A_cA_e product can be chosen from Eq. 8–7.

The power-handling capabilities of the four often-used cores of Figs. 8–1, 8–2, and 8–6 are calculated from Eq. 8–7 and tabulated in Fig. 8–8. This is done for peak flux densities of 1,000, 1,500, and 2,000 G and frequencies of 10, 15, 20, 30, 40, and 50 kHz at primary and secondary current densities of 250, 500, and 1,000 circular mils/ampere.

It is seen in Fig. 8–8 that quite high power levels can be handled at current densities down to 250 circular mils/ampere. Now an often used "industry" rule of thumb for current density in magnetic components is 1,000 circular mils/ampere. But current densities down to 250 circular mils/ampere or even less are easily possible without excessive coil temperature rise. This depends on thermal resistance between coils and case, between case and ambient

Fig. 8–8. Power-handling capability for various ferrite cores from Eq. 8–7. Power in watts for various cores, frequency, B_{max}, and current density. Assumed winding area for cup core is that of double-section bobbin. For E–E core, it is that of the only available single-section bobbin.

Core	$B_{max} = 2,000$ G						$B_{max} = 1,500$ G						$B_{max} = 1,000$ G						
	10 kHz	15 kHz	20 kHz	30 kHz	40 kHz	50 kHz	10 kHz	15 kHz	20 kHz	30 kHz	40 kHz	50 kHz	10 kHz	15 kHz	20 kHz	30 kHz	40 kHz	50 kHz	
1F10–UU Toroid	2328	3492	4656	6984	9312	11640	1746	2619	3492	5238	6984	8,730	1164	1746	2328	3492	4656	5820	250 circular mils/ampere
144T500 Cup	3081	4622	6162	9243	12324	15405	2311	3467	4622	6933	9244	11,556	1541	2312	3081	4623	6164	7705	
4229 E–E	398	597	796	1194	1592	1990	299	449	598	897	1196	1495	199	299	398	597	796	995	
783–608	379	568	757	1136	1514	1893	284	426	568	852	1136	1420	190	285	379	569	758	948	
1F10–UU Toroid	1162	1743	2324	3486	4648	5810	872	1308	1744	2616	3488	4360	581	872	1162	1743	2324	2905	500 circular mils/ampere
144T500 Cup	1541	2312	3082	4623	6164	7705	1156	1734	2312	3468	4624	5780	771	1157	1541	2313	3084	3855	
4229 E–E	199	299	398	597	796	995	149	224	298	447	596	745	100	150	199	300	400	500	
783–608	190	285	379	569	758	948	142	213	284	426	568	710	95	143	190	285	380	475	
1F10–UU Toroid	581	872	1162	1743	2324	2905	436	654	872	1308	1744	2180	291	437	581	873	1164	1455	1,000 circular mils/ampere
144T500 Cup	771	1157	1542	2313	3084	3855	578	867	1156	1734	2312	2890	386	579	771	1158	1544	1930	
4229 E–E	100	150	200	300	400	500	75	113	150	225	300	375	50	75	100	150	200	250	
783–608	95	143	190	285	380	476	71	107	143	214	285	356	48	71	95	143	196	238	

244

(or case to heat sink if transformer is tied to a heat sink), and power level. Further details on coil current density will be presented in Sect. 8.8.1.

Hysteresis losses for the cores of Figs. 8-1, 8-2, and 8-6 are shown in Fig. 8-9. It is seen that the hysteresis losses at the highest frequency of Fig. 8-9 are under 0.5% of the power-handling capabilities shown in Fig. 8-8 for current density of 1,000 circular mils/ampere and a peak flux density of 2,000 G. At a peak flux density of 1,000 G, hysteresis losses are under 0.25% of the power-handling capability at a current density of 1,000 circular mils/ampere.

8.3   Selection of Number of Turns per Winding

With a specific core selected to have the required $A_c A_e$ product calculated from Eq. 8-7, the next step in the transformer design is the selection of the number of turns for each winding.

Primary turns are calculated from Eq. 8-3A. Values of peak flux density $B_{\max}$, frequency f, and core area A_e have already been tentatively fixed from the core selection in the calculations of Eq. 8-7. Now if there are variations in the magnitudes of these parameters about their nominal values, these must be considered.

There is no problem if $B_{\max}$ had been chosen low enough—say, 1,000 G—for nominal values of f and P_o. For then, from Eq. 8-3, if f decreases and E_{dc} increases by 10%, for a given A_e $B_{\max}$ will increase by 20% to 1,200 G. At this flux density, hysteresis losses are still sufficiently low. But if N_p is chosen from Eq. 8-3 for $B_{\max} = 2,000$ G, at nominal values of f and E_{dc} similar variations of f and E_{dc} would increase $B_{\max}$ by 20% to 2,400 G.

It is seen from Fig. 8-7A that this is already on the low slope into the core saturation region where hysteresis losses and primary magnetizing current are increasing rapidly. Thus, if there are tolerances in f and E_{dc} in Eq. 8-3, N_p should be chosen so that at minimum value of f, maximum value of E_{dc} (ripple on E_{dc} should be considered). $B_{\max}$ is no more than 2,000 G.

Now for any desired secondary voltage, V_s, its turns, N_s, are

$$N_s = \frac{N_p V_s}{E_{dc} - V_{ce(sat)}} \tag{8-8}$$

And if a secondary voltage V_o is required after rectification with diode drop V_d, then

$$N_s = \frac{N_p (V_o + V_d)}{E_{dc} - V_{ce(sat)}} \tag{8-9}$$

Now $V_{ce(sat)} \cong 0.8$ and $V_d \cong 1.0$, thus making a fairly unique rectified secondary voltage available for a constant E_{dc}. But if an exact output voltage is required, tolerances in V_d, $V_{ce(sat)}$, and E_{dc} must be considered.

8.4   Winding Copper Losses

Wire size has in effect been chosen when a core has been selected from Eq. 8-7 for a tentatively chosen value of current density. For a given value of peak current I_p and chosen current density D_{cma}, the circular mils area is

Core type	$B_{max} = 2,000$ G						$B_{max} = 1,500$ G						$B_{max} = 1,000$ G					
	10 kHz	15 kHz	20 kHz	30 kHz	40 kHz	50 kHz	10 kHz	15 kHz	20 kHz	30 kHz	40 kHz	50 kHz	10 kHz	15 kHz	20 kHz	30 kHz	40 kHz	50 kHz
1F10–UU Toroid	0.77	1.23	2.04	2.88	4.21	6.32	0.42	0.60	0.95	1.36	2.07	3.16	0.14	0.21	0.33	0.46	0.67	1.05
144T500 Cup	0.83	1.33	2.20	3.11	4.55	6.83	0.46	0.65	1.02	1.48	2.24	3.42	0.15	0.23	0.36	0.49	0.72	1.14
4229 E-E	0.40	0.64	1.06	1.49	2.18	3.28	0.22	0.31	0.49	0.71	1.07	1.64	0.07	0.11	0.17	0.24	0.35	0.55
783–608	0.39	0.62	1.03	1.45	2.13	3.19	0.21	0.30	0.48	0.69	1.04	1.59	0.07	0.11	0.17	0.23	0.34	0.53

Fig. 8–9. Hysteresis losses in watts for various B_{max}, frequency, and core types from Fig. 2–6.

$I_p D_{cma}$. Wire tables such as in Fig. 8–10 then give the required wire size and, hence, resistance and power dissipation for the known current in each winding.

But if the transformer is used up to the maximum power as given in Eq. 8–7, it must be verified either by thermal calculations or measurement that, with the resulting copper losses and various thermal resistances, the coil temperature rise is within specified or safe limits for the selected class of transformer-insulating materials and wire-insulating coatings.

If winding temperature rise is excessive for the materials chosen, either higher-temperature materials must be used or lower current densities chosen. This means larger wire diameter, which perhaps results in insufficient winding space (A_c of Eq. 8–7). Then higher values of B_{max} must be permitted, thus decreasing the number of winding turns (N_p of Eq. 8–3). Since core hysteresis losses are generally lower than copper losses, values of B_{max} up to 2,000 G are acceptable. As a last resort, the next larger-sized core having larger coil winding space, thus permitting larger wire size, can be used.

Current densities in Eq. 8–7 can range from 1,000 down to 250 circular mils/ampere or even less. An often-used "industry" rule of thumb for safe current density in magnetic components is 1,000 circular mils/ampere. But the only real criteria are temperature rise and temperature limitations of the materials used. The step-by-step procedure in the design of the coil is thus as follows:

1. Select a core with the required $A_e A_c$ product from Eq. 8–7. Inputs to the equation are P_o, f, a desired safe value of B_{max}, and an initial estimate of 500 circular mils/ampere for D_{cma}.
2. Calculate the number of primary turns from Eq. 8–3A and the number of secondary turns for each winding from Eq. 8–9.
3. Select a wire size in circular mils from $(cm)_n = I_{pn} D_{cma}$, where $(cm)_n$ is the number of circular mils in the nth winding, I_{pn} is the peak current in the nth winding in amperes, and D_{cma} is circular mils per ampere equaling 500.

Now from wire tables such as in Fig. 8–10, selecte the wire size for the calculated number of circular mils.

4. Calculate resistance of each winding from

$$R_n = R_{tn} N_n$$
$$= mlt \, R1 \, N_n$$

where R_n is the resistance in ohms of the nth winding, N_n is the number of turns in the nth winding (from Eq. 8–9), R_{tn} is the resistance per turn of the nth winding, mlt is the mean length of a single turn in feet (calculated from geometry or given in core data sheets), and R1 is the resistance of the given wire size in ohms per one foot, from wire tables.
5. Calculate total copper losses:

$$P_{tc} = \Sigma I_n^2 R_n$$

where P_{tc} is the total copper losses in watts, I_n is rms current ampere in the nth winding, and R_n is the resistance of the nth winding in ohms.

MAGNET WIRE TABLE

ROUND HEAVY FILM INSULATED

AWG	Diameter Over Bare (Inches)			Nominal Circular Mil Area	Insulation Additions		Diameter Over Insulation		Pounds per M Feet	Weight		Resistance at 20°C (68°F)			Turns		AWG
	Min.	Nom.	Max.		Min.	Max.	Min.	Max.		Feet per Pound	Pounds per Cubic Inch	Ohms per M Feet	Ohms per Pound	Ohms per Cubic Inch	Per Linear Inch	Per Square Inch	
4	.2023	.2043	.2063	41740.	.0037	.0045	.2060	.2098	127.20	7.86	.244	.2485	.001954	.0004768	4.80	24.0	4
5	.1801	.1819	.1837	33090.	.0036	.0044	.1837	.1872	100.84	9.92	.243	.3134	.003108	.0007552	5.38	28.9	5
6	.1604	.1620	.1636	26240.	.0035	.0043	.1639	.1671	80.00	12.50	.242	.3952	.004940	.001195	6.03	36.4	6
7	.1429	.1443	.1457	20820.	.0034	.0041	.1463	.1491	63.51	15.75	.241	.4981	.007843	.001890	6.75	45.6	7
8	.1272	.1285	.1298	16510.	.0033	.0040	.1305	.1332	50.39	19.85	.240	.6281	.01246	.002791	7.57	57.3	8
9	.1133	.1144	.1155	13090.	.0032	.0039	.1165	.1189	39.98	25.0	.239	.7925	.01982	.004737	8.48	71.9	9
10	.1009	.1019	.1029	10380.	.0031	.0037	.1040	.1061	31.74	31.5	.238	.9988	.03147	.007490	9.50	90.3	10
11	.0898	.0907	.0916	8230.	.0030	.0035	.0928	.0948	25.16	39.8	.237	1.26	.0501	.0119	10.6	112.	11
12	.0800	.0808	.0816	6530.	.0029	.0035	.0829	.0847	20.03	49.9	.236	1.59	.0794	.0187	11.9	142.	12
13	.0713	.0720	.0727	5180.	.0028	.0033	.0741	.0757	15.89	62.9	.235	2.00	.126	.0296	13.3	177.	13
14	.0635	.0641	.0647	4110.	.0032	.0038	.0667	.0682	12.60	82.9	.230	2.52	.200	.0460	14.8	219.	14
15	.0565	.0571	.0577	3260.	.0030	.0035	.0595	.0609	10.04	99.6	.229	3.18	.317	.0726	16.6	276.	15
16	.0503	.0508	.0513	2580.	.0029	.0034	.0532	.0545	7.95	126	.228	4.02	.506	.115	18.5	342.	16
17	.0448	.0453	.0458	2050.	.0028	.0033	.0476	.0488	6.33	158	.226	5.05	.798	.180	20.7	428.	17
18	.0399	.0403	.0407	1620.	.0026	.0032	.0425	.0437	5.03	199	.224	6.39	1.27	.284	23.1	534.	18
19	.0355	.0359	.0363	1290.	.0025	.0030	.0380	.0391	3.99	251	.223	8.05	2.02	.450	25.9	671.	19
20	.0317	.0320	.0323	1020.	.0023	.0028	.0340	.0351	3.18	314	.221	10.1	3.18	.703	28.9	835.	20
21	.0282	.0285	.0288	812.	.0022	.0027	.0302	.0314	2.53	395	.219	12.8	5.06	1.11	32.3	1043.	21
22	.0250	.0253	.0256	640.	.0021	.0026	.0271	.0281	2.00	500	.217	16.2	8.10	1.76	36.1	1303.	22
23	.0224	.0226	.0228	511.	.0020	.0026	.0244	.0253	1.60	625	.215	20.3	12.7	2.73	40.2	1616.	23
24	.0199	.0201	.0203	404.	.0019	.0025	.0218	.0227	1.26	794	.211	25.7	20.4	4.30	44.8	2007.	24
25	.0177	.0179	.0181	320.	.0018	.0023	.0195	.0203	1.00	1000	.210	32.4	32.4	6.80	50.1	2510.	25
26	.0157	.0159	.0161	253.	.0017	.0021	.0174	.0182	.794	1259	.208	41.0	51.6	10.7	56.0	3136.	26
27	.0141	.0142	.0143	202.	.0016	.0021	.0157	.0164	.634	1577	.205	51.4	81.1	16.6	62.3	3831.	27
28	.0125	.0126	.0127	159.	.0016	.0020	.0141	.0147	.502	1992	.202	65.3	130.	26.3	69.4	4816.	28
29	.0112	.0113	.0114	128.	.0015	.0019	.0127	.0133	.405	2469	.200	81.2	200.	40.0	76.9	5914.	29
30	.0099	.0100	.0101	100.	.0014	.0018	.0113	.0119	.318	3145	.197	104	327.	64.4	86.2	7430.	30
31	.0088	.0089	.0090	79.2	.0013	.0018	.0101	.0108	.253	4000	.193	131.	520.	100.	96.	9200.	31
32	.0079	.0080	.0081	64.0	.0012	.0017	.0091	.0098	.205	4900.	.191	162.	790.	151.	106.	11200.	32
33	.0070	.0071	.0072	50.4	.0011	.0016	.0081	.0088	.162	6200	.189	206.	1270.	240.	118.	13900.	33
34	.0062	.0063	.0064	39.7	.0010	.0014	.0072	.0078	.127	7900	.189	261.	2060.	388.	133.	17700.	34
35	.0055	.0056	.0057	31.4	.0009	.0013	.0064	.0070	.101	9900	.187	331.	3280.	613.	149.	22200.	35
36	.0049	.0050	.0051	25.0	.0008	.0012	.0057	.0063	.0805	12400	.186	415.	5150.	959.	167.	27900.	36
37	.0044	.0045	.0046	20.2	.0008	.0011	.0052	.0057	.0655	15300	.184	512.	7800.	1438.	183.	33500.	37
38	.0039	.0040	.0041	16.0	.0007	.0010	.0046	.0051	.0518	19300	.183	648.	12500.	2289.	206.	42400.	38
39	.0034	.0035	.0036	12.2	.0006	.0009	.0040	.0045	.0397	25200	.183	847.	21300.	3904.	235.	55200.	39
40	.0030	.0031	.0032	9.61	.0006	.0008	.0036	.0040	.0312	32100	.183	1080.	34600.	6335.	263.	69200.	40
41	.0027	.0028	.0029	7.84	.0005	.0007	.0032	.0036	.0254	39400	.183	1320.	52000.	9510.	294.	86400.	41
42	.0024	.0025	.0026	6.25	.0004	.0006	.0028	.0032	.0203	49300	.182	1660.	81800.	14883.	328.	107600.	42

Fig. 8–10. Magnetic wire table. (*Courtesy* Belden Corp.)

8.5   Transformer Thermal Design

Total copper plus hysteresis losses and a knowledge of the various thermal resistances theoretically permit calculation of the winding temperature rise, but this calculation is very difficult to do exactly, since the heat-flow paths and the thermal resistances along these paths are not known.

If the transformer is enclosed and dissipates its hysteresis and copper losses through various surfaces, and, if there are various encapsulating materials and copper and ferrite paths with differing thermal conductivities involved, this becomes a three-dimensional heat-flow problem. The calculation of temperature rise consists of analyzing a network of many thermal resistances interconnected in a multinode mesh. A quite precise temperature calculation can be made with a computer, but, generally, a fairly good estimate of winding temperature rise can be made by making simplifying assumptions as to the heat-flow paths. This effectively reduces the calculation to a one-dimensional heat-flow path. Thermal resistances along the path can be calculated as in Sect. 4.3.3 from simplifying assumptions as to the average geometry. Such calculations can predict temperatures to within 10°C and are in most cases sufficient for initial design purposes.

Winding temperature rise depends on the way the internal heat is dissipated. If the transformer is encapsulated and cased and the case is thermally connected to a heat sink at a known temperature, the thermal resistances involved are those of heat sink to case and winding to case. If the transformer is open and not attached to a heat sink, the thermal resistances involved are primarily those of outer coil surface area to ambient (which can be read from Fig. 4–7) and the smaller and often-negligible resistance from interior of the winding to its outer surface.

Following are some typical simplified thermal resistance calculations for various-shaped transformer cores.

8.5.1 Thermal Resistance of a Typical Ferrite Cup Core Transformer

Consider the 4229 cup core of Fig. 8–2. Assume the coil is wound on the single-section bobbin of Fig. 8–2. Also, as in Fig. 8–11, assume the cup core is encapsulated in a metal case with a thickness of 0.10 in. of silicone rubber potting material (G.E. Type RTV) between the outer periphery of the cup and the inner periphery of the metal case.

Assume the round case sits snuggly in a round hole in the solid metal heat sink kept at a temperature T_{hs}. Then, to a close approximation, the heat generated in the windings will flow radially out through the windings themselves, the outer lip of the ferrite core, the 0.1 in. of potting material, the metal case, and into the heat sink.

Assume the heat-flow path is radially outward and confined to a height D of Fig. 8–11 (D corresponds to the dimension D of the bobbin in Fig. 8–2). Then total thermal resistance from the windings to the heat sink is

$$R_t = R_{cu} + R_f + R_p + R_c$$

where R_t is the total thermal resistance in °C/watt, R_{cu} is the thermal resistance radially out through the copper windings alone in °C/watt, R_f is the thermal resistance of the outer lip of the ferrite core in °C/watt, R_p is the thermal re-

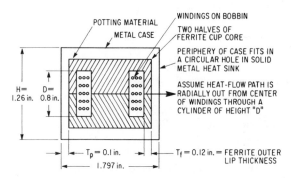

Fig. 8–11. Thermal resistance calculation for a 4229 ferrite cup core potted in a metal case with 0.1-in. wall of silicone rubber (G.E. type RTV) potting material. Metal case is snugly embedded in a circular hole in a solid metal heat sink.

sistance of the potting material in °C/watt, and R_c is the thermal resistance of the case in °C/watt. Thermal resistances will be calculated as in Sect. 4.3.2. by

$$R = \left(\frac{1}{K}\right)\left(\frac{L}{A}\right)$$

where R is the thermal resistance in °C/watt, K is thermal conductivity in watts/sq cm/cm/°C, $= 0.0173$ (thermal conductivity in Btu/hour/sq ft/ft/°F), L is the length of heat-flow path in centimeters, and A is the area through which heat flows — normally to the direction of flow in square centimeters.

Now, since the thermal conductivity of the copper windings is 4.0 W/°C/sq cm/cm as compared to 0.0020 for the potting material and 0.063 for ferrite (Fig. 4–5), it will be assumed $R_{cu} \simeq 0$ and that there is negligible temperature difference between the inner and outer portions of the coil windings.

Then, for the ferrite lip, the heat-flow path length is the thickness of the lip, which from Fig. 8–2 is

$$\frac{A - B}{2} = \frac{1.697 - 1.457}{2} = 0.12 \text{ in.} = 0.30 \text{ cm}$$

The area through which the heat flows is the area of the lip normal to the radius. From Fig. 8–2, this is

$$A = \pi\left(\frac{A + B}{2}\right)K$$

$$= \pi\left(\frac{1.697 + 1.45}{2}\right)(0.816) = 4.0 \text{ sq in.} = 26 \text{ sq cm}$$

Then thermal resistance of the ferrite lip is

$$R_f = \left(\frac{1}{K_f}\right)\left(\frac{L}{A}\right) \qquad [K_f = 0.063 \text{ W/sq cm/cm/°C (from Fig. 4–5)}]$$

$$= \left(\frac{1}{0.063}\right)\left(\frac{0.30}{26}\right) = 0.18°\text{C/watt}$$

The thermal resistance of 0.1 in. thickness of silicone rubber potting compound is

$$R_p = \left(\frac{1}{K_p}\right)\left(\frac{L}{A}\right) \quad [K_p = 0.0026 \text{ W/sq cm/cm/°C (from Fig. 4–5)}]$$

$$L = 0.1 \text{ in.} = 0.25 \text{ cm}$$

$$A = \pi DH$$
$$= \pi(1.79)(0.8) \quad \text{[from Fig. 8–8]}$$
$$= 4.5 \text{ sq in.} = 29.1 \text{ sq cm}$$

Then

$$R_p = \left(\frac{1}{0.0026}\right)\left(\frac{0.25}{29.1}\right)$$
$$= 3.3 \text{ °C/watt}$$

Assume in the aluminum case that the heat flow is normal to the cup radius through the same area (πDH) as through the potting material. Then, for a 20-mil-thick aluminum case of thermal conductivity of 2.25 W/°C/sq cm/cm

$$R_c = \left(\frac{1}{K_c}\right)\left(\frac{L}{A}\right) = \left(\frac{1}{2.25}\right)\frac{(0.02)(2.54)}{29.1}$$
$$= 0.0008°\text{C/watt} \simeq 0$$

Thus, total thermal resistance between coils and outside of case is

$$R_t \cong R_f + R_p = 0.18 + 3.3$$
$$= 3.5°\text{C/watt}$$

Thus, if the case is kept in good thermal contact with the heat sink, for every watt of copper losses, the coil will rise only 3.5°C above the heat sink temperature.

If the case is isolated on a PC board and loses its heat only by radiation and convection to the ambient air, the thermal resistance from case to ambient must be considered. This thermal resistance is mainly a function of the outside case area alone. Its thermal resistance can be read from the θ_{vs} area curves for finned heat sinks given in Fig. 4–7. This case area in Fig. 8–8 is

$$\frac{\pi(1.792)^2}{4} + \pi(1.797)(1.26)$$

$$= 2.54 + 7.11 = 9.7 \text{ sq in.}$$

And from Fig. 4–7, it is seen that for 9.7 sq in. of surface area, the thermal resistance is 16°C/watt at a 1-W power level. Assuming an internal dissipation of 10 W, Fig. 4–8 shows at that power level, thermal resistance is 70% of its 1-W value or $\theta = (0.70)(16) = 11.2°\text{C/watt}$ at the 10-W level. Thus, total thermal resistance of the transformer of Fig. 8–11 from coil to ambient air is

$$R \text{ (coil to ambient air)} = R \text{ (coil to case)} + R \text{ (case to ambient air)}$$
$$= 3.5 + 11.2 = 14.7°\text{C/watt}$$

This compares to 3.5°C/watt if the case has a low thermal impedance to a heat sink.

8.5.2 Winding Temperature Rise in a
Typical Cup Core Transformer

Consider the transformer of Fig. 8–11. Assume it has been used at 20 kHz at a B_{max} of 1,500 G at a peak current density in all its windings of 500 circular mils/ampere.

Then, from Fig. 8–8, at these parameters it has a power-handling capacity of 298 W. Assume it is used in a square-wave converter such as in Fig. 2–1 with a 30-V supply voltage and a center-tap secondary generating an output of 5 V. Copper losses and winding temperature rise are calculated in the following sections.

Primary Copper Losses

For 300 W of input power at 30 V dc, peak current in each half primary is $300/30 = 10$ A. Since the transformer is to be designed for 500 circular mils/peak ampere, the total number of circular mils in each half primary is $(500)(10) = 5,000$ circular mils. From the wire table of Fig. 8–10, this calls for a No. 13 wire (5,180 circular mils). The winding can be either one strand of No. 13 or two parallel strands of No. 16 (2,580 circular mils area). The two parallel strands having about the same area may be easier to wind, since the thinner wire is more flexible. The number of turns per half primary is calculated from Eq. 8–3 as

$$N_p = \frac{E_{dc}(10^{+8})}{4fB_{max}A_e}$$

A_e, the core area in square centimeters is obtained from Fig. 8–2 as 2.66 sq cm. For $B_{max} = 1,500$ G at 20 kHz

$$N_p = \frac{30 \times 10^{+8}}{4(2 \times 10^{+4})(1.5 \times 10^{+3})(2.66)} = 9.39 \cong 10 \text{ turns}$$

Thus, the primary consists of a 20-turn center-tap winding of No. 13 wire. From Fig. 8–2, the mean length of turn on the bobbin is 3.39 in. or 0.28 ft. From the wire table in Fig. 8–10, No. 13 wire has a resistance of 2 ohms/1,000 ft. Resistance of the 10-turn half primary is thus $(10)(2/1,000)(0.28) = 0.0056$ ohms. Since the primary current flows as a 10-A square-current pulse switched alternately on half cycles to one or the other half primary, the total primary dissipation is

$$PD_p = I_p^2 R_p = (10^2)(0.0056) = 0.56 \text{ W}$$

Secondary Dissipation

For 300 W of output power at a 5-V level, secondary current is $300/5 = 60$ A. At 500 circular mils/ampere, the secondary winding has an area of $(500)(60) = 30,000$ circular mils. From the wire table in Fig. 8–10, wire size must be between No. 5 (33,090 circular mils) and No. 6 (26,240 circular mils). If No. 6 wire is chosen, the wire may be single strand No. 6 or a number of paralleled wires of the same total circular mil area to permit easier wiring.

Assume 1 V drop in the diode rectifiers. Then secondary voltage must be 6 V for a rectified 5-V output. Number of secondary turns is

$$N_s \cong N_p(V_s/V_p) = 10(6/30) = 2 \text{ turns}$$

From the wire table, No. 6 wire has a resistance of 0.40 ohms per 1,000 ft. For a mean length of turn of 0.28 ft (Fig. 8–2), the resistance of each half secondary is

$$R_{total} = N_sR_s(\text{per turn}) = 2(0.28/1,000)(0.40)$$
$$= 0.00022 \text{ ohms}$$

Secondary power dissipation is

$$PD_s = I_s^2R_{total} = (60)^2(0.00022) = 0.79 \text{ W}$$

Total copper losses are then

$$PD_{total} = PD_p + PD_s = 0.56 + 0.79 = 1.35 \text{ W}$$

From Fig. 8–9, core hysteresis losses at 1,500 G and 20 kHz for the 4,229-cup core are 0.49 W. These losses, as predicted, are small compared to the copper losses and will be neglected.

Now, from Sect. 8.5, the coil thermal resistance to heat sink is 3.5°C/ watt. Thus, with 1.35 W of internal dissipation, the coil will rise (1.35)(3.5) = 4.7°C above the heat sink.

If the transformer is not thermally tied to a heat sink, its thermal resistance to ambient air for its 9.7 sq in. of outer surface area is 14°C/watt at the 1.35-W power level (Figs. 4–7 and 4–8). Thus, its temperature rise is (as calculated in Sect. 8.5.1), $\Delta T = (3.5 + 14)(1.35) = 23.6$°C.

With temperature rise so low, the choice of 500 circular mils/peak ampere is seen to have been quite conservative. At 250 circular mils/peak ampere in the primary and secondary, primary and secondary resistance and total copper losses would have doubled. This would increase the winding temperature rise to only 9.4°C for the heat sunk transformer to 48°C for the nonheat sink unit – easily safe enough values in most cases.

8.5.3 Winding Fit within Available Winding Space

In the derivation of Eq. 8–7, it was assumed the primary plus secondary windings used only 80% of the total available area. Since a bobbin was used in the above design, it must be checked that the windings as calculated in Sect. 8.5.2 still fit within the available winding space. Thus, total primary winding space is the number of turns times area per turn. (Assume area per turn is D^2 rather than $\pi D^2/4$.) Then for 20 turns of No. 13 wire (diameter 0.074 in.), the area occupied by the primary is

$$A_p = 20(0.074)^2 = 0.11 \text{ sq in.}$$

Total secondary winding space for four turns of No. 6 wire of diameter 0.16 in. = $4(0.16)^2$ = 0.10 sq in. Thus, required winding space for primary plus secondary is 0.11 + 0.10 = 0.21 sq in. And, from Fig. 8–2, the available winding space for the single-section bobbin is 0.217 sq. in. Thus, the coil will just about make it. The fact that the area occupied by one turn is actually $\pi D^2/4$ rather than D^2 may make the coil fit. The fit is so close, because in the initial selection of a core, Eq. 8–7 considers that the full core winding area is available for winding the coil. Actually, the area available for winding the coil is that offered by the bobbin. This may be only 70 to 80% of the winding area of the core itself.

If the fit is actually too close, smaller-sized wire can easily be used as in Sect. 8.5.2, in which it was seen that a current density of 500 circular mils/

ampere was conservative. Even at 250 circular mils/ampere, it was shown in Sect. 8.5.2 that the coil temperature rise is only 9.4°C for the heat sink transformer and 48°C for the nonheat sunk transformer.

8.5.4 Coil Temperature Rise in Unpotted Transformers without Heat Sinks

In the previous section it was seen that the largest temperature rise was due to the high thermal resistance of the potting material in enclosed transformers. For nonheat sunk transformers, the case-to-ambient temperature rise was greatest.

In most instances, U–U or toroidal core transformers will not be heat sunk and, hence, the coil-to-ambient air temperature rise is most serious. For open transformers, a good estimate of temperature rise (accurate to within 5–10°C) can be obtained from the average surface area of the outer surface of the windings. Thermal resistance can be obtained from this area from the curves of Fig. 4–7 and 4–8. With its thermal resistance and the copper losses calculated from the wire size and current as in Sect. 8.5.1, the coil temperature rise can be calculated.

As an example, the thermal resistance (coil to ambient air) will be calculated for a transformer using the toroidal core 1F10 of Fig. 8–1. Assume winding occupies most of the inside hole in the toroid and extends say 0.125 in. radially beyond the 2.9-in. outer diameter of the core. Also the height of the winding extends 0.125 in. above and below the 0.5-in. height of the toroid. Then the total radiating surface area of the winding is approximately

$$A_t = 2\left(\frac{\Pi D^2}{4}\right) + \Pi D H$$
$$= 2\left(\frac{\Pi(2.9 + 0.25)^2}{4}\right) + \Pi(2.9 + 0.25)(0.5 + 0.25)$$
$$= 15.6 + 7.4 = 23 \text{ sq in.}$$

And, from Fig. 4–7, the thermal resistance to ambient air at a 1-W power level is 8.4°C/watt. From Fig. 4–8, at a 5-W power level (the approximate internal dissipation in this size transformer), its thermal resistance is $(0.78)(8.4) = 6.5$°C/watt. From this and the core plus copper losses, coil temperature rise can be calculated.

8.5.5 Coil Temperature Rise Measurements

Coil temperature rise can be calculated as in the previous sections to an accuracy of 5–10°C, but these calculations should be verified by actual measurements on the transformer in its final packaged configuration in the actual power supply. Coil temperature rise is best measured by using the copper winding itself as a resistance thermometer. Since its thermal coefficient of resistance is 0.39%/°C, measurement of any winding resistance before the application of input power and after its application when temperature equilibrium is reached gives the coil temperature rise in the actual operating environment as follows.

Resistance of any winding (preferably the innermost one on the core) is measured as R_o at a reference temperature t_o. This temperature t_o is the ambient air temperature if the transformer is not heat sunk and the heat sink temperature if it is heat sunk. Now, power is applied to the power supply in its final packaged configuration at maximum input voltage with maximum loads at all outputs. After a 30-min wait for temperature equilibrium to be established, power is removed and the winding resistance quickly measured as, say, R_{t1}. If the second measurement is done within 30–60 sec, thermal inertia of any but the smallest transformer will keep temperature constant. Then

$$R_{t1} = R_o[1 + 0.0039(t_1 - t_o)]$$

or (maximum coil temperature under worst-case operating conditions) is

$$t_1 = t_o + \frac{R_{t1} - R_o}{R_o(0.0039)}$$

or $$t_1 = t_o + 256 \left(\frac{R_{t1} - R_o}{R_o}\right) \tag{8-10}$$

If it is not practical to run the entire supply in its final operating and packaged configuration, the transformer's thermal resistances can be measured with dc in the primary alone.

Thus, both ends of the primary are shorted and a dc current is run from the primary center lap through to the shorted primary ends. This current is adjusted to give about the same power dissipation as the worst-case total transformer losses in actual operation. The transformer is isolated on a low-thermal-conductivity surface so that it loses heat by convection and radiation only.

Now, the transformer is operated thus until it comes to thermal equilibrium. Case temperature and primary resistances are measured initially and after temperature equilibrium. From Eq. 8–10, the coil temperature at the given power dissipation is calculated. Then the thermal resistances are

$$R_{wc} = \text{thermal resistance (winding to case) in } °C/\text{watt}$$
$$= (t_{wh} - t_{ch})/PD$$

where t_{wh} is the temperature of the winding when hot, as calculated from Eq. 8–10, t_{ch} is the measured case temperature when hot, and PD is dc power dissipation. R_{ca} is thermal resistance from case to ambient air in $°C/\text{watt}$. Then

$$R_{ca} = (t_{ch} - t_a)/PD$$

where t_a is ambient air temperature and t_{ch} and PD are as defined above. Now with these thermal resistances, winding temperature for any power dissipation and cooling means is calculated as

$$t_w = R_{wc}PD + R_{ca}PD + t_a$$

for a transformer cooled by radiation and convection alone. PD is the sum of hysteresis and copper losses. And for a transformer embedded in a heat sink at a temperature t_{hs}

$$t_w = R_{wc}PD + R_{chs}PD + t_{hs}$$

Here, R_{chs} is the thermal resistance across the heat sink to case interface. This can usually be kept under 0.5°C/watt and may be neglected.

It should be noted that all of the above is predicated on a uniform temperature inside the transformer windings. Since transformers for frequencies of 10 kHz and above are small and have few turns with negligible layers of insulation, the coils can be considered one uniform mass of copper of high thermal conductivity. Since most of the internal heat is generated in the copper windings,

Transformer class	Maximum operating temperature (°C)
Q	85
R	105
S	130
V	155
T	170
U	>170

			Permissible rise in °C above 40°C ambient	
Class	Insulating material	Limiting insulation temperature (hottest spot) in °C	By thermometer	By resistance or imbedded detector
O	Cotton, silk, paper and similar organic materials when neither impregnated nor immersed in a liquid dielectric	90	35	45
A	(1) Cotton, silk, paper, and similar organic materials when either impregnated or immersed in a liquid dielectric; or (2) molded and laminated materials with cellulose filler, phenolic resins and other resins of similar properties; or (3) films and sheets of cellulose acetate and other cellulose derivatives of similar properties; or (4) varnishes (enamel) as applied to conductors	105	50	60
B	Mica, glass fiber, asbestos, etc., with suitable binding substances. Other materials or combinations of materials, not necessarily inorganic, may be included in this class if by experience or acceptance tests they can be shown to be capable of operation at class-B temperature limits	130	70	80
H	Silicone elastomer, mica, glass fiber, asbestos, etc., with suitable binding substances such as appropriate silicone resins. Other materials or combinations of materials may be included in this class if by experience or acceptance tests they can be shown to be capable of operation at class-H temperature limits	180	100	120
C	Entirely mica, porcelain, glass, quartz, and similar inorganic materials	No limit selected	—	—

Fig. 8–12. Characteristics of various classes of transformer-insulating materials from AIEE standard No. 1, "General Principles Upon Which Temperature Limits Are Based in the Design of Electrical Machines."

it is a safe assumption that there are negligible temperature gradients inside the copper windings.

8.5.6 Coil Temperature Limitations

In the previous sections, it was shown how coil temperatures are calculated. The actual limitations on temperature are dictated either by the specified "class" of transformer if the transformer must conform to "Military Specifications on Transformers — Mil T-27" or by the temperature at which the insulating material between layers of wire or wire film coatings degrade.

The various "classes" of transformers defined by Mil T-27 specification are shown in Table 8–1. "Maximum operating temperature" is defined therein as maximum ambient temperature plus temperature rise measured as in Sect. 8.5.5. Presumably, for a transformer embedded in a heat sink, "maximum operating temperature" is defined as maximum heat sink temperature plus temperature rise above the heat sink.

Materials used as insulators between winding layers or between primary and various secondaries are grouped in classes having different temperature limitations. These insulator classes are defined in A1EE Standard Number 1[3] and are shown in Fig. 8–12.

Temperature limitations of the various magnet wire coatings are defined in "Military Specification — Magnet Wire — Mil Spec. W-583C" classes and their capabilities are shown in Fig. 8–13.

8.6   Transistor-Type Selections and Circuit Decisions

Transistor-type selection has been taken up in detail in Sect. 2.1.9. The step-by-step design choice can be summarized as follows for a two-transistor, push–pull converter.

1. Choose a transistor with a vendor's maximum V_{ceo} (or V_{cbo}) rating in accordance with Eq. 2–2.
2. Choose a transistor with a peak collector-current capability given in Eq. 2–3 and having a current gain β equal to at least 20 at that current level.
3. Select a transistor with minimum rise, fall, and storage times at the maximum operating current.
4. Design the base drive circuit so that the worst-case base input current is $\frac{1}{10}$ of the peak current calculated from Eq. 2–3. This ensures an overdrive factor of two at least and results in fast turnon.
5. Design the base circuit to minimize transistor rise, fall, and storage times. This can be done as discussed in Sect. 2.1.9 by using a Darlington configuration for the inverter or antisaturation feedback diodes as shown in Fig. 2–9.

     Alternatively, various circuit tricks providing large reverse-base currents at turnoff can be used. Some possibilities are: capacitively coupling a negative base current spike at turnoff; momentarily turning on a very fast lower-current transistor to short the base to ground or to a

---

[3] "General Principles upon Which Temperature Limits Are Based in the Rating of Electrical Machines."

Wire with single and multiple insulation

Class 90 — For use in insulation systems rated to operate at a maximum temperature of 90°C*

    Types C, C2 — Cotton insulation

    Types S, S2 — Silk insulation

    Types F, F2 — Synthetic-fiber insulation

Class 105 — For use in insulation systems rated to operate at a maximum temperature of 105°C

    Types E, E2 — Oleoresinous-film insulation

    Types T, T2, T3, T4 — Film insulation

Class 130 — For use in insulation systems rated to operate at a maximum temperature of 130°C

    Types GV, G2V — Glass-fiber-treated-with-varnish insulation

    Types B, B2, B3, B4 — Film insulation

    Types Dg, Dg2 — Glass-and polyester-fiber-combination insulation

    Type AV — Asbestos treated-with-varnish insulation

Class 155 — For use in insulation systems rated to operate at a maximum temperature of 155°C

    Types L, L2, L3, L4 — Film insulation

Class 180 — For use in insulation systems rated to operate at a maximum temperature of 180°C

    Types H, H2, H3, H4 — Film insulation

Class 200 — For use in insulation systems rated to operate at a maximum temperature of 200°C

    Types GH, G2H — Glass-treated-with-a-high-temperature-varnish-or-resin insulation

    Types K, K2, K3, K4 — Film insulation

Class 220 — For use in insulation systems rated to operate at a maximum temperature of 220°C

    Types M, M2, M3, M4 — Film insulation

Wire with combination insulations: Combination insulations are designated by a combination of the type designators listed above. The elements designating the type are listed in the order of application of the insulation to the bare wire.

Class 130 — For use in insulation systems rated to operate at a maximum temperature of 130°C

    Types TGV, TG2V, T2GV, T2G2V, BDg, BDg2, B2Dg, B2Dg2, BGV, BG2V, B2GV, B2G2V

Class 155 — For use in insulation systems rated to operate at a maximum temperature of 155°C†

    Types LDg, LDg2, L2Dg, L2Dg2, LGV, LG2V, L2GV, L2G2V

---

* It is expected that this class will be deleted from the next revision of this specification. Users are urged to utilize more modern types of magnet wire.

† The G servings must be bonded with Class 155 (F) varnish and the Dg servings must be either fused or bonded with Class 155 (F) varnish.

Fig. 8–13. Classes of magnetic wire insulation as defined in military specification Mil W-583C.

lower-negative voltage source. Since the current and voltage requirements to provide the necessary reverse-base drive current pulse to the power inverter are low, there are many transistors available having the required high speed and low storage times.

6. Ensure the selected power transistor has adequate forward- and reverse-bias second-breakdown ratings (Sect. 2.1.9).
7. Calculate the transistor's dc and ac power dissipations as in Sect. 2.1.9. From this and the thermal resistances from junction to case (θ_{jc}) and case to ambient air or case to heat sink, calculate maximum junction temperature as in Sect. 2.1.9. Ensure that the temperature is within the derating guidelines for the type of equipment (less than 105°C for military equipment, less than 135–150°C for commercial equipment).

8.7 Recurrent Circuit Problems in Converter Designs

With the selection of the inverter transistor type, transformer core, and the design of the transformer windings for the desired output voltages, about 90% of the design decisions have already been made.

Thermal design must now be verified. The maximum inverter transistor junction temperature must be calculated as in Sect. 2.1.9 and the transformer winding temperature calculated and measured as in Sect. 8.5. The details of the inverter transistor base drive circuit must be worked out so as to yield enough forward current for fast turnon and adequate reverse drive for fast turnoff.

With all these details tended to, the converter design is practically complete. Yet, attention must be paid to some frequently occurring circuit problems, which can result in catastrophic failures. Some of these problems and failure modes are as follows.

8.7.1 Simultaneous Inverter Conduction

This problem arises from the possibility that at the moment the on-turning inverter receives its base turn-on signal, the off-turning one, although it has lost its base drive signal, still remains on because of collector storage time.

Thus, consider the conventional inverter of Fig. 8–14A. The base drive signals are square waves 180° out of phase. The transitions between high and low are exactly time coincident for the two inputs, but storage time in the turn-off transistor keeps the collector on and at $V_{ce(sat)}$ of 1 V for times of 1–5 μsec. Since turn-on time is considerably shorter than storage time, until the end of the storage interval both transistors are simultaneously on.

This can lead to catastrophic failure, for as long as the off-turning transistor is in storage, it keeps a voltage V_{cc} across its half primary. By transformer action, the opposite collector is held at a potential of $2V_{cc}$ and cannot begin moving down to saturation. But since this transistor has received a base turn-on signal at the start of storage of the opposite device, it carries a very high current (about βI_b) at a collector voltage of $2V_{cc}$.

This spike of high dissipation occurs once each full cycle for each transistor. At a duty cycle that is high enough, the average power can raise the junction temperature to the failure point. This average dissipation per transistor is $PD = 2V_{cc}\beta I_b f_o t_s$, where f_o is the square-wave frequency and t_s is the storage time.

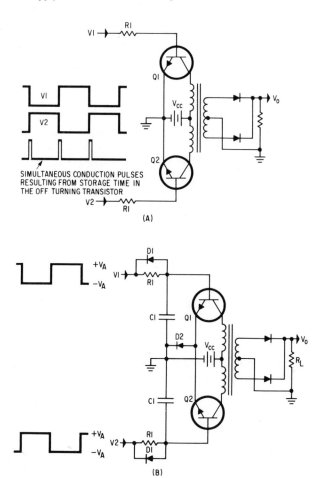

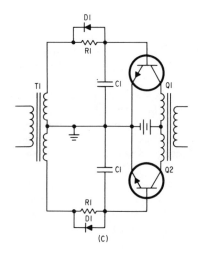

Fig. 8–14. (A) A conventional inverter with each inverter driven on for a full half cycle may have both inverters on at each transition because of storage time. (B) A capacitor-diode combination at each base to delay turnon and speed up turnoff for avoiding simultaneous inverter conduction. (C) Providing base drive via transformer T1 offers the dc level below ground required by diodes D1 for discharging the stored base charge in Q1, Q2.

Even if the average power is not sufficient to destroy the transistor, second-breakdown effects may destroy it. Thus, Fig. 2–10C shows safe-area, forward-biased, voltage-current limits for a typical high-speed transistor. This curve shows that for times under 20 μsec the operating limits are not significantly lower than the maximum dc voltage and dc current limits.

But safe-area curves such as in Fig. 2–10C are for single nonrepetitive pulses. Vendor data are not readily available for second-breakdown limitations on high-power, high-frequency pulses. Thus, to be safe, circuit means should be devised to avoid simultaneous inverter conduction. Two such schemes are as follows.

RC Turn-On Slow-Up to Avoid Simultaneous Conduction

The obvious way to avoid simultaneous conduction is either to reduce the storage time holding the turn-off transistor on too long or to delay the turnon of the turn-on device. The use of Darlington inverters or antisaturation feedback diodes (Sect. 2.1.9) or large reverse-base drives serves to reduce storage time. Even with these means of reducing storage delay, it is still necessary to delay turnon.

A simple and inexpensive means to delay turnon is shown in Fig. 8–14B. Capacitors C1 are added from each base to ground to integrate and delay the positive-going turn edge of the square-wave input signals. The input resistors R1 are paralleled by diodes in the polarity shown. For positive-going inputs, they are reverse biased and effectively out of the circuit. For negative-going signals, resistors R1 are shunted by forward-biased diodes D1, which quickly discharge C1 and draw large reverse currents from the turn-off base.

In order for diodes D1 to be effective, the lowermost dc level of the input signal must be at a potential of at least 0.8 V below ground potential. This permits forward-biasing diodes D1 when their anodes are at the halfway-on/halfway-off base potential of about 0.5 V during base turnoff.

If it is impractical for the lowermost base potential to be below ground, a diode D2 can be added as shown. This raises the common emitters by only about 0.8 V and the "on" base potential to about +1.7 V. Now a lowermost input level of zero volts is enough to forward bias diodes D1 and quickly discharge C1 and the stored base charge. The added dissipation in diode D2 is not very significant.

A simple way of providing the dc level below ground to discharge the Q1 and Q2 bases is to supply input drive from a transformer (Fig. 8–14C) whose normal output voltage levels are equally spaced around ground. Peak-to-peak drive amplitudes should be less than 8 V to provide margin against exceeding the reverse base-emitter potentials, which are normally about 5 V. This avoids adding diode D2 in Fig. 8–14B.

Pulsed Delay between Turnon and Turnoff to Avoid Simultaneous Conduction

The resistor–capacitor delay of Fig. 8–14B has no uniquely defined edges and its magnitude is temperature dependent. At higher temperatures when storage delay is greatest and turn-on delay should be longer, it is actually shorter, for the turn-on point in time is fixed by the base turn-on threshold, which decreases with temperature.

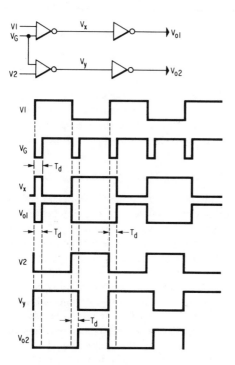

Fig. 8–15. Logic circuits to produce a set of drive pulses, V_{o1} and V_{o2}, each of whose positive-going edge is delayed a time T_d beyond the negative-going edge of the opposite pulse. This prevents simultaneous inverter conduction.

A better means of providing the needed delay is shown in Fig. 8–15. Here a delay pulse of width T_d is generated by a one-shot multivibrator at the start of each half cycle. Positive logic NAND gates are used in Fig. 8–15 to combine the negative-going delay pulse V_g with the full half-cycle square waves $V1$ and $V2$. The resulting outputs V_{o1} and V_{o2} are seen to be positive-going waveforms whose positive-leading edges are delayed by T_d from the start of each half cycle. Their negative-going edge is time coincident with the end of each half cycle.

It can thus be seen that the positive-going turn-on edge of either V_{o1} or V_{o2} is delayed by T_d from the negative-going turn-off edge of the opposite drive pulse.

8.7.2 Capacitive Load Problems

Power dissipation in the inverter is generally low because of the fast rise and fall of collector voltage and current. Any significant overlap of high voltage and current during turnon and turnoff contributes greatly to power dissipation.

The time required to charge a capacitance on amount ΔV with a constant current I is $\Delta t = C\Delta V/I$.

Thus, for large C and small, limited current I, Δt can be quite large. Normally, any capacitive loads in the square-wave inverter retain their charge once charged up, since they operate with a fixed dc voltage across them and are called on to discharge and deliver load current only in the narrow time interval between one inverter turning on and the other turning off.

But, at initial turnon, the time to bring a capacitance to its full voltage can be long. During this charging time, the capacitor can present such a low impedance to the inverter transistor that, with the limited current, the collector does not saturate over many half cycles.

Thus, over these many half cycles, collector voltage and current are simultaneously high and power dissipation is high. With a sufficiently large capacitive load, the inverters can fail either because of excessive dissipation or because of operation outside the safe-area limits curves such as in Fig. 2–1C. Such failures, if they occur, happen at power supply turnon.

In most cases, capacitive loads on inverters are low and this is not a problem, but the one instance often overlooked is in inverters used to generate high voltage (12,000–15,000 V) for CRT displays. Such voltages are generated by voltage multipliers in the secondary of a high-voltage step-up transformer. Usual practice is to step up either to 1,000 and use a $\times 12$ voltage multiplier or to 3,000 and use a voltage tripler for 12,000 V.

Thus, if the dc supply voltage for the inverter is 30 V, the high-voltage step-up ratio for 3,000 V at the secondary is 100. Then any capacitance C_s at the secondary is reflected into the primary by the square of the turns ratio. The effective capacitance at the primary is then $C_s(100)^2$ or $10,000C_s$. Often the input capacitance to a voltage multiplier is an $0.01\text{-}\mu\text{F}$ capacitor. This, then, is seen at the primary as $(01)(10,000)$ or $100\ \mu\text{F}$. Depending on the power rating of the inverter transistors, this heavy capacitive load can easily result in failure at turnon.

Thus, it is important to avoid heavy capacitive loads in inverters. Capacitors at the secondary of a high-voltage step-up transformer are particularly troublesome. In the instance cited above, an isolating resistor should be used in series between the transformer secondary and the input to the voltage multiplier.

A useful empirical test for inverters is to switch them on and off 100 or so times at maximum input voltage and maximum load at all outputs. Many of the subtle failure modes occur at turnon and are often overlooked or are not predictable in the initial paper-and-pencil design.

8.7.3 Overcurrent Protection

Overcurrent protection is a very useful feature to have in dc/dc converters. Even brief duration shorts or overcurrent impulses can destroy the inverter transistors.

A convenient way to implement the overcurrent feature is by a current transformer (as in Fig. 8–16A). This is simply a high-frequency transformer with a large current step down between secondary and primary. Secondary current is then $I_p(N_p/N_s)$. By selection of the magnitude of the secondary load resistor, the secondary voltage is then a measure of primary current being monitored. This current transformer square-wave secondary voltage is rectified and the dc voltage sensed by a threshold detector. When the threshold is exceeded, the inverter base drive may be removed permanently by setting an "overcurrent" flip-flop. Or it may be removed intermittently by setting an "overcurrent one-shot multivibrator," which will remove the inverter drive and restore it after a delay. Such a "try-again" feature is useful if the overcurrent was simply a momentary one. In the event of a prolonged short, the supply continues to turn on and off producing a characteristic "beeping" overcurrent tone.

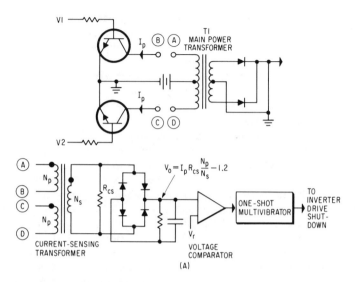

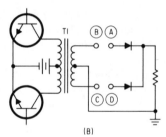

Fig. 8–16. (A) A current-sensing transformer for over-current protection. (B) The same current-sensing transformer monitoring peak secondary current in the main power transformer.

The current being sensed can be either that in the primary or any secondary of the main power transformer. Operation of the inverter is not affected. Because of the large current transformer turns ratio, the impedance reflected into the current-sensing point can be made negligibly small.

The circuit is shown in Fig. 8–16A, in which it senses current in the main power transformer primary. The two primary windings are placed in series with the two collectors in the polarity shown. The turns ratio and R_{cs} (the current calibrating resistor) are selected as follows.

Assume a peak current of 5 A in each collector is to result in maximum voltage at V_o, and assume at 5 A the drop across AB or CD—the current transformer primaries—shall be negligibly small so as not to interfere with circuit operation. Let this drop be 0.05 V, and assume when 5 A flows in either AB or CD, the voltage across the secondary is 5 V. The current transformer step-down ratio is then $N_s/N_p = 5/0.05 = 100$.

For 5 A in the primary and a current step-down ratio 0.01, the secondary current is 5/100 = 50 mA. Then for 5 V across the secondary, at 50 mA secondary current, the bridge rectifier and its load will be chosen to take a current significantly less than 50 mA. Thus, R_{cs} (the calibrating resistor) is 5/0.05 = 100 ohms.

Output voltage from the bridge will be 5 V less two bridge rectifier diode drops, or about $5 - 1.6 = 3.4$ V. The relation between V_o and power transformer primary current is linear and is given by

$$V_o = I_s R_{cs} - 2V_d \qquad (8-11)$$

Now, the current-sensing transformer core must be selected and its turns chosen. Assume it is ferrite core and in each half cycle flux density moves from $-1,000$ to $+1,000$ G. Then, from Eq. 8–1, assuming the inverter operates at 20 kHz (half period $= 25$ μsec)

$$A_e = \frac{e \Delta t \times 10^{+8}}{N_s \Delta B}$$

Now, $N_s/N_p = 100$. Let $N_p =$ one turn and $N_s = 100$ turns. Since there are to be 5 V across the secondary, the core area is

$$A_e = \frac{5(25) \times 10^{-6} \times 10^{+8}}{(100)(2,000)} = 0.063 \text{ sq cm}$$

From the Ferroxcube "Linear Ferrite" catalog, find a toroidal core whose area is at least 0.063 sq cm. The smallest toroid is the Series 266 core, which has an OD of 0.375 in., ID of 0.187 in., and thickness of 0.125 in. This toroid must support one 100-turn winding carrying 50 mA and two one-turn windings—each carrying 5 A on alternate half cycles.

Now, assume the winding area of 0.187 in. diameter is 50% filled by the windings and that half that area is occupied by the 100-turn secondary, half by the two one-turn primary. Thus, windings will occupy an area of

$$\tfrac{1}{2}(\pi D^2/4) = \tfrac{1}{8}\pi(0.187)^2 = 0.014 \text{ sq in.}$$

The area of one turn of the 100-turn primary is $(1/100)(0.014/2) = 0.00007$ sq in. The closest wire size to this area is No. 30; this wire can easily carry the 50-mA secondary current.

Area available for the two one-turn primaries is 0.007 sq in. Area per turn is 0.0035 sq in. The nearest wire size of this area is No. 15, which can easily handle 5 A on alternate half cycles.

The Series 266 core of 0.187-in. OD is thus large enough to support the required windings. Larger cores can be used with no change. For a 1/100 step-up ratio, and the same value of R_{cs}, the relationship between rectified dc and peak primary current will still be as given by Eq. 8–11. Larger area cores will simply move over a lesser excursion in flux density as can be seen from Eq. 8–1.

Current sensing may be done in the secondary of the main power transformer as shown in Fig. 8–16B. Since the transformers are small, there is no problem in sensing each secondary individually and "oring" their outputs so that overcurrent in any single output will remove inverter base drive. The turns ratio and calibrating resistors may be different for the different outputs being sensed.

8.7.4 Collector Spike Problems

Leakage reactance in the main power transformer acts like a small inductor in series with the power transistor collector leads. When current in either transistor is turned off, this leakage reactance causes an overshoot spike (Fig. 8–17) at the leading edge of the positive-going collector waveform.

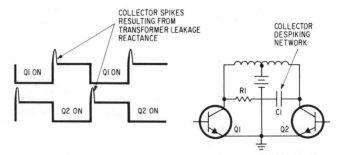

Fig. 8–17. Collector spikes resulting from transformer leakage reactance and RC despiking network.

This spike rises above the level of $2V_{cc}$ and, unless it is damped or limited otherwise, the energy stored in the leakage reactance is dissipated each half cycle in the transistor collector by causing momentary collector breakdown. At sufficiently high collector currents and operating frequency, such overshoot spikes can cause transistor failure.

The overshoot spike is usually damped down to an adequately safe amplitude by the despiking network R1–C1 bridged from collector to collector as shown in Fig. 8–17. The value of R1 is chosen empirically to limit the amplitude of the spike to less than 20% of $2V_{cc}$. The time constant of R1–C1 should be sufficiently small that C1 is completely charged in a small fraction of a half cycle. Generally, with R1 chosen to limit the spike amplitude as above, C1 is chosen so that 3R1C1 is 5% of a half period. The voltage rating for C1 should be at least $(1.1)(2V_{cc})(1.2)$ or $2.6V_{cc(nom)}$. With a derating factor added, the voltage rating of C1 should be three times the nominal value of V_{cc}.

8.7.5 High-Voltage, High-Current Overlap at Turn-On/Turn-Off Transitions

Slow transistor current fall time at turnoff results in an overlap of high voltage and current as seen in Fig. 8–18. The duration of this overlap depends on transistor switching speed and circuit tricks to speed up turn-off time (Figs. 2–9A and 2–9B).

Generally, since turn-off time is longer than turnon, the overlap is more serious at turnoff. Overlaps generally range from 0.3 to 3 μsec with present-day transistors. At switching frequencies of 20 kHz and above, these overlap switching losses can exceed the dc dissipation of $I_c V_{ce(sat)}$.

It is essential in any final design to monitor the overlap with a current and voltage probe on a fast oscilloscope time base. Excessive overlap can result in failure either because of high overlap dissipation or second-breakdown effects.

8.7.6 Power Transformer Vertical Drift along Its Hysteresis Loop

The operating locus of a driven inverter's power transformer on its hysteresis loop (Fig. 2–18) must be kept centered about the zero flux density point. If some circuit mechanism allows it to move off center, it can "walk" upward or downward into core saturation.

If it is in magnetic saturation during the part of a half cycle while transistor base drive still exists, the inverter transistors can be destroyed, since, as

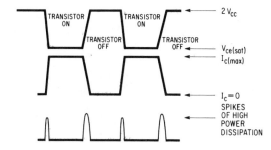

Fig. 8–18. Overlap of high voltage and current at transition times— especially turn-off times—can cause transistor failure.

the transformer moves into saturation, its impedance drops toward zero, and its magnetizing current starts rising exponentially. For a given base drive, a point is reached when the transistor's collector can no longer be kept in saturation. Collector voltage and current are simultaneously high, and the transistor can be destroyed either by the increased power dissipation or by exceeding the boundary of forward-biased safe-area curves.

The mechanism by which the transformer core "walks" up or down its hysteresis loop can be seen from Eq. 8–2. In a push–pull-driven inverter such as in Fig. 2–1, that equation states the core flux change during each half cycle is proportional to the volt second area applied to the core. During one half cycle, the core flux change is

$$+\Delta B = \frac{10^{-8}}{N_p A_e} \int_0^{T/2} e \, dt$$

In the next half cycle, since the primary is center tapped, the flux change is

$$\frac{-10^{-8}}{N_p A_e} \int_0^{T/2} e \, dt$$

Now, even if the volt second areas are minutely unequal, at the end of the second half cycle, the flux starts slightly above or below its initial starting point. After many cycles, the core has "walked" up so that at the end of one or the other half cycles, the core is in saturation, voltage can no longer be sustained across it, and transistor collector current rises steeply.

This "walking" process ceases when the volt second areas balance out automatically. The initial unbalance can arise from highly unequal base-to-emitter or collector-to-emitter saturation voltages making the voltage applied to each half winding in its conducting half cycle unequal. It can also arise from unequal storage times in the two transistors, making the time voltages applied to the half windings unequal despite equal "on" time drives at the bases. Depending on the nature of the base drive circuitry, it may, of course, also arise from unequal base time drives.

Small initial unbalances in volt second areas can be tolerated and will automatically equalize by the core "walking" toward saturation. As saturation is approached, the larger current in the transistor producing the larger volt second area results in larger $V_{ce(sat)}$ and, hence, subsequent lesser volt second area applied to that half winding. This causes the core to cease "walking" before a disastrous condition exists, or, at the end of a half cycle as core saturation occurs, the transistor comes out of saturation, applying less voltage to that half winding and automatically balancing the core.

The effect and an assessment as to whether a dangerous condition exists can be observed with an oscilloscope current probe in series with the transformer center tap. This shows both transistor currents simultaneously, and the effect can be seen by a concave upward rise in current in one or the other transistors toward the end of the conducting half cycle. Peak currents should be equal to within 25%.

The core flux density "walking" effect can be minimized by using inverter transistors matched in V_{be} and $V_{ce(sat)}$ and ensuring equal "on" time drive at the transistor bases. Use of antisaturation feedback diodes (Sect. 2.1.9, and Fig. 2–9) helps considerably in balancing the volt second areas by minimizing and equalizing storage times and equalizing the transistor "on" voltages. Adding an air gap in the transformer core flattens the hysteresis loop and prevents sudden disastrous increases in magnetizing current as core saturation is approached.

Addition of a transformer air gap, matching V_{be} and $V_{ce(sat)}$, and use of antisaturation feedback diodes are almost always sufficient to avoid disastrously large current imbalances. In some cases, designers add feedback networks to equalize the peak currents in each half cycle. Current-sensing transformers and peak detectors can be used to give dc voltages proportional to the peak currents in each half cycle. These dc voltages can be used to produce slight alterations in the width of each half-cycle drive and thus produce equal volt second areas independent of transistor storage times, V_{ce}, and V_{be}. In a bridge inverter, a capacitor in series with the transformer primary has been used[4] to avoid this effect.

8.7.7 Switching Noise Voltage on Power Supply Chassis

Power supply specifications often require that the output ground be dc isolated from the power supply chassis itself. The intent is usually to dc connect the output ground to the chassis somewhere in the system external to the power supply but only at a single point. Many systems designers feel that by connecting the output ground to the system frame or chassis ground at only one point, they can better control ground loop currents and keep noise voltages on the output ground to a minimum.

But generally the one point where the output ground and chassis are made to have a common dc connection is at the end of long wires from the power supply itself. Thus, although the dc impedance between output and chassis or frame ground is zero, because the inductance of the wiring to the common tie point is high, the ac impedance or impedance to narrow noise spikes is high.

In switching supplies, this results in some fraction of the high-amplitude square waves at the switching transistor collectors or power transformer secondaries appearing as a noise voltage between the output ground and power supply chassis. This occurs because there is always a capacitive voltage divider (resulting from wiring capacities) bridged across the internal square-wave signal

---

[4] R. J. Haver, "Switched Mode 5 Volt, 40 Ampere Power Supply," Motorola Application Note AN 737; and P. Wood, "Design of a 5 Volt 1000 Watt Power Supply," TRW Application Note.

generators. These capacities are from one end of a signal source to the chassis, from the chassis to the output ground, and from the output ground to the other end of a signal source. Thus, unless the capacitance from the output ground to the chassis is high, a large fraction of the square-wave voltage appears between the output ground and chassis of the power supply.

Even though ripple and noise voltage between an output voltage node and the output ground is very low, this noise voltage between the chassis and output ground can cause problems in systems which have high-gain amplifiers and 5-V logic circuits. This noise voltage travels down the output ground wire to the common tie point to the system frame and has a different phase at different points on the output ground bus. Thus, two points spaced apart along the output ground bus will have a noise voltage between them. If these points are at the input to a receiving amplifier and the output of a transmitting amplifier, the noise voltage on ground bus will be in series with the transmitter output voltage. With high-gain-receiving amplifiers or computer logic circuits, this can result in false outputs.

Noise between the output ground and frame generally appears as spikes or high-frequency shocked damped oscillations at the leading and trailing edge of square waves generated internally in the power supply. Their amplitude and duration depends on the inductance of the wiring from the output ground to the common tie point to the system frame. If the power supply is not connected to the system frame (feeding only isolated dummy loads), the noise voltage between the output ground and system frame may be square wave in shape.

Most often, it is essential to add high-frequency capacitors (about 0.1 μF) between all output-voltage ground nodes and the power supply chassis. This makes the capacitive voltage divider described above such that only a negligible fraction of the internal signal source appears from the output ground to the chassis. Without such capacitors, a system can be plagued with noise problems even though ripple and noise between an output voltage node and its ground or "return" node is negligible.

8.8   Typical dc/dc Converter Designs

8.8.1 Design of a 400-W dc/dc Converter with Rectified Preregulated Line Voltage Input and Five Output Voltages (Fig. 8–19)

As a typical problem, design a dc/dc converter to operate from a preregulator whose input is the rectified ac line voltage as in Fig. 3–1. From Fig. 3–8 it is seen that the rectified 115-V ac line voltage with $\pm 10\%$ tolerances will yield dc outputs after bridge rectification of 140 V minimum, 156 V nominal, and 172 V maximum.

Assume a series-switch step-down preregulator that can yield with equally good efficiency any dc voltage below the bottom of the rectifier ripple triangle. Assume an overall efficiency as in Fig. 3–8 of 70%. Then for 400 W of output, input power is $300/0.7 = 571$ W. At the minimum of 140 V dc output from the rectifier, this is a current of $571/140 = 4.08 \cong 4$ A. Now to keep filter capacity size down, assume only 1,000 μF of line rectifier filter capacity. Then for 60 Hz line frequency, the filter capacity must supply load current for about one half cycle or for $1/2(60) = 8.3 -$ say, 8 msec.

Then for 4 A of load current and 1,000 μF of filter capacity, peak-to-peak ripple is

$$\Delta V = \frac{It}{c} = \frac{4(8 \times 10^{-3})}{1,000 \times 10^{-6}} = 32 \text{ V}$$

For a minimum dc line voltage of 140 V, the bottom of the ripple triangle is at a voltage level of $140 - 32/2 = 124$ V. Thus, the preregulator must regulate to a voltage no higher than this. Assume, then, the preregulator generates a dc voltage of 120 V, constant to $\pm 0.5\%$ over all line and load changes. With this dc input, assume it is required to build a dc/dc converter with the outputs after secondary rectification shown in Table 8–2.

Table 8–2. Required Output Voltages and Current in a Typical Design

Volts	Amperes	Watts
5	30	150
+30	2	60
−30	2	60
+15	3	45
−15	3	45
	40	360

Now for conventional silicon rectifier diodes with about 1 V forward drop, the total rectifier dissipation alone at 40 A of load current is 40 W. Thus, the power to be handled at the transformer input (not including transformer loss) is 360 W of load power plus 40 W of diode rectifier losses for a total of 400 W. At 120 V of input, this is a peak square-wave primary current of 3.3 A.

8.8.2 Design of Power Transformer

Core Selection and Winding Current Density

Choose an operating frequency of 20 kHz and a maximum flux density of 1,500 G. From Fig. 8–8, it is seen the 4229 cup core at a current density of 500 peak circular mils/ampere has a power-handling capability of only 298 W. At 2,000 G peak, it can handle 398 W. But to avoid the possible excursion into core saturation if there is current unbalance in the two halves of the primary, it is safer to stay at 1,500 G peak.

Now, it was seen in Sect. 8.5.2 that safe thermal designs are easily possible with current densities considerably greater than 500 circular mils/ampere. Since from Eq. 8–7 power-handling capability is inversely proportional to current density in circular mils per ampere, then at, say, 350 circular mils/ampere, the 4229 cup core can handle 298 (500/350) = 426 W. Thus, choose the 4229 cup core and design the windings for a current density of 350 circular mils/ampere.

Number of Turns per Winding

From Eq. 8–3, the number of turns either side of center tap on the primary is

$$N_p = \frac{(E_{\text{dc}})10^{+8}}{4fA_eB_{\text{max}}} = \frac{120 \times 10^{+8}}{4(2 \times 10^{+4})(2.66)(1,500)} = 37.5 \quad \text{or 38 turns}$$

Now, from Eq. 8–9, the number of turns either side of center tap for the 5-V winding is

$$N_s = \frac{N_p(V_o + V_d)}{E_{dc} - V_{ce(sat)}} = \frac{(38)(5.0 + 0.8)}{120 - 0.8} = 1.84 \qquad \text{or, say, two turns}$$

With a two-turn winding, the 5-V output after the rectifier is exactly from Eq. 8–9:

$$V_o = (120 - 0.8)(2/38) - 0.8 = 5.47 \text{ V}$$

This is somewhat high for computer logic circuits (T^2L logic circuits are specified for a supply voltage of 5.00 ± 0.25 V). By reducing the $+120$ V, the $+5$ can be made exactly 5.0. But a value closer to 5.0 can be achieved by choosing the primary turns to be 40 and keeping the 5-V winding at two turns. At 40 turns on the primary, the flux density is somewhat lower from Eq. 8–3. Then for a two-turn secondary and 40-turn primary, the 5-V output after rectification is

$$V_o = (120 - 0.8)(2/40) - 0.8 = 5.16 \text{ V}$$

which is close enough. Then the number of turns for the 15-V output is, from Eq. 8–9,

$$N_{15} = \frac{40(15 + 0.8)}{120 - 0.8} = 5.3 \qquad \text{or, say, five turns}$$

The 30-V winding will have

$$N_{30} = \frac{N_p(30 + 0.8)}{120 - 0.8} = \frac{40(30.8)}{119.2} = 10.33 \qquad \text{or 10 turns}$$

Actually, because only an integral number of turns on the transformer is possible, the 15-V output with 5.0 rather than 5.3 turns will be at

$$\begin{aligned} V_{15} &= (E_{dc} - V_{ce})_{sat} (N_s/N_p) - V_p \\ &= (120 - 0.8)(5/40) - 0.8 = 14.1 \text{ V} \end{aligned}$$

The 30-V output will be at

$$V_{30} = (120 - 0.8)(10/40) - 0.8 = 29.0 \text{ V}$$

These low voltages are typical of a problem in dc/dc converters with multiple secondaries. Any one output can be made close to what is required by adjusting the input voltage and turns ratio, but this fixes the other outputs. They can be changed in magnitude by the voltage corresponding to a single turn only. Thus, in Eq. 8–1

$$\frac{e}{N} = \frac{(A_e B)10^{-8}}{t} = \frac{A_e(2B_{max})10^{-8}}{T/2} = 4fB_{max}A_e \times 10^{-8} \qquad (8\text{–}12)$$

And for the 4229 core at $B_{max} = 1{,}500$ G, $A_e = 2.66$ sq cm

$$e/N = 4(2 \times 10^{+4})(2.66)(1{,}500)10^{-8} = 3.1$$

This is exact if B_{max} is exactly 1,500 G. Actually, B_{max} is fixed by the primary turns and primary voltage and thus the exact value of e/N is

$$\frac{E_{dc} - V_{ce(sat)}}{N_p} = \frac{120 - 0.8}{40} = 2.98 \text{ V/turn}$$

Hence, changing any secondary by one turn will change its output by 2.98 V. Thus, adding one turn to the "15-V" winding will bring the output up from +14.1 to +17.1; adding one turn to the "30-V" winding will bring that output up to +32 V.

In most cases, an exact numerical rectified output is not essential — it is only important that the ripple and regulation about the actual output is low. When a specific output is required, there is little choice but to follow the rectified output with a series-pass or switching regulator as in Figs. 3–10 and 3–11. Efficiency is still high even with a series-pass postregulator, since the dc/dc converter output is constant to ±0.50% because its preregulated input is constant to 0.5%.

If the addition of a postregulator is not practical, rectified secondary voltages closer to desired values are still possible as can be seen from Eq. 8–12. That relation shows that volts per turn is proportional to B_{max}/T, where B_{max} is the maximum flux density and T is the switching period. By operating at a lower

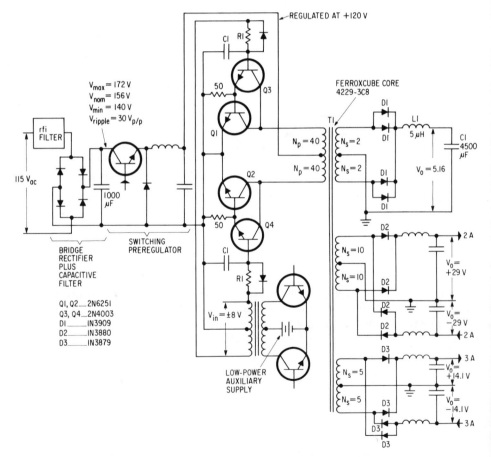

Fig. 8–19. A 400-W, five-output-voltage dc/dc converter operating at 20 kHz from a preregulated 120 V dc.

B_{max} or lower frequency, volts per turn may be lowered to the point when a one-turn change can yield the desired output voltage. But, of course, as can be seen from Fig. 8–7, lower B_{max} and operating frequency lowers the power-handling capability of the transformer core, and a larger core would be required.

But for the present purpose, it will be assumed that the low 15- and 30-V outputs are acceptable. The transformer and means of deriving the various outputs are shown in Fig. 8–19.

Winding Wire Size and Copper Losses

It was tentatively decided earlier to operate each winding at a current density of 350 circular mils/ampere. Characteristics of each winding at that current density are shown in Table 8–3.

Table 8–3 is self-explanatory. For a tentatively assumed current density of 350 circular mils/ampere, and specified currents, the wire size is calculated. From the mean length of turn for the bobbin (Fig. 8–2) and the

Table 8–3. Transformer Winding Characteristics for a 400-W, Five-Output Voltage Transformer

	Winding					
	Primary	*+5 V*	*+30 V*	*−30 V*	*+15 V*	*−15 V*
Number of turns, each side of center tap	40	2	10	10	5	5
Wire length in feet, for mean length per turn of 0.28 ft	11.2	0.56	2.8	2.8	1.4	1.4
Peak amperes	3.3	30	2	2	3	3
Total circular mils at 350 circular mils/ampere	1155	10,500	700	700	1050	1050
Nearest wire size for required circular mils	20	10	22	22	20	20
Ohms/foot for wire size	0.010	0.001	0.016	0.016	0.010	0.010
Resistance each side of center tap	0.11	0.00056	0.0448	0.0448	0.014	0.014
Power dissipation (watts)	1.20	0.50	0.18	0.18	0.13	0.13
Wire diameter in inches ($= D$)	0.035	0.106	0.028	0.028	0.035	0.035
Wire area per turn in square inches ($= D^2$)	0.00123	0.0112	0.000784	0.000784	0.00123	0.00123
Total wire area (square inches)	0.098	0.045	0.0157	–	0.0123	–
Total primary wire losses	1.20	watts				
Total secondary wire losses	1.12	watts				
Total copper losses	2.32	watts				
Total area occupied by windings	0.171	sq in.				
Available bobbin winding area (from Fig. 8–2)	0.195	sq in.				

number of turns, the wire and resistance per foot (Fig. 8–10) for the calculated wire size and the coil resistance each side of center tap may be calculated. The coil resistance and specified currents yield copper losses in each winding. This gives total primary plus secondary copper losses of only 2.32 W.

From the wire size, number of turns and area per turn of wire (assumed D^2 rather than $\pi D^2/4$), the area occupied by each winding and the total winding area may be calculated. Table 8–3 shows the total required winding area is 0.171 sq in., and the two-section bobbin of Fig. 8–2 shows 0.195 sq in. is available. There is thus no problem of fitting the windings in the available space.

Coil Temperature Rise

Section 8.5.1 showed that the 4229 cup core had a thermal resistance from coils to outside of case of 3.5°C/watt. Its thermal resistance from case to ambient air at a 1-W power level for its 9.7 sq in. surface area is 16°C/watt from Fig. 4–7, and from Fig. 4–8 at a 2-W power level this drops to 0.9(16) = 14.4°C/watt.

Then, if the transformer is heat sunk around its outer periphery, with 2.32 W of copper losses, its temperature rise above the heat sink is 2.32(3.5) = 8.1°C. And for a nonheat sunk transformer, the coil will rise above ambient by 14.4(2.32) = 33.4°C.

With proper choice of insulating materials (Fig. 8–12) magnetic wire coatings (Fig. 8–13), and with a maximum bobbin temperature of 130°C, the above temperature increases present no problem even at a maximum ambient or heat sink temperature of 70°C.

For a maximum ambient of 70°C and a rise of 33°C for a nonheat sunk temperature, maximum coil temperature is 103°C. If this were a Mil T-27 transformer specified as Class R (Table 8–1), this would be too close to the specified limit of 105°C. Either the transformer would have to be heat sunk or larger wire sizes used. The single-section bobbin with insulation between primary and secondaries would permit larger wire size.

Hysteresis losses have thus far been ignored. Figure 8–6 shows that at 20 kHz and 1,500 G, these contribute 0.49 W. At 14.4°C/watt for a nonheat sunk transformer, hysteresis loss increases temperature by only 14.4(0.49) = 7.1°C.

8.8.3 Power Transistor Selection

There are a number of choices possible for the main power transistor, and newer improved types become available from various vendors every year. Thus, a list of types in current frequent use is likely to be obsolete in a period of 1–2 years. Yet, a history of types in frequent use over the past 5 years is of value and is given in Fig. 8–20. The types shown are only high-energy types— those having high-voltage and high-current capabilities. Types with low collector-voltage ratings (150 V or less) are far more numerous and will not be listed here.

The types shown in Fig. 8–20 are those used in inverters operating either directly off the rectified ac line (115 or 208) or from preregulators off the rectified ac line and generating dc voltages in the range of 75–150 V.

With a regulated 120-V output from the preregulator, the inverters are subjected to 2(120) = 240 V plus a possible 20% turn-off spike. The maximum

Type No.	$I_{c(max)}$ (amps)	Type	V_{ceo} at I_c (volts/amps)	V_{cbo} (volts)	V_{cer} (volts)	Minimum f_s (mHz)	Maximum Switching Time in Microseconds at I_c (amps)/I_b (amps)			θ_{jc} (°C/watt)	Minimum h_{fe} at I_c (h_{fe}/amps)	Case
							t_r at $\{I_c/I_b\}$	t_f at $\{I_c/I_b\}$	t_s at $\{I_c/I_b\}$			
2N3439	1	npn	350/0.05	450		15.0				17.5	40/0.02	TO5
2N5416	1	pnp	300/0.05	350	350	15.0				17.5	30/0.05	TO5
2N5663	2	npn	300/0.01	400	400	20.0	$0.25\{0.5/0.025\}$	$1.2\{0.5/0.025\}$		6.7	15/1.0	TO5
2N6212	2	pnp	300/0.2	350	325	20.0	$0.6\{1.0/0.125\}$	$0.6\{1.0/0.125\}$	$2.5\{1.0/0.125\}$	5.0	10/1.0	TO66
2N6213	2	pnp	350/0.2	400	375	20.0	$0.6\{1.0/0.125\}$	$0.6\{1.0/0.125\}$	$2.5\{1.0/0.125\}$	5.0	10/1.0	TO66
2N6214	2	pnp	400/0.2	450	425	20.0	$0.6\{1.0/0.125\}$	$0.6\{1.0/0.125\}$	$2.5\{1.0/0.125\}$	5.0	10/1.0	TO66
2N5661	2	npn	300/0.01	400	400	20.0	$0.25\{0.5/0.025\}$	$1.2\{0.5/0.025\}$		5.0	15/1.0	TO66
2N3585	2	npn	300/0.2	500		10.0	$3.0\{1.0/0.1\}$	$3\{1.0/0.1\}$	$4\{1.0/0.1\}$	5.0	8/1.0	TO66
2N5667	3	npn	300/0.01		400	20	$0.25\{1.0/0.05\}$	$2.0\{1.0/0.05\}$		6.67	25/1.0	TO5
2N5840	3	npn	350/0.2	375	375	5.0	$1.75\{2/0.2\}$	$1.5\{2/0.2\}$	$3.0\{2/0.2\}$	1.75	10/2.0	TO3
2N5665	3	npn	300/0.01		400	20.0	$0.25\{1.0/0.05\}$	$2.0\{1.0/0.05\}$		3.3	15/3.0	TO66
2N3902	3.5	npn	325/0.1	700		2.5	$0.8\{1.0/0.1\}$	$1.7\{1.0/0.05\}$		0.75	10/2.5	TO3
2N6235	5	npn	325/0.02	350	350	20.0	$0.5\{1.0/0.1\}$	$0.5\{1.0/0.1\}$	$3.5\{1.0/0.1\}$	3.5	10/3.0	TO66
2N6542	5	npn	300/0.1	650	650	6.0	$0.7\{3/0.6\}$	$0.8\{3.0/0.6\}$	$4.0\{3.0/0.6\}$	1.75	7/3.0	TO3

Fig. 8–20. High-energy power transistors in frequent use in off-the-ac-line switching regulators and dc/dc power converters.

Type No.	$I_{c(max)}$ (amps)	Type	V_{ceo} at I_c (volts/amps)	V_{cbo} (volts)	V_{cer} (volts)	Minimum f_t (mHz)	Maximum Switching Time in Microseconds at I_c (amps)/I_b (amps)			θ_{jc} (°C/watt)	Minimum h_{fe} at I_c (h_{fe}/amps)	Case
							t_r at $\{I_c/I_b\}$	t_f at $\{I_c/I_b\}$	t_s at $\{I_c/I_b\}$			
2N6543	5	npn	400/0.1	850	850	6.0	$0.8\left\{\frac{3.0}{0.6}\right\}$	$0.8\left\{\frac{3.0}{0.6}\right\}$	$4.0\left\{\frac{3.0}{0.6}\right\}$	1.75	7/3.0	TO3
2N5805	5	npn	300/0.2	375		15.0	$0.5\left\{\frac{5.0}{0.5}\right\}$	$2\left\{\frac{5.0}{0.5}\right\}$	$3.5\left\{\frac{5.0}{0.5}\right\}$	1.60	10/5.0	TO3
2N6544	8	npn	300/0.1	650	650	6.0	$0.75\left\{\frac{5.0}{1.0}\right\}$	$1\left\{\frac{5.0}{1.0}\right\}$	$4.0\left\{\frac{5.0}{1.0}\right\}$	1.4	7/5.0	TO3
2N6545	8	npn	400/0.1	850	850	6.0	$0.75\left\{\frac{5.0}{1.0}\right\}$	$1\left\{\frac{5.0}{1.0}\right\}$	$4.0\left\{\frac{5.0}{1.0}\right\}$	1.4	7/5.0	TO3
2N6307	8	npn	300/0.1	600		5.0	$0.6\left\{\frac{3.0}{0.6}\right\}$	$0.4\left\{\frac{3.0}{1.5}\right\}$	$1.6\left\{\frac{3.0}{1.5}\right\}$	1.4	4/8.0	TO3
2N6308	8	npn	350/0.1	700		5.0	$0.6\left\{\frac{3.0}{0.6}\right\}$	$0.4\left\{\frac{3.0}{1.5}\right\}$	$1.6\left\{\frac{3.0}{1.5}\right\}$	1.4	3/8.0	TO3
2N6546	10	npn	300/	650	650	6.0	$0.75\left\{\frac{10.0}{2.0}\right\}$	$0.8\left\{\frac{10.0}{2.0}\right\}$	$4.0\left\{\frac{10.0}{2.0}\right\}$	1.0	6/10	TO3
2N6547	10	npn	400/	850	850	6.0	$0.75\left\{\frac{10.0}{2.0}\right\}$	$0.8\left\{\frac{10.0}{2.0}\right\}$	$4.0\left\{\frac{10.0}{2.0}\right\}$	1.0	6/10	TO3
2N6251	10	npn	350/0.2	450	375	2.5	$2.0\left\{\frac{10}{1.67}\right\}$	$1.0\left\{\frac{10}{1.67}\right\}$	$3.5\left\{\frac{10}{1.67}\right\}$	1.0	6/10	TO3
Non-JEDEC-registered types												
SVT300–3	3	npn	300/0.05	325		80	$0.2\left\{\frac{3.0}{0.6}\right\}$	$0.3\left\{\frac{3.0}{0.3}\right\}$	$1.0\left\{\frac{3.0}{0.6}\right\}$	1.5	15/3	TO3
SVT300–5	5	npn	300/0.05	325		70	$0.2\left\{\frac{5.0}{1.0}\right\}$	$0.3\left\{\frac{5.0}{1.0}\right\}$	$1.5\left\{\frac{5.0}{1.0}\right\}$	1.5	15/5	TO3
SVT300–10	10	npn	300/0.05	325		50	$0.2\left\{\frac{10.0}{2.0}\right\}$	$0.3\left\{\frac{10.0}{1.0}\right\}$	$1.0\left\{\frac{10.0}{2.0}\right\}$	1.2	15/10	TO3

SVT450-3	3	npn	450/0.05	450		$0.1\left\{\frac{3.0}{0.6}\right\}$	$0.15\left\{\frac{3.0}{0.6}\right\}$	$1.5\left\{\frac{3.0}{0.6}\right\}$	1.5	15/3	TO3
SVT450-5	5	npn	450/0.05	450		$0.1\left\{\frac{5.0}{1.0}\right\}$	$0.15\left\{\frac{5.0}{1.0}\right\}$	$1.5\left\{\frac{5.0}{1.0}\right\}$	1.2	15/5	TO3
SDT13301	10	npn	300/0.1	300	15	$0.25\left\{\frac{5.0}{0.5}\right\}$	$0.35\left\{\frac{5.0}{0.5}\right\}$	$1.6\left\{\frac{5.0}{0.5}\right\}$	0.8	10/5	TO3
SDT13302	10	npn	350/0.1	350	15	$0.25\left\{\frac{5.0}{0.5}\right\}$	$0.35\left\{\frac{5.0}{0.5}\right\}$	$1.6\left\{\frac{5.0}{0.5}\right\}$	0.8	10/5	TO3
SDT13303	10	npn	400/0.1	400	15	$0.25\left\{\frac{5.0}{0.5}\right\}$	$0.35\left\{\frac{5.0}{0.5}\right\}$	$1.6\left\{\frac{5.0}{0.5}\right\}$	0.8	10/5	TO3
SDT13304	10	npn	450/0.1	450	15	$0.25\left\{\frac{5.0}{0.5}\right\}$	$0.35\left\{\frac{5.0}{0.5}\right\}$	$1.6\left\{\frac{5.0}{0.5}\right\}$	0.8	10/5	TO3
SDT13305	10	npn	500/0.1	500	15	$0.25\left\{\frac{5.0}{0.5}\right\}$	$0.35\left\{\frac{5.0}{0.5}\right\}$	$1.6\left\{\frac{5.0}{0.5}\right\}$	0.8	10/5	TO3
Darlington types—nonregistered											
IR-SVT-6253	10	npn	450/2	500		$0.25\left\{\frac{5.0}{0.5}\right\}$	$1.0\left\{\frac{5.0}{0.5}\right\}$	$2.5\left\{\frac{5.0}{0.5}\right\}$	1.5	140/5	TO3
IR-SVT-6002	15	npn	400/2	500		$0.4\left\{\frac{10.0}{1.0}\right\}$	$1.0\left\{\frac{10.0}{1.0}\right\}$	$2.5\left\{\frac{10.0}{1.0}\right\}$	1.3	60/10	TO3
IR-SVT-6062	20	npn	400/2	450		$0.4\left\{\frac{10.0}{1.0}\right\}$	$1.0\left\{\frac{10.0}{1.0}\right\}$	$2.5\left\{\frac{10.0}{1.0}\right\}$	1.3	40/15	TO3

Fig. 8–20. (*Cont'd.*) High-energy power transistors in frequent use in off-the-ac-line switching regulators and dc/dc power converters.

voltage the transistors will be subjected to is thus $1.2(240) = 288$ V. For a margin of safety, operation should be at no more than 80% of vendor's maximum rating. Vendor maximum rating should thus be $288/0.8 = 360$ V.

Peak collector current for 400 W at 120 V is 3.3 A. The selected transistor should thus have a V_{cer} (collector-to-emitter voltage with a resistor of less than 50 ohms from base to emitter) rating of at least 360 V. It should have a maximum current rating of at least 3.3 A with minimum current gain of at least 20 at 3.3 A. Thermal resistance should be minimized.

It can be seen from Fig. 8–20 that there are a number of transistor types meeting the above requirements in most respects. Characteristic shortcomings in any particular area can almost always be overcome by proper circuit design.

Hence, as a reasonable choice meeting most of the requirements, choose the 2N6251. Its junction-to-case thermal resistance (θ_{jc}) is relatively low at 1°C/watt. Its current rise and fall times at a 4-A current level are under 0.4 μsec at I_c/I_b (forward) and I_c/I_b (reverse) of 10 (Fig. 2–8). Its typical gain of 50 at 4A is relatively high. With 50 ohms base-emitter resistance, V_{cer} is 375 V, and it thus meets the minimum required value of 360 V. Its maximum continuous current rating of 10 A is comfortably above the required 3.3-A level.

Power Transistor Base Drive Circuitry

Figure 2–8B shows that at 3.3 A collector current and a base current of 3.3/10 or 0.33 A, collector current rise time is 0.3 μsec. Figure 2–8C shows at turnoff a reverse-base drive of 3.3/8 or 0.41 A gives a current fall time of 0.38 μsec.

But Fig. 2–8D shows a storage time of about 4 μsec for a reverse-base drive I_b equal to the forward-base drive ($I_c/10$). This is too long a time and, hence, the transistor will not be permitted to saturate. Storage time will be reduced essentially to zero by going to a Darlington configuration (Sect. 2.1.9). The added gain of the Darlington driver makes the 0.33-A forward-base drive easily available from a low-power driver at the base of the Darlington driver. The circuit is thus shown in Fig. 8–19.

There are many choices available for the Darlington driver. Some possibilities are the 2N3585, 2N3439, 2N6079, 2N5661, and 2N5663. These, as almost any others with adequate V_{cer} ratings have relatively long storage times (of the order of 1–3 μsec) and should have large reverse-base drives to reduce these times.

The resistor-capacitor combination R1–C1 in Fig. 8–19 provides the turn-on delay effect discussed in Sect. 8.7.1. The transformer drive at the input to the Darlington driver should have a peak-to-peak voltage of no more than about 8 V, for, on the turn-off half cycle, V_{in} minus one diode drop is applied as a reverse-base bias to Q3 and Q4. These have reverse-base voltage limits of 6 V, which should not be exceeded. The 4-V peak limit provides a margin of safety and helps avoid second-breakdown effects, which are very sensitive to excessive reverse base-emitter bias.

Integrated Power Darlingtons

An apriori best-transistor choice cannot always be made without breadboard testing, for characteristics needed to predict performance under specific operating conditions are not always available from vendors' data sheets. Roughly equal performance is possible with a large range of power inverters and Darlington drivers chosen from Fig. 8–19.

But one interesting and valuable choice is to use integrated power Darlingtons that have the power stage and its driver on one chip in the same TO3 package. Thus, TRW SVT 6250 series devices meet the above requirements and provide useful space and assembly cost savings. The power Darlington has the useful feature that characteristics must be specified for one unit only rather than on the inverter and its driver.

Power Transistors with Antisaturation Feedback Diodes

The low-storage-time advantage of the Darlington configuration is fully realized only if the Darlington driver has low storage time. By its nature, in a Darlington configuration the output power inverter is not permitted to have its base-collector junction forward biased. In this nonsaturated condition, its storage time is low. But the Darlington driver does have its base-collector junction forward biased and large reverse-base currents are required to reduce its storage time. A study of Fig. 8–21 shows the various possibilities, since Darlington drivers themselves have storage times in the range of 1–4 μsec.

Thus, if sufficient base drive is available to achieve fast turnon (I_c/I_{b1} = 10) with a single transistor, the antisaturation scheme of Fig. 2–9A may be preferable to the Darlington configuration. Storage delay will be negligible and a reverse-base drive of $I_c/I_{b2} = 10$ will yield fast current fall time. In the scheme shown in Fig. 8–21, diodes D1 and D2 provide the antisaturation effect discussed in Sect. 2.1.9. Resistors R_a are small in value and can be used to keep the voltage drop in R_a and D1 in series about 0.1 V greater than the drop in D2. This ensures that the transistor base-collector junction cannot take on a forward bias and reduces storage delay essentially to zero.

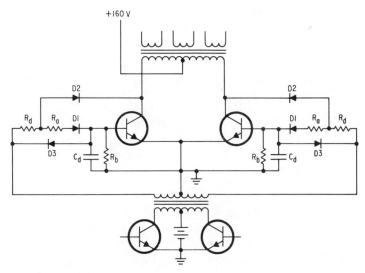

Fig. 8–21. Antisaturation feedback diodes (D1, D2, R_a) for reduced storage delay and RC-delayed turnon (R_dC_d) plus diode pullthrough (D3) for turn-off speed-up.

Diodes D2 must be ultrafast recovery types (Unitrode UTX125) to keep their reverse recovery current spikes low. Such diodes have reverse recovery times of about 75 nsec but generally have low reverse-voltage ratings, and two in series would be required to sustain the 360-V reverse voltage.

Elements R_a, R_d, and C_d provide the delayed turn-on feature of Fig. 8–14B. Diodes D3, on the negative half cycle, reach around $R_a + R_d$ to pull large reverse-base currents and decrease storage time.

With sufficient base drive available from the input transformer, this scheme can result in faster overall switching speed than the Darlington configuration. But the antisaturation diode scheme of Fig. 2–9A can still be used with a Darlington configuration to reduce drive requirements from the input transformer and to reduce Darlington driver storage time.

Capacitive Overdrive for Fast Switching Times

If the positive-edge, delayed, square-wave voltages of Fig. 8–15 are available, resistive base drives with speed-up capacitors across the base resistors can be used to give large turn-on and turn-off base currents as shown in Fig. 8–22. The differentiated spikes of high current at the leading and trailing edges of input voltage waveforms result in fast turnon and turnoff.

But this scheme is only possible without the risk of simultaneous conduction if the positive-going edges of input voltage square waves are delayed with

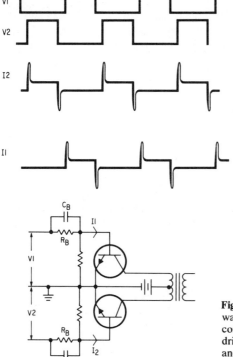

Fig. 8–22. If positive-edge-delayed, square-wave voltage drive of Fig. 8–15 is available, conventional capacitance speed-up overdrive can be used to obtain large forward- and reverse-base currents without danger of simultaneous conduction.

respect to the negative-going turn-off edges of the opposite inverter. Note in Fig. 8–22 that the high-current, positive-going spikes occur after the high-current, negative-going turn-off spikes.

Power Transistor Junction Temperature

The thermal design must be performed to verify maximum junction temperature is below some preassigned safe value. Junction temperature is calculated as noted in Sect. 4.3.1 by

$$T_j = T_a + \Delta T_{hsa} + \Delta T_{jhs} \tag{8–13}$$

where ΔT_{hsa} is the temperature rise of the heat sink above ambient air temperature and ΔT_{jhs} is the temperature rise of the transistor junction above the heat sink. But

$$\Delta T_{hsa} = \theta_{hsa} P_{hs}$$

where θ_{hsa} is the thermal resistance of the heat sink above ambient air (obtained from its surface area and curves as in Figs. 4–7 and 4–8 and P_{hs} is the total power flowing into the heat sink. Now

$$\Delta T_{jhs} = (\theta_{jc} + \theta_{chs}) P_t$$

where θ_{jc} is the transistor's junction-to-case thermal resistance equaling 1°C/watt for the 2N6251, θ_{chs} is the thermal resistance from case to heat sink ($= 0.5$°C/watt for a TO3 case through a standard 2-mil mica washer), and P_t equals dc plus ac power dissipation of all power transistors on the heat sink.

Now assume that the heat sink absorbs the heat from only the two power inverters. Other heat-dissipating elements such as power rectifiers and the transformer will have their own thermally isolated heat sinks, which, it can be safely assumed, will dissipate their heat directly into the ambient air without delivering any heat to the power inverter heat sink. Then

$$P_{hs} = 2P_t$$

and

$$T_j = T_a + \theta_{hsa}(2P_t) + 1.5P_t \tag{8–13}$$

Now

$$P_t = P_{dc} + P_{ac} \tag{8–14}$$

where $P_{dc} =$ dc power dissipation per inverter $= (V_{ce(on)} I_{dc(max)})/2$. And for a Darlington transistor, $V_{ce(on)}$ is the sum of the base-emitter potential of the power inverter in its "on" state (about 0.8 V) plus the saturated collector-to-emitter potential of the Darlington driver (about 0.4 V). Then, for a maximum inverter collector current of 3.3 A

$$P_{dc} = (0.8 + 0.4)(3.3)/2 = 1.98 \text{ W}$$

The ac transistor losses result from the overlap of high voltage and current at turnon and turnoff. The transistor current rise time is generally so fast that there is no substantial overlap of voltage and current at turnon.

But at turnoff (as shown in Fig. 8–23), we can assume current that falls linearly from $I_{c(max)}$ to zero in a time t_f and that collector voltage rises linearly from zero to $2V_{cc}$ in a time t_f. Then the ac losses averaged over a time t_f may be obtained as follows:

$$P_{t_f} = \frac{1}{t_f} \int_0^{t_f} ei \, dt$$

$$= \frac{1}{t_f} \int_0^{t_f} 2V_{cc}\left(\frac{t}{t_f}\right)\left[I_{c(max)}\left(1 - \frac{t}{t_f}\right)\right]dt$$

$$= \frac{2V_{cc}I_{c(max)}}{t_f^2} \int_0^{t_f}\left(t - \frac{t^2}{t_f}\right)dt$$

$$= \frac{2V_{cc}I_{c(max)}}{t_f^2}\left|\frac{t^2}{2} - \frac{t^3}{3t_f^2}\right|_0^{t_f} = \frac{2V_{cc}I_{c(max)}}{t_f^2}\left(\frac{t_f^2}{2} - \frac{t_f^2}{3}\right)$$

$$= 2V_{cc}I_{c(max)}\left(\frac{1}{2} - \frac{1}{3}\right) = \frac{V_{cc}I_{c(max)}}{3}$$

And the power dissipation averaged over a complete cycle of period t is

$$P_{av} = \frac{V_{cc}I_{c(max)}\,t_f}{3T} \qquad\qquad (8-15)$$

Now for the 2N6251, t_f is about 1 μsec. For most of the transistors in Fig. 8–20, t_f will range between 1 and 3 μsec. Then at 20 kHz, the average ac power dissipation per inverter transistor is

$$P_{ac} = \left(\frac{V_{cc}I_{c(max)}}{3}\right)\left(\frac{1}{50}\right)$$

And for $V_{cc} = 120$ V, $I_{c(max)} = 3.3$ A

$$P_{ac} = \left(\frac{120 \times 3.3}{3}\right)\left(\frac{1}{50}\right) = 2.64 \text{ W}$$

Then in Eq. 8–14

$$P_t = P_{dc} + P_{ac} = 1.98 + 2.64 = 4.52 \text{ W}$$

And from Eq. 8–13

$$T_j = T_a + \theta_{hsa} \,(2)(4.52) + 1.5(4.52)$$
$$= T_a + \theta_{hsa} \,(9.04) + 6.78$$

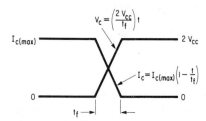

Fig. 8–23. Overlap of falling current and rising collector voltage results in power losses equal to or greater than dc losses. Overlap losses (P_{ac}), for overlap at current turnoff only, averaged over a time t_f, is

$$P_{ac} = 1/t_f \int_0^{t_f} ei \, dt = I_{c(max)}(V_{cc}/3)$$

Now if the maximum ambient air temperature is 70°C and if maximum junction temperature permitted is to be 135°C (Sect. 2.1.9) then

$$\theta_{hsa} = \frac{T_j - T_a - 6.78}{9.04}$$

$$= \frac{135 - 70 - 6.78}{9.04}$$

$$= 6.44°C/watt$$

And from Figs. 4–7 and 4–8 for a heat sink-to-ambient thermal resistance of 6.4°C/watt at a 4.5-W power level, the heat sink area must be 25 sq. in.

Now in a realistic design, there would not be a separate heat sink for the invertor transistors and all other power-dissipating elements. All the high-power dissipating elements would likely be located on one heat sink. From Sect. 8.8.1, the total rectifier losses are 40 W. Then, if these 40 plus the 9.04 W are poured into the heat sink, from Eq. 8–13

$$T_j = T_a + \theta_{hs} (49.04) + 6.78$$

or
$$\theta_{hs} = \frac{135 - 70 - 6.78}{49.04} = 1.2°C/watt$$

And from Figs. 4–7 and 4–8 for 1.2°C/watt at a 49-W power level, a heat sink of 180 sq in. of area would be required.

8.8.4 Output Rectifier Dissipation

The total rectified load current as specified in Sect. 8.8.1 is 40 A. The fast recovery rectifiers of Fig. 2–4 have forward voltage drops of close to 1 V over a large range of currents. If these types are used in the rectifiers of Fig. 8–16, rectifier diode losses alone will be 40 W.

Rectifier diode losses can be cut almost in half by use of the "Schottky" diode, which has become available with reliable, useful characteristics within the past few years. Original versions of this device proved erratic in their characteristics, had a maximum junction temperature limit of 100°C, and were limited to 20 V peak reverse voltage.

Present versions (TRW-SD41 and SD51) have reverse voltages of 35–45 V and maximum junction temperature ratings of 150°C. Current carrying capacity is high—thus, the TRW-SD51 is rated at 60 A at a forward drop of 0.6 V with a 125°C case temperature (Fig. 8–24).

At 30 A in the 5-V output of Fig. 8–19, the forward drop with SD51 rectifiers would be 0.6 V maximum (Fig. 8–24) and the resulting dissipation would be 18 W. In Fig. 8–19, in which two IN3909s are used in parallel for each half cycle, the forward drop at 30 A is 1.0 V and dissipation is 30 W. If only one 1N3909 were used per half cycle, the forward drop would be 1.1 V and the rectifier dissipation at 30 A would be 33 W.

Since, in the full-wave rectifier, the maximum reverse voltage experienced by the rectifier is twice the peak, the 45-V reverse voltage diodes could not be used on the ±30-V outputs, but they could be used with an adequate safety margin on the ±15-V outputs. Thus, using the SD51 in the ±5- and ±15-V outputs and the 1N3880 in the ±30-V outputs results in total rectifier losses of only 23 W as compared to 40 W with the original complement of rectifiers.

Characteristics of the SD51 rectifier diodes are shown in Fig. 8–24, and a comparison of the SD41 and SD51 rectifiers is given in Table 8–4.

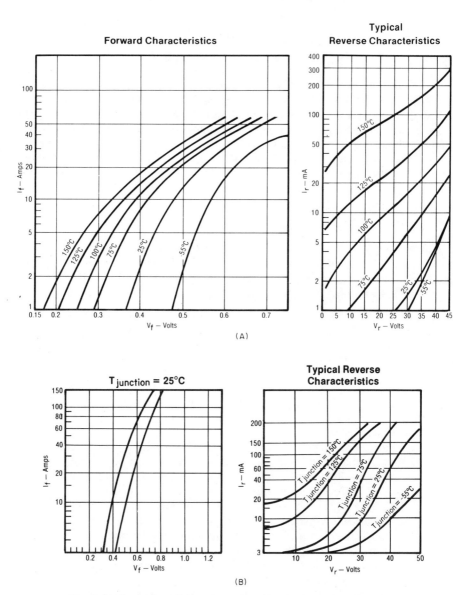

Fig. 8–24. Low-forward-drop Schottky-type rectifiers. (A) TRW-type SD 41 Schottky diode. (B) TRW-type SD 51 Schottky diode. (*Courtesy* TRW, Inc.)

Table 8-4. Comparison of SD41 and SD51 Rectifier Characteristics

	SD41	SD51
Peak reverse voltage (volts)	35	45
Maximum average forward current (amps)	30	60
Thermal resistance (°C/watt)	2.0	1.0

8.8.5 Output Filters

In Sect. 2.1.4 it was pointed out that there was a notch at the rectifier output (Fig. 2–3B) at the instant of switchover from one inverter to the other. During this interval, an output filter capacitor is required to hold the output voltage constant and supply output load current.

The magnitude of the filter capacitor depends on load current and the permissible voltage droop at the instant of the notch. Since the voltage droop is small compared to the absolute value of output voltage, the capacitor must supply an essentially constant current equal to the full load current for a time equal to half the sum of the rise plus fall time. Then, for a permissible droop ΔV, the magnitude of the capacitor is

$$C = \frac{I\Delta t}{\Delta V} = \frac{I}{\Delta V}\left(\frac{t_r + t_f}{2}\right)$$

Thus, for the 5-V, 30-A output, for an allowable droop of 0.1 V, rise time of 0.5 and fall time of 1.0 μsec, the size of the filter capacitor would be

$$C = \frac{30(1.5 \times 10^{-6})}{0.1\ (2)} = 225\ \mu\text{F}$$

This would be the required size of the output filter capacitor if it appeared at its output terminals as a pure capacitor, but all types of electrolytic (and tantalum) capacitors behave as if they have an equivalent series resistor (ESR) in series with their stated capacity. Then, during the notch, when the full load current is supplied by the capacitor, the output voltage dips an amount ΔV_o = I_{load} (ESR). For large load currents, output voltage can dip down to the bottom of the input notch for a sufficiently high ESR.

Values of ESR depend on type of capacitor and details of its construction and assembly, voltage rating, and temperature. For many electrolytic and tantalum capacitors, used primarily as filters at 60 or 400 Hz line frequency, ESR is small compared to the capacitive reactance and is not specified in vendors' data sheets. Values of ESR can vary from 0.27 ohms for a 10-V 4,200-μF capacitor (roughly 1.13 ohms1,000 μF) to 0.37 ohms for a 50-V, 800-μF capacitor (roughly 0.31 ohms/1,000 μF).

Thus, at notch times such as in Fig. 2–3B, if the load current had to be supplied by the filter capacitor, the ESR would cause output voltage to dip to zero. To avoid this, an inductor L1 is placed in series between the rectifier cathodes and output capacitor as in Fig. 8–25. It serves two purposes. First, during the notch time as the rectifier diodes move below the output voltage, since current in an inductance attempts to remain constant; as one anode goes negative and the opposite cathode has not yet risen to the conduction level, the input end

Fig. 8–25. Output LC filter is required to eliminate the commutation notch of Fig. 2–3B. L1 is
required because the relatively large valve of
ESR does not permit C1 to hold the output up
at notch time.

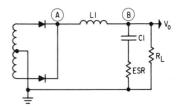

of L1 has a negative inductive impulse and follows the falling anode down. Therefore, current continues to flow through the off-turning diode until the on-turning
one has risen high enough to supply load current. Now, the load current need
not be supplied through the output capacitor, and its ESR and output does not
dip.

A further advantage of L1 is that during turnon, the transient impedance
reflected into the transformer primary is not that of the low-impedance filter
capacity, but that of L1 in series with it. The criteria used in selecting L1 and C1
are as follows:

1. During notch time, assume potential at A (Fig. 8–25) is a vertical-sided
   waveform dipping to ground for a time $t_r + t_f \approx 1.5$ μsec. Now, since
   point B is to remain at V_o, the voltage across L1 is V_o, and assume there is
   only a 5% droop of current in L1 for 1.5 μsec. Then

   $$V_o = L1\left(\frac{\Delta i}{\Delta t}\right) = \frac{L1(0.05I_L)}{t_r + t_f}$$

   or $$L1 = \frac{V_o(t_r + t_f)}{0.05I_L} \qquad (8\text{–}16)$$

   For the 5-V, 30-A output

   $$L1 = \frac{5(1.5 \times 10^{-6})}{1.5} = 5 \ \mu\text{H}$$

2. It can be shown that if a step of load current ΔI is drawn through the
   node B (effectively, L1 and C1 in parallel) the resultant transient voltage
   at the node is an exponentially decaying sinusoidal "ring." The first
   half cycle has an amplitude of $\Delta V_o = \Delta I(L/C)^{1/2}$ and a base width of
   $\pi(LC)^{1/2}$. Then, for a step of load current of 10% of the maximum,
   choose C1 so that ΔV_o is some maximum preassigned value – say, 0.1 V.
   Then, for the 5-V, 30-A output

   $$\Delta V_o = 0.1 \text{ V} = 0.1I_m(L/C)^{1/2}$$

   or $$(L/C)^{1/2} = \frac{0.1}{0.1 \ (30)} = 0.033 \text{ ohms}$$

   $$L/C = 1.1 \times 10^{-3}$$

   and $$C = \frac{L}{1.1 \times 10^{-3}} = \frac{5 \times 10^{-6}}{1.1 \times 10^{-3}} = 4,500 \ \mu\text{F}$$

L1 must be designed to have the specified inductance with the maximum
dc load current. This requires a magnetic core with an air gap or a powdered iron

case that will not saturate with a dc current in it. Design of such inductors with specified inductance at various dc load currents will be taken up in Chap. 9.

Now, it must be verified that at turnon there is no transient overshoot of output voltage at the output of the L1–C1 filter. It is well known that a step of voltage applied to the input of an LC filter can cause a ringing overshoot at the capacitor output if the circuit is underdamped. Damping, which prevents a ringing overshoot, can be provided either by the shunt load resistor R_L or by the equivalent series resistor (ESR) in series with the capacitor.

$$\text{If } R_L < 0.5(L/C)^{1/2} \text{ or if (ESR)} > 2(L/C)^{1/2}$$

the circuit is overdamped and there will be no ringing overshoot. The damping, which avoids overshoots, is more often supplied by ESR, which generally is not specified by the vendor and is very temperature dependent. It is generally simpler to check for ringing overshoots by oscilloscope examination than by calculation because of the uncertainty in ESR.

It is important to check for ringing overshoot at turnon because even a single high-voltage pulse can destroy voltage-sensitive semiconductors.

8.8.6 Output Line and Load Regulation

With dc input from the preregulator, constant to ±0.5% for a ±10% input line variation, all rectified secondary outputs are also constant to ±0.5% for the same input line variation.

Load regulation is due primarily to effective impedance of the rectifier diodes, for transformer primary and secondary dc resistances and resistance of the output inductor are generally insignificant.

Impedance of the rectifier diodes for small current changes is their slope at their operating points. For the 1N3909 diodes (Fig. 2–4D) used in the 5-V output of Fig. 8–19, slope is seen to be about 0.1 ohm at a 30-A current level. Thus, for a 10% load change from 30 to 27 A, output voltage will increase by only $(0.1)(3) = 0.3$ V. This is generally good enough, since for 5-V logic circuits dc load current generally remains constant.

For a step change of load current, ΔI_o, there is an initial step change of output voltage $\Delta I_o(L1/C1)^{1/2}$. In Sect. 8.8.5 it was shown that dynamic filter impedance, $(L1/C1)^{1/2}$, was designed to be 0.033 ohm and give only a 0.1-V change for a 10% load change.

PROBLEMS

8.1 What are the hysteresis losses of cup core types 4229, 3622, 3019, and 2616 at a peak flux density of 1,500 G at frequencies of 20, 50, and 100 kHz? Assume 3C8 ferrite core material.

8.2 What is the power-handling capability of Ferroxcube cores 3622, 3019, and 2616 in 3C8 ferrite material at 20, 30, and 50 kHz at a peak flux density of 1,500 G and wire current densities of 250 and 500 circular mils/ampere? Assume a double-section bobbin.

8.3 Assume a square-wave dc/dc converter, such as in Fig. 2–1, operating from a preregulated dc of 120 V. Select an integral number of primary turns that yields a peak flux excursion of about 2,000 G at an operating frequency of 30 kHz.

a. What is the actual peak flux excursion for the integral number of primary turns of $V_{dc} = 120$ V?

b. What is the number of volts per turn of this design?

c. What is the closest we can approach to 5 V output after secondary rectifier (assume 1 V forward drop) with this design? How many secondary turns does this require?

d. For 5 V output after the output rectifiers assuming 1 V rectifier drop, for one-, two-, and three-turn secondaries, calculate the number of primary turns for primary voltages of 114, 120, and 126 V. What is the required dc supply voltage for each of these cases? What is the peak flux excursion in each case? What is the volts per turn characteristic for each case? What is the power-handling capability in each case, assuming a current density of 250 circular mils/ampere for the 3622 core?

e. Assume 300 W of primary power and a lossless transformer. What are the primary and secondary currents for N_p/N_s of 19, 20, and 21?

f. At 250 circular mils/ampere ($N_p/N_s = 20$), what are the required circular mil areas of the primary and secondary windings? What are the required wire sizes?

g. What are the wire diameters and total spaces occupied by primary and secondary windings for the cases of $N_p/N_s = 20$, $N_s = 1,2,3$?

h. What is the total available winding space of the bobbin for the 3622 core? Which of the three cases of Prob. 3g can be handled by the 3622 core?

8.4 In Prob. 3, for $V_{dc} = 121$, $N_p = 40$ turns, and $N_s =$ two turns (each side of primary), assuming primary wire size in No. 22 and secondary in No. 10, what are the primary and secondary resistances (each side of center tap) and what are the total copper losses?

8.5 In a push-pull inverter as in Fig. 2–1, operating off $V_{cc} = 300$ V, at a peak current of 4 A, assume current fall and collector voltage rise times are 1.5 μsec. Assume they overlap as in Fig. 8–23. What is the ac power dissipation in the transistor at a switching frequency of 10 kHz?

9
Switching Regulators

9.1 Width-Modulated, Step-Down Switching Regulator

This is sometimes referred to as a "down chopper." Its basic circuit configuration is shown in Figs. 1–5 and 9–1, and its merits relative to series-pass regulators were discussed in Sect. 1.2.

It was pointed out in Sect. 1.2 that its chief advantage is its high efficiency and its efficiency being independent of input voltage. The efficiency of a step-down switching regulator, it was shown, can be as high as $V_o/(V_o + 2)$ whatever the input voltage is. In contrast, the series-pass regulator efficiency is $V_o/V_{in(max)}$.

Since switching operation occurs at frequencies of 10–40 kHz, filter, inductors, and capacitors are small. With the smaller heat sink volume permitted by high efficiency (Fig. 4–11), small filter components, and no need for a power frequency input transformer, packing densities of 1–4 load watts/cubic inch are possible using switching-regulator techniques. In contrast, conventional-power transformer–series-pass regulator power supply systems yield packing densities averaging about 0.3 W/cubic inch.

In many complex electronic systems, overall specifications on volume and efficiency can only be met using switching regulators in some of the block diagram combinations discussed in Chap. 3. The step-down switching regulator is the heart of many of these new power supply systems and details of its design will be presented in this chapter.

9.1.1 Voltage and Current Waveforms in Step-Down Switching Regulator

The basic block diagram of the regulator is reproduced in Fig. 9–1. A study of its waveform (Fig. 9–2) at critical points clarifies many of the design decisions to be made.

The basic circuit operation is to close switch transistor Q1 for a time T_{on}, and open it for T_{off} at a switching period T. When Q1 is closed, it is in saturation at a voltage drop of $V_{ce(sat)}$, which is approximately 1 V. When Q1 is opened, the inductive kick in L2 drives its left-hand end negative until "free-wheeling" diode D1 latches in and conducts – initially at the same instantaneous current

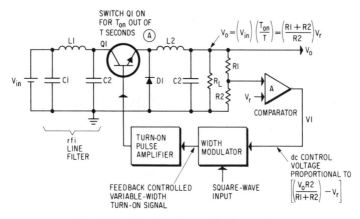

Fig. 9–1. Basic step-down switching regulator.

that had been flowing in Q1 just prior to its opening. The voltage at point A, Fig. 9–1, is then only $V_{ce(\text{sat})}$ or about 1 V below V_{in} when Q1 is closed and V_{D1} or about 1 V below ground when Q1 is open.

Assuming for the moment the 1-V drops of $V_{ce(\text{sat})}$ and V_{D1} can be neglected, the voltage at point A is shown in Fig. 9–2B. It is at $+V_{in}$ for the time Q1 is closed (T_{on}) and at ground for the time Q1 is open ($T - T_{on}$). The filter L2–C2 averages out the peak-to-peak ripple voltage of V_{in} volts and produces at V_o a constant dc output voltage whose average value is

$$V_o = V_{in}(T_{on}/T) \tag{9-1}$$

With the feedback network shown in Fig. 9–1, the "on" time T_{on} is automatically adjusted so that

$$V_o = V_{in}(T_{on}/T) = [(R1 + R2)/R2]V_r$$

Ripple voltage at V_o can be set at any arbitrarily low value by proper choice of L2 and C2. Selection of these components is perhaps the most important decision to be made in the regulator design.

Output voltage V_o is regulated by controlling the ratio of T_{on}/T. The frequency or period T may be fixed and T_{on}, the duration of the "on" time, may be varied, or T_{on} may be fixed and the switching period varied. Generally, operating at a fixed frequency and varying T_{on} leads to a simpler design. Further, many systems require fixed operating frequency to keep any generated noise pulses locked in time relationship to fundamental parameters such as computer clock frequency or horizontal sweep rate in display systems. Noise pulses generated at the instant the switch Q1 closes or opens can be tolerated more easily when they are locked in time phase to these other system frequencies.

Currents in the switch Q1, diode D1, and inductor L2 have the waveform shown in Figs. 9–2C to 9–2E. The dc or average value of current flowing in the inductor L2 must always equal the dc load current, but the current in L2 ramps upward linearly when Q1 is closed and ramps down linearly when Q1 is open. The upward ramp of current flows through Q1 when it is closed and the downward ramp of current flows through D1 when Q1 is open. Thus, Q1 current is zero when Q1 is open, and D1 current is zero when Q1 is closed. The dc value of current about which the current ramps in L2 are centered is equal to the average dc load current.

The explanation for the linear current ramps can be seen as follows: When Q1 is closed, since it is assumed the potential at V_o is constant and relatively ripple free, there is a constant voltage across L2 equal to $V_{in} - V_o$. Since voltage across an inductor is $E = L(di/dt)$, then for a fixed voltage of $V_{in} - V_o$ across L2 for a time T_{on}, the current change in it is an upward ramp of magnitude:

$$+\Delta I_L = \frac{(V_{in} - V_o)T_{on}}{L2}$$

and from Eq. 9–1,

$$+\Delta I_L = \frac{V_o}{V_{in}} (V_{in} - V_o) \frac{T}{L2} \tag{9-2}$$

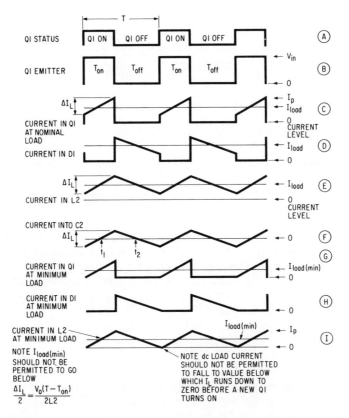

Fig. 9–2. Critical waveforms in the step-down switching regulator of Fig. 9–1.

When Q1 is open for a time $(T - T_{on})$, the inductive kick in L2 forces point A to ground (actually,-1 V) and a constant voltage of V_o is impressed across L2. But this time the voltage polarity across L2 is reversed and the current ramps downward linearly by an amount

$$-\Delta I_L = \frac{V_o(T - T_{on})}{L2} \tag{9-3}$$

and, again, from Eq. 9-1,

$$-\Delta I_L = \frac{V_o(V_{in} - V_o)T}{V_{in}L2} \tag{9-3A}$$

When Q1 opens, since the current in an inductor cannot change instantaneously, the inductive kick in L2 instantaneously drops V_A to ground where "free-wheeling" diode D1 latches in and conducts. The current in diode D1 at the moment it latches in is equal to I_p, the peak current in Q1 at the instant it turned off. The current in D1 at the end of the Q1 off time is

$$I_p - \Delta I_L = I_p - \frac{V_o(T - T_{on})}{L2}$$

where the peak current is the average dc load current plus one-half the peak-to-peak current ramp. Then, the peak current in D1 when it is on is

$$I_{D1(max)} = I_{dc} + \frac{V_o(T - T_{on})}{2L2} \tag{9-4}$$

and the minimum current in D1 when it conducts is

$$I_{D1(min)} = I_{dc} - \frac{V_o(T - T_{on})}{2L2} \tag{9-5}$$

And during the Q1 off time, the current in D1 ramps linearly between these values. Maximum and minimum values of current in Q1 are identical to those of Eqs. 9-4 and 9-5. Current in Q1 ramps upward between these values during Q1 "on" time and current in D1 ramps downward between these values during the Q1 "off" time.

Current in L2 (Fig. 9-2E) is the sum of the transistor Q1 current (Fig. 9-2C) and diode D1 current (Fig. 9-2D). DC power dissipations in D1 and Q1 may be calculated on the basis of 1-V drop in these elements. Thus, since Q1 conducts only during its "on" time, its average dc dissipation is $I_{av}V_{av}(T_{on}/T)$ or

$$PD_{dc(Q1)} = (I_{dc(load)})(1)(T_{on}/T) \tag{9-6}$$

And similarly, dc dissipation in D1 is

$$PD_{dc(D1)} = (I_{dc(load)})(1)(T_{off}/T) \tag{9-7}$$

Overlap of high voltage and current during turnon and turnoff (Sect. 2.1.3) will increase these dissipations. The exact amount of the increase depends on circuit details fixing the voltage rise and fall times. Integration of the instantaneous voltage and current during rise and fall times gives the exact ac overlap or switching losses. As a first approximation, it should be assumed overlap or "switching" dissipation in both the diode and transistor will be equal to their respective dc dissipations.

9.1.2 Minimum Load Current in Step-Down Switching Regulator

Current in L2 at the bottom of the current ramp is given by Eq. 9–5 (diode D1 current at that time is equal to current in L2). It can be seen from Eq. 9–5, that when the minimum load current is equal to half the peak-to-peak ramp current $V_o(T - T_{on})/2L2$, the current in L2 falls to zero. This condition should be avoided either by choosing a value of L2 large enough so that

$$\frac{(V_{in} - V_o)T_{on}}{2L2} < I_{\text{dc load(min)}} \tag{9–8}$$

Or, for a preselected value of L2, minimum value of dc load current should be restricted so that the above inequality holds.

If the above inequality does not hold and L2 current at the negative tip of the current triangle (Fig. 1–9E) does fall to zero before the next Q1 turn-on interval, voltage at V_o can rise to V_{in} and possibly damage some of the load elements.

This rise, uncontrollable by the feedback network, can be seen in the limit case when dc load current falls to zero. For if load current falls to zero, and there is a net average current through L2 over one Q1 "on" and Q1 "off" cycle, that average current must flow somewhere. If the load current is truly zero, that current flows into the capacitor, charging it to a higher potential. Then potential at V_o rises until there is no voltage across L2 during the "on" cycle and, hence, there can be no net current flow into L2 and, hence, no load current. Thus, with zero load current, V_o would rise to the peak input voltage or V_{in}.

The filter thus effectively becomes a capacitive rather than an inductive input type. For load currents between zero and $V_o(T - T_{on})/2L2$, dc output voltage varies roughly linearly between V_{in} and $V_r[(R1 + R2)/R2]$. This can be seen as follows. As long as V_{in} and V_o are constant, the average dc current supplied at the input to L2 is $V_o(T - T_{on})/2L2$. For decreasing T_{on} would decrease V_o. Thus, if the load impedance increased so that at the output node, the current $V_o(T - T_{on})/2L2$ could not be carried away, V_o would have to rise so that current flowing into the output node via L2 is equal to that carried out by the load impedance.

The detailed manner in which the output rises can be seen in Fig. 9–3. In Fig. 9–3A, load current is so low that at the minimum of the current ramps, the L2 current just falls to zero. Now if the dc load current were decreased further and L2 current ramped down to zero at time $T1$, before the start of the next period, since di/dt is zero, no voltage can appear across L2 and the potential at the input to L2 drifts up to that at the output end $-V_o$. Thus, the average voltage at the input to L2, the area under the V_a curve of Fig. 9–3B, goes up.

This phenomenon—the current in L2 running down to zero before the start of the next period—is often referred to as the inductor "running dry." When it occurs, voltage and current waveforms become erratic and output voltage commences rising and can no longer be controlled by the feedback loop.

This rising output voltage at currents below a certain minimum is very similar to the behavior of a choke input filter in an ac line frequency rectifier–filter network. It will be recalled such choke input filters have a critical minimum value of inductance at a unique frequency. For a given inductance, output voltage for current above a certain minimum is the average of the rectified half sine wave and is independent of load current. For load currents less than the minimum, the output filter capacitor starts charging toward the peak of the rectified input sine wave rather than remaining at the average value.

9.1.3 Input and Output Currents and Dissipation

Current in Q1, which is also the current taken from the input source, is seen in Fig. 9–2C to be a series of pulses having the characteristic shape of a ramp placed on top of a step. During the Q1 "on" time, the average load current is supplied from Q1 (i.e., the current from Q1 averaged over the Q1 "on" time is equal to the dc load current). During the Q1 "off" time, the dc load current is supplied from L2 and flows via D1 into the load. This current averaged over the Q1 "off" time is also equal to the dc load current. Thus, total current in L2 averaged over the entire period is equal to the dc load current. But the current from Q1 alone, averaged over a whole period, which is the average or dc current taken from the input source, is only $I_{dc}(T_{on}/T)$. Thus, power taken from the dc input source is

$$P_{in} = (V_{in(\text{average})})(I_{in(\text{average})}) = V_{in}I_{dc}(T_{on}/T) \qquad (9\text{–}9)$$

Assuming no internal losses for the moment, the output power is at a lower voltage $[V_o = V_{in}(T_{on}/T)]$ but at a high average output current (I_{dc}) than the average input, which is $I_{dc}(T_{on}/T)$. Output power is then

$$P_o = (V_{o(\text{average})})(I_{o(\text{average})}) = V_{in}(T_{on}/T)I_{dc} \qquad (9\text{–}10)$$

which is equal to the input power. This, of course, was what should be expected, since it was postulated that there are no internal losses.

The step-down switching regulator thus has the interesting property of a step-down transformer. It takes a high input voltage V_{in} at a low average input current $I_{dc}(T_{on}/T)$ and transforms it to a lower input voltage $V_{in}(T_{on}/T)$ at a higher output current, I_{dc}.

9.1.4 Switching Regulator Efficiency

The width modulation and low-level control circuitry of Fig. 9–1 generally dissipate negligible power, usually in the range of 1-2 W. Most of the internal dissipation is in the 1-V drop across Q1 when it is on and in saturation and in free-wheeling diode D1 when it is on. These respective dissipations from Eqs. 9–6 and 9–7 are

$$I_{dc}(T_{on}/T)(1) + I_{dc}(T - T_{on}/T)(1) = I_{dc}(1) \text{ watts}$$

Then, assuming ac overlap losses are equal to dc losses, total internal dissipation is $2I_{dc}$. For an output power of $P_o = V_oI_{dc}$, input power is

$$P_{in} = V_oI_{dc} + 2I_{dc} = I_{dc}(V_o + 2) \qquad (9\text{–}11)$$

Then efficiency of the step-down switching regulator is

$$E = \frac{P_o}{P_{in}} = \frac{I_{dc}(V_o)}{I_{dc}(V_o + 2)} = \frac{V_o}{V_o + 2} \qquad (9\text{–}12)$$

9.1.5 Filter Inductance Calculation

Filter inductance (L2 of Fig. 9–1) is selected large enough so that, at the top of the current ramp, the peak current given by Eq. 9–4 is not significantly

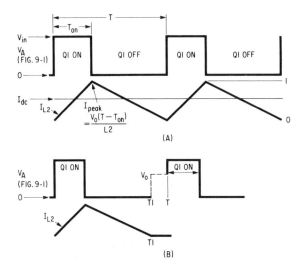

Fig. 9–3. Effect of lowering dc load current. (A) Voltages and current for $I_L = 0$ at end of "off" time. (B) When switching inductor current runs down to zero before the next turnon, waveforms become erratic and output and feedback network lose control.

greater than I_{dc}. The higher the peak current is, the larger is the required Q1 base drive. Further, if the inductance is too small, it requires a high minimum dc load current to satisfy the inequality of Eq. 9–8.

But the disadvantage of too large a filter inductance is that it degrades the transient response to steps of load current. Generally, the time constants in the feedback network do not permit too fast a change in (T_c/T) ratios to accommodate a steep step change in load current. Thus, the circuit depends on a low output impedance at the output node to avoid too large a bump or droop in output voltage for a step change in load current.

It can be shown to a first approximation that a step change $\pm\Delta I$ in output current from a node such as V_o (an inductor and capacitor in parallel) results in a half-sinusoidal bump or dip in output voltage whose peak amplitude is $\Delta I \sqrt{L/C}$. Width of the output voltage is roughly that of a half sinusoid whose period is $2\pi \sqrt{LC}$. Thus, the V_o node output impedance for load current steps, $\sqrt{L2/C2}$, should be minimized to avoid large output voltage transients for step load changes.

As a compromise, the peak current at the top of the current ramp (Fig. 9–2C) is often taken as 20% above the nominal dc load current. This permits a minimum dc load current of 20% of I_{nom} (from Eq. 9–8). This is adequate, since minimum current will rarely be less than 20% of its nominal value. Then

$$\Delta I_L = V_o[(T - T_{on})/L2] = 0.4 I_{dc(nom)} \tag{9–13}$$

or
$$L2 = \frac{2.5 V_o(T - T_{on})}{I_{dc(nom)}}$$

And, since $V_o = V_{in}(T_{on}/T)$ for nominal input voltage $V_{in(nom)}$,

$$L2 = \left(\frac{2.5V_o}{I_{dc(nom)}}\right)\left(T - \frac{V_oT}{V_{in(nom)}}\right)$$

$$= \frac{2.5V_oT(V_{in(nom)} - V_o)}{(I_{dc(nom)}V_{in(nom)})} \qquad (9-14)$$

And for instances in which this large a value gives poor load transient responses, L2 may be decreased at the price of a higher minimum dc load current in accordance with Eq. 9–8. Also, peak transistor current during the "on" time will be greater (Fig. 9–2C), thus requiring a larger dc base drive.

9.1.6 Filter Capacitance Calculation

After the filter inductance has been selected in accordance with Eq. 9–14, the next design decision is the selection of filter capacitance C2 (Fig. 9–1). C2 is chosen to provide a specified minimum output ripple voltage at the output node. This ripple is calculated from the average current per cycle taken from C2 and its duration. In Fig. 9–2E, it is seen the inductor current ramps between $I_{dc} - \Delta I_L/2$ and $I_{dc} + \Delta I_L/2$, where ΔI_L is given by Eq. 9–3.

Now referring to Fig. 9–1, it is obvious that, at any instant, the sum of the currents in L2 and C2 must equal the dc load current. Then in Fig. 9–2E at the midpoint of the "on" time, current in L2 is equal to the dc load current. Hence, at this instant there is no current flowing either into or out of C2 – the entire load current is supplied from L2. At the end of the "on" time, L2 current is $I_{dc} + \Delta I_L/2$. Since the load current is still I_{dc}, the excess from L2 must flow into C2 to replenish the charge lost when current was taken out of C2 earlier in the "on" time.

At the start of the "on" time, since current supplied from L2 is $(I_{dc} - \Delta I_L/2)$ and the load still demands I_{dc}, the balance of $\Delta I_L/2$ is supplied by current taken out of C2.

The current waveform in C2 is thus shown in Fig. 9–2F. It is centered about zero, of course, has a peak-to-peak amplitude of ΔI_L, and crosses through zero in the positive direction at the center of the "on" time. It crosses through zero in the negative direction at the center of the "off" time. Then from the center of the "on" to center of the "off" time (T_1 to T_2), current flows into C2 producing a ripple voltage

$$\Delta V = \frac{1}{C2}\int_{T_1}^{T_2} i\, dt$$

The average current during this time interval, which is $(T_{on}/2 + T_{off}/2)$, is $\Delta I_L/4$, where ΔI_L is given by Eq. 9–3. Thus, the ripple voltage rises in a triangular fashion an amount

$$\Delta V_{p/p} = \frac{1}{C2}\int_{T_1}^{T_2} i\, dt$$

$$= \frac{\Delta I_L}{4C2}\left(\frac{T_{on} + T_{off}}{2}\right) = \frac{(\Delta I_L)(T)}{8C2}$$

$$= \frac{V_oT(T - T_{on})}{8(L2)(C2)} \qquad \text{(from Eq. 9–3)}$$

But from Eq. 9–1, $T_{on} = (V_o/V_{in})T$. Then peak-to-peak ripple voltage is

$$\Delta V_{p/p} = V_o\left(T - \frac{V_o T}{V_{in}}\right)\left(\frac{T}{8L2C2}\right) = \frac{V_o T^2(V_{in} - V_o)}{8V_{in}L2C2}$$

Or for a predetermined peak-to-peak ripple voltage, $\Delta V_{p/p}$, the required filter capacity is

$$C2 = \frac{V_o T^2(V_{in} - V_o)}{8(L2)V_{in}\Delta V_{p/p}} \qquad (9–15)$$

where the period T is in seconds; L2 in henrys; and V_{in}, V_o, and $V_{p/p}$ in volts for C2 in farads.

Filter Capacitance Equivalent Series Resistance

A capacitor selected in accordance with Eq. 9–15 for a certain specified ripple voltage will actually yield a larger ripple voltage. This is so because high capacitance capacitors – either aluminum, electrolytic, or tantalum – are not pure capacitors. Between their input terminals, a more exact equivalent circuit at frequencies up to 20 kHz is a capacitor in series with a resistance, usually referred to as the "equivalent series resistance" or ESR (Fig. 9–4A).

This resistance arises from the detailed internal construction of the capacitor: how connections are made from the external leads to the equivalent capacitor "plates" and nature of the plates. ESR is a function mainly of capacitance and somewhat of voltage rating as voltage rating affects internal construction, which in consequence affects ESR. Even for the same capacitance and voltage rating, ESR will vary with physical dimensions of the capacitor can, since this affects to some extent those parameters determining ESR.

Most vendors do not specify ESR in their data sheets but can supply maximum values for their various types on request. There is general confusion among users and also among capacitor vendors as to just what is meant by "ESR." Some vendors use the term "ESR at 120 Hz" or "maximum impedance at 120 Hz." This is the impedance measured on a bridge at 120 Hz. For an equivalent circuit of a resistor in series with a capacitor, the impedance measured thus (Fig. 9–4B) is

$$Z = \left((ESR)^2 + X_c^2\right)^{1/2} = \left((ESR)^2 + \frac{1}{2\pi 120C}\right)^{1/2}$$

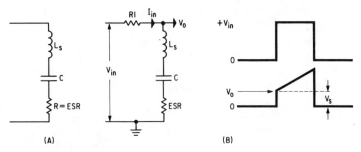

Fig. 9–4. (A) Equivalent circuit of an electrolytic or tantalum capacitor. L_s is only significant at very high frequencies. (B) Applying an input current step to measure ESR. ESR $= V_s/I_{in}$.

It might be thought that given a measured value of Z, ESR could be calculated from the above. But ESR from the above is $\text{ESR} = (Z^2 - X_c^2)^{1/2}$. Since Z^2 and X_c^2 are large numbers and almost equal, small errors in either give large errors in their difference and hence in ESR. The impedance Z is given as a maximum value and represents essentially the impedance of the minimum capacitance in the production spread. Thus, what is often called "maximum ESR at 120 Hz" has no relation at all to the value of the equivalent resistance in series with the capacitor.

If ripple magnitudes are important, true ESR must be obtained from the vendor or measured. This contribution to ripple from ESR is simply $V_{\text{ripple(p/p)}} = (\text{ESR})\Delta I_L$, where ΔI_L is given by Eq. 9-2

$$\Delta I_L = \frac{V_o T(V_{in} - V_o)}{V_{in} \, \text{L2}}$$

This ESR ripple contribution should be added linearly to that given by Eq. 9-15 for a preselected value of C2.

ESR Measurements

Because ESR is most often not quoted in capacitor data sheets and difficult to obtain from vendors, it is simplest to measure it. A simple scheme for doing this is shown in Fig. 9-4B. A step of current is applied to the top of the capacitor. For R1 >> ESR, the current is approximately $I_{in} = V_{in}/\text{R1}$. Voltage at the capacitor output will have the waveform shown in Fig. 4-9B. The series inductance is generally negligible and, hence, the output voltage will have an initial upward step of magnitude $V_s = I_{in}(\text{ESR}) = (V_{in}/\text{R1})(\text{ESR})$. After the initial step, the output will rise upward as shown with a $dV/dt = I_{in}/C$. ESR is calculated from $\text{ESR} = V_s/I1$. For large capacitors having low ESR, the current step must be quite large to get a significant V_s. A current step of 1–5 A from a 10-V V_{in} is a convenient test signal. If the input source voltage droops on application of the capacitor load, it is important that this should be measured. Actually, if it does droop, the input current can still be measured by measuring voltage at both ends of R1 when the load is applied.

9.1.7 Design of Input, Filter, and Power Components for a Typical Off-the-ac-Line Step-Down Switching Regulator

A specific example will clarify the various calculations for a step-down switching regulator.

Assume a step-down switching regulator to produce a regulated output from a directly "off-the-ac-line" bridge rectifier as in Fig. 9-5. The regulated output cannot be used directly as it is not dc isolated from the ac line. Rather, it is used as the preregulated input to a dc/dc converter as in some of the block diagrams of Chap. 3 (Figs. 3-1, 3-2, 3-9, and 3-12). Rectified secondary output voltages in the dc/dc converter are dc isolated from the ac line and can be put at any dc level.

Assume input ac is 60 Hz single phase at a nominal voltage of 120 V with $\pm 10\%$ steady-state tolerance limits. The switching regulator will produce a regulated voltage sufficiently low so that at 10% low line voltage, at the bottom of the ripple triangle at the input bridge rectifier–filter capacitance, the voltage is still high enough to allow safe switching regulation operation.

The criterion for safe switching regulation operation is taken to be that the ratio $T_{on}/T = V_o/V_{in}$ (Eq. 9–1) should not be greater than 90% at minimum instantaneous input voltage. "On" times of greater than $0.9T$ can result in problems because of storage time delay in the transistor switch Q1.

LC Filter Calculations

At nominal ac input of 120 V, the input filter capacitance will charge up to a peak voltage equal to the peak of the ac sine wave or $(1.41)(120)$V. Peak-to-peak ripple voltage at the top of the input capacitor C1 is determined by the average load current drawn out of node V_a and the magnitude of C1. Assume an average load current of 2 A and select C1 from Eq. 5–3 for a peak-to-peak ripple voltage of 20 V. Lesser ripple voltage will require bulkier and more expensive filter capacitors, which in any case take up a large fraction of the allotted regulator space. Then, from Eq. 5–3, the required input capacitor C1 is

$$C1 = (8.3 \times 10^{-3})I/\Delta V = (8.3 \times 10^{-3})(2/20) = 830 \ \mu F$$

Thus, at nominal ac line voltage, the top of the triangular ripple voltage is at $+169$ V (actually two rectifier diode drops or 1.8 V below that). The bottom of the triangular ripple is at $167 - 20 = +147$ V. Average dc voltage at V_a is $167 - 10 = +157$ V.

Then at 10% low ac line voltage, the average or dc voltage at V_a is $0.9(157) = +141$ V, and the bottom of the ripple triangle is at $0.9(147) = +132$ V.

Now design the step-down switching regulator so that, at the bottom of the ripple triangle, the "on" time duty cycle of the switch Q1 is no more than 90%. To make it closer to 100% may be troublesome as Q1 will have to turn on too soon after the end of its previous turn-on time. Then from Eq. 9–1

$$V_o = V_{in}(T_{on}/T)$$

or $T_{on}/T = V_o/V_{in}$

or $V_o = 0.9(132) = 119$ V

Reduce this to 110 V for an additional margin of safety.

Thus, whatever the input ac line voltage or at whatever level V_a is, on its 20-V peak-to-peak ripple triangle, the feedback-controlled T_{on}/T ratio will be such as to keep V_o at $+110$ V.

Let the switching frequency be 20 kHz or $T = 1/(20 \times 10^{+3}) = 50 \ \mu sec$. Calculate L2 from Eq. 9–14:

$$L2 = \frac{2.5 V_o T (V_{in(nom)} - V_o)}{I_{dc \ (nom)} V_{in(nom)}}$$

In the above it was assumed that at nominal line voltage the average current from the bridge rectifier (or average current into the switch Q1) is 2 A. Assume for the moment that there are, say, only 5% power losses from V_a to V_o. Then for nominal ac line voltage, for $V_a = 157$ V, I = 2 A,

$$P(\text{at } V_o) = 0.95 P(\text{at } V_a) = 0.95(157)(2) = 298 \text{ W}$$

And for $V_o = +110$ V, the dc (or average load current) at nominal line input is

$$I_{dc(nom \ at \ V_o)} = 298/110 = 2.71 \text{ A}$$

Now from Eq. 9–14

$$L2 = \frac{2.4(110)(50 \times 10^{-6})(157 - 110)}{2.71(157)} = 1.5 \text{ mH}$$

The filter capacitance C2 is now calculated from Eq. 9–15:

$$C2 = \frac{V_o T^2 (V_{in} - V_o)}{8 V_{in} (L2) \Delta V_{p/p}}$$

Assume now a ripple output $\Delta V_{p/p}$ of 0.1% of V_o or $(0.001)(110) = 0.11$ V. Then

$$C2 = \frac{110(157 - 110)(50 \times 10^{-6})^2}{8(157)(1.5 \times 10^{-3})(0.11)} = 62 \ \mu\text{F}$$

This value of capacitance, if there were no ESR in it, would yield the calculated 0.1% or 0.11-V ripple. But there will be an additional peak-to-peak ripple voltage due to $\Delta I_{L(ESR)}$. Now from Eq. 9–3A

$$\Delta I_L = \frac{V_o T (V_{in} - V_o)}{V_{in} L2} = \frac{110(50 \times 10^{-6})(157 - 110)}{157(1.5 \times 10^{-3})} = 1.09 \text{ A}$$

The additional ripple component due to ESR is then (1.09)(ESR), where ESR is obtained either from the vendor or measurements in Sect. 9.1.6.

Transistor Switch Base Drive and Minimum dc Load Current

Note that the peak-to-peak value of the ripple current in the inductor has been calculated as 1.09 A (ΔI_L). Thus, the peak current in switch transistor Q1 is $2.71 + (1.09/2) = 3.26$ A. The base drive of Q1 will have to be sufficient to turn on 3.26 A at minimum current gain. For a minimum β of, say, 15, this requires a base drive of 217 mA.

This may require a Darlington driver ahead of the switch transistor. The Darlington driver (Sect. 2.1.9) is a valuable addition, since Q1, being a large power transistor, has relatively long storage and fall times. The Darlington driver keeps Q1 from saturating and reduces total turn-off time considerably.

Fast turnoff of switch transistor Q1 is essential for minimizing ac switching losses and avoiding catastrophic failures at these relatively high input voltages. Circuit tricks to speed up turn-off time are considered in Sect. 9.2.4.

The inductor ripple current of 1.09 A peak to peak permits going down to a minimum dc load current of $\Delta I_L/2 = 1.09/2$ or 0.55 A before the inductor current runs down to zero at the end of the turn-off time (Sect. 9.1.2).

Power Dissipation, Heat Sink, and Temperature Rise Calculations

The major power dissipating elements are the transistor switch Q1 and free-wheeling diode D1. Their dissipations are calculated as follows:

The transistor dissipates significant power only during its "on" time. Hence

$$PD_{(Q1)} = V_{ce(sat)} I_{dc}(T_{on}/T) \qquad \text{(from Eq. 9–6)}$$

Now from Fig. 9–2C, current in Q1 during the on time (even though it is a ramp on top of a step) is approximated by a square-topped pulse of amplitude

I_{dc}. Maximum (T_o/T) ratio occurs when input voltage is low. For 10% low ac voltage, $V_{in(min)} = 157(0.9) = 141$ V. Then from Eq. 9–1

$$(T_o/T)_{max} = (V_o/V_{in})_{max} = 110/141 = 0.78$$

And for $V_{ce(sat)}$ of 1 V, I_{dc} of 2.71 A at 298 W of output power (Sect. 9.1.7):

$$PD_{Q1} = 1(2.71)(0.78) = 2.1 \text{ W}$$

Then, assuming as in Sect. 9.1.4 that ac switching overlap losses are equal to dc losses, Q1 dissipation is

$$PD_{Q1} = (2)(2.1) = 4.2 \text{ W}$$

There is dc dissipation in free-wheeling diode only during the Q1 off time. Its dissipation is (from Eq. 9–7)

$$PD_{D1} = V_{D1}I_{D1}(T - T_{on})/T$$

The ratio $(T - T_{on})/T$ is a maximum when T_{on} is a minimum. This occurs at a maximum input voltage or

$$V_{in} = 1.1(157) = 173 \text{ V}$$

Then
$$[(T - T_{on})/T]_{max} = 1 - (T_{on}/T)_{min} = 1 - (V_o/V_{in})_{min}$$
$$= 1 - 110/173 = 0.36$$

and assuming a 1-V drop on diode D1,

$$PD_{D1} = 1(2.71)(0.36) = 0.98 \text{ W}$$

Diode D1 must be of the fast recovery type (Fig. 2–4). If recovery time to a high reverse resistance following forward current is too slow, the overlap of high voltage and current during turnoff can result in ac dissipation two to three times the dc dissipation. Reverse recovery time is a function of the specific circuitry: achievable di/dt in Q1 when it turns on, forward current just prior to turnoff, and temperature (Motorola IN3879 data sheet). Assuming a recovery time dissipation twice the dc value, the total diode dissipation is still only 3 W.

Thus, total Q1 and D1 dissipation = $4.2 + 3 = 7.2$ W. For a heat sink temperature rise of, say, 20°C above ambient, its thermal resistance must be $\Delta T/\Delta W = 20/7 = 2.85$/watt.

Now Fig. 4–8 shows that a heat sink at a 7-W power level has a thermal resistance of 0.75 times its resistance at a 1-W power level. Thus, the required 1-W thermal resistance is $2.85/0.75 = 3.8$°C/watt. Finally, Fig. 4–7 shows that for 3.8°C/watt, a heat sink area of 75 sq in. is required.

Junction temperature rise above heat sink is calculated from Eq. 4–1

$$\Delta T = PD(\theta_{hsc} + \theta_{jc})$$

Assume a thermal resistance of heat sink to case (θ_{hsc}) through a mica washer of 0.5°C/watt and transistor thermal resistance junction to case of 1°C/watt (2N6251 transistor). Then

$$\Delta T = 4.2(0.5 + 1.0) = 6.3°C$$

Thus, the transistor junction temperature will rise above ambient by ΔT (heat sink to ambient) $+ \Delta T$ (junction to heat sink) $= 20 + 6.3 = 26.3$°C.

The free-wheeling diode (IN3892) has a thermal resistance of 2°C/watt and dissipation of 3 W. For an insulating washer thermal resistance of 0.5°C/watt, it will thus rise $3(2 + 0.5) = 7.5$°C above the heat sink or 27.5°C above ambient.

To keep junction temperatures to 105°C maximum, temperature rise of this magnitude permits a worst-case ambient temperature of $105 - 27.5 \cong 78$°C. This is above the maximum usually specified for military equipment. Higher ambient temperatures may, of course, be tolerated with somewhat larger heat sink area (Fig. 4–7).

It should be noted, of course, that if other power-dissipating elements in the supply are located on the same heat sink, its area must be selected to yield the same desired 20°C rise for the sum of all power dissipations flowing into the heat sink.

ESR and Ripple Current Ratings in Input and Output Capacitors

Current drawn from the input capacitor (Fig. 9–5) is a series of "ramp-on-a-step" or trapezoid pulses as shown in Fig. 9–2C, which may be approximated by a series of square-topped pulses of amplitude $I_{dc(load)}$.

An often-overlooked problem with switching regulators is that this current has a large ripple current at the switching frequency. This high ripple current, which must flow through the input capacitor, can dissipate enough power in its ESR to heat it to the point of destruction.

In Fig. 5–2 it is seen that with a capacitive input filter, the capacitor itself supplies the load current for most of the ac line period and, hence, the ripple current component of the above waveform must flow through the input filter capacitor. In the regulator designed in the previous sections, the current drawn through the filter capacitor is approximated by a series of square-topped pulses having an amplitude of 2.71 A and an "on" time-to-period ratio (T_{on}/T) of 0.78 (see section on power dissipation, heat sink, and temperature rise calculation).

It is well known that the rms value of a rectangular waveform at a level of I_p for T_{on} time units and at zero for $T - T_{on}$ time units is $I_{rms} = I_p(T_{on}/T)^{1/2}$. Thus, the rms value of the ripple current supplied by the input capacitor is $2.71(0.78)^{1/2} = 2.39$ A. The capacitor must thus have a ripple current rating of at least this value at the operating temperature and frequency.

Many vendors do not supply ripple current ratings, however. This is a design parameter that must be taken seriously, for, although most power supply failures are in semiconductors, capacitors will fail if these ripple ratings are exceeded.

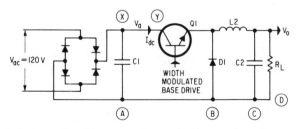

Fig. 9–5. An ac-line-driven step-down switching regulator for sample calculations of L2 and C2.

Vendors who do supply maximum ripple current ratings generally supply them at a frequency of 120 Hz and the maximum temperature for the capacitor type.[1] They also suggest a multiplying factor for higher frequencies and temperatures. As a typical example, for the Sprague type 32D aluminum electrolyte capacitors, ripple current ratings at frequencies above 1 kHz are 1.4 times their ratings at 120 Hz. Also, at temperatures up to 65°C, ripple current ratings are 1.5 times their value at 85°C – the maximum temperature for this type.

Thus, the input filter capacitor was calculated earlier in this section as 830 μF. If a Sprague type 32D, 250-V, 800-μF capacitor is used, the vendor specifies its 120 Hz, 85°C ripple rating as 2.8 A. At 65°C, 20 kHz, its ripple rating is 2.8(1.5)(1.4) = 5.88 A – quite an adequate safety margin for the actual ripple current of 2.39 A.

Ripple current rating in the output capacitor must also be considered. Thus, in Fig. 9–2F, it is seen that the ripple current in the output capacitor is a triangle of peak-to-peak amplitude of ΔI_L or 1.09 A. It can be shown that the rms value of a triangle of peak-to-peak amplitude ΔI_L is $\Delta I_L/\sqrt{3}$ or in this case $1.09/\sqrt{3} = 0.63$ A. Earlier in this section, the output filter capacitor was calculated as 62 μF. When a Sprague-type 34D, 75-μF, 200-V capacitor is used, the data sheet indicates a ripple rating of 0.43 A at 120 Hz and 85°C. For this type, the multiplying factor up to 65°C is 1.5 and that for frequencies above 1 kHz is 1.2. This gives a ripple current rating of 0.43(1.5)(1.2) = 0.77 A, also an adequate margin of safety for an actual rms ripple current of 0.63 A.

Noise and Cross Talk on Switch Input and Output Wires

One of the major practical problems in building switching regulators is to ensure that the high-current, high-voltage, fast-rise-time signals at the switch input and output do not couple into the inputs of high-gain amplifiers. With all other design decisions correct and worst-case-safe, such cross talk resulting from poor wire harness, wire routing, and wire shielding practices can be the undoing of a design.

In Fig. 9–5, it is seen that the emitter of the switch transistor and all other wires connected to it move up and down an amount V_{in} volts. With V_{in} as high as 170 V (or about 340 V for a 230V_{ac} input) and with voltage rise and fall times generally under 0.5 μsec, there is a great likelihood of electrostatic (via capacitance between wires) cross talk. Such cross talk can generally be minimized by using a shielded wire for any wire that has a large $\Delta V/\Delta t$.

Electromagnetic cross talk (via magnetic fields around high-current-carrying wires producing a magnetic flux change through other wire loops) is more difficult to control. The electrostatic wire shield does not, of course, confine the magnetic fields. These can be confined only by having, for each wire carrying an ac current in one direction, a close-by wire twisted with it and carrying an equal current in the opposite direction. The equal and opposite currents produce canceling magnetic fields. Shielding twisted wire pairs are often effective when twisting alone is insufficient.

Thus, in Fig. 9–5, every time switch Q1 closes, a high-amplitude, fast-rise-time current flows from the top of C1 into the collector of Q1. Its return path

---

[1] Sprague Electric Co., Engineering Bulletin 3441, p. 14.

is initially through D1 until that becomes reverse biased and then via L2 and C2 and along the return wire in the opposite direction from the bottom end of C2 (point C), picking up the bottom end of D1 and then the bottom end of C1 (point A). Thus, the wires from the bottom ends of D1 and C2 should be brought to a common tie point with leads as short as possible. That tie point should be brought with a lead as short as possible close to the wire running between the top end of C1 to the Q1 collector and twisted with it before running back to pick up the bottom end of C1 at point A. Or briefly the wire A–B should be twisted with X–Y. All wires off the emitter of Q1 (to cathode of D1, input of L2) should be short as possible, and, similarly, wires from bottom ends of D1, C2 should be as short as possible.

All of the above-mentioned wires carrying high-current pulses should run in their own separate wire harnesses and should, as far as possible, not be in, close to, or parallel to other wires in other wire harnesses.

Probably the largest ΔI and $\Delta I/\Delta t$ occurs at the instant switch Q1 turns on, for at that instant, and until the free-wheeling diode D1 is starved down to zero forward current and then recovers to its high reverse impedance, Q1 is turning on into a short circuit. Current is limited only by β of Q1 and its base drive. The resulting large $\Delta I/\Delta t$ in the wire X–Y and A–B produce large magnetic fields, which can be canceled by twisting wire A–B with wire X–Y.

But the wire X–Y has inductance and with the shunt capacity at the collector of Q1 forms a series-resonant circuit. The large $\Delta I/\Delta t$ produces a ring or shocked high-frequency oscillation at the collector of Q1, which can cross talk into other circuits. Generally, a small nonelectrolytic capacitor of 0.05–0.10 or 0.50 μF from the collector of Q1 to the nearest ground point can reduce the amplitude of the ring and, by also reducing its frequency, can make it less capable of coupling significant voltage into other circuits or wires.

In general, eliminating cross talk is a black art and almost any new design is a problem in itself. The general rules one can follow are: avoid large spacing between wires carrying high currents in opposite directions; twist them if possible; electrostatically shield wires with large-voltage, fast rise and fall times; keep impedance at inputs to amplifiers—transistors and SCRs—as low as pos-

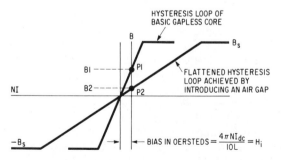

Fig. 9–6. A dc current in an inductor biases it up to $B1$ close to saturation. The permissible ΔB before saturation occurs is $B_{sat} - B1$. By introducing an air gap, the slope of the $B–H$ curve is flattened and the same dc bias current sets operating point at P2 and now the permissible ΔB is $B_{sat} - B2$.

sible (say, under 200 ohms); keep wires with high-voltage, high-current signals out of other wire harnesses; and keep such wires short and, if possible, remote from and not parallel to other wires.

In general, it is easier to avoid cross-talk problems by silencing the noise generators rather than reducing the sensitivity of circuits to noise, for there are far fewer noise generators than potential circuits sensitive to noise.

Often, a noise source probe is of value in locating the troublesome noise generator. This can be made by winding a few (one to five) turns of a $\frac{1}{2}$-in. diameter coil and connecting it via a short twisted pair to the input to a high-gain oscilloscope. Probing with this "direction-finding" pickup coil around various wires and orienting the plane of the coil in various directions can usually isolate the troublesome noise-generating wires. If the interfering signal is an electrostatic one, probing with the input probe of an oscilloscope can often find an offending wire.

9.1.8 Output Filter Inductance Design for Direct Current in Inductor

The filter inductance (L2 of Fig. 9–5) in a switching regulator carries a direct current equal to the dc load current. This produces magnetic bias close to the top of the hysteresis loop (Fig. 8–7A) and prevents it from being able to sustain a voltage when the ac voltage is in such a direction as to move it further up the loop toward saturation. This can be seen more clearly in Fig. 9–6. A given dc current, I_{dc}, forces the operating point in H to $H = 0.4\pi NI_{dc}/L$ where H is in oersteds for N in turns, L (magnetic path length) in centimeters. If this value of H sets operating point at P1, then the quiescent operating point in B is $B1$. Any ac voltage applied to the inductor can only produce a B in the positive half cycle of twice $(B_s - B1)$ before the core saturates. If the volt second area in the positive half cycle is $(E\Delta T)$, then the amount the core moves up in B during this half cycle is

$$\Delta B = \frac{E\Delta T \times 10^{+8}}{NA} \tag{9-16}$$

where ΔB is in gauss for E in volts, ΔT in seconds, A in square centimeters, and N in turns. The area under the positive half cycle of the input waveform is thus limited by Eq. 9–16 so that $\Delta B = B_s - B1$. At volt second areas greater than this, the core will saturate and the voltage will collapse to zero.

Saturation is avoided by introducing an air gap in series in the magnetic path. The effect of this is to flatten out the hysteresis loop as shown in Fig. 9–6. The same dc current sets operating point in B, further down from saturation to a point like P2. Now a ΔB in the positive half cycle of $B_s - B2$ can be sustained across the inductor before it saturates.

Gapped Core Design for Preventing Magnetic Core Saturation

The design of a gapped core to avoid saturation under conditions of a dc bias current involves selection of the core itself and calculating the number of required turns and width of the necessary air gap. The design decisions stem from some well-known magnetic fundamentals, which will be reviewed here.

The fundamental relation in magnetic circuits is Ampere's law:

$$\oint Hdl = 0.4\pi NI$$

This states the line integral around a closed loop of length l of the dot product of field intensity H and element of length dl is equal to $0.4\pi NI$, where NI is the ampere turns enclosed by the loop. Here, H is in oersteds, l in centimeters, I in amperes. and N in turns.

Consider, as in Fig. 9–7, a toroidal magnetic path of length l_i in the magnetic material and an air gap of length l_a. Take the line integral around the inside of the toroid and across the air gap. Everywhere along this path inside the iron, the field intensity is parallel to the path of integration and constant at an intensity of H_i. Across the air gap, to a close approximation, the field intensity is constant, equal to H_a and parallel to the path of integration. Thus

$$\oint H dl = H_i l_i + H_a l_a = 0.4\pi NI$$

If the air gap is narrow and there is no bulging or fringing of magnetic flux as it crosses the air gap, then the flux density in iron, B_i, is equal to that in air, B_a. Then, $H_i = B_i/\mu_i$ where μ_i is the average iron permeability and $H_a = B_a/\mu_a = B_i$, since $B_i = B_a$ and permeability of air, μ_a, is unity. Then

$$B_i l_i/\mu_i + B_i l_a = 0.4\pi NI$$

or
$$B_i = \frac{0.4\pi NI}{l_i/\mu_i + l_a} = \frac{0.4\pi NI \mu_i}{l_i + \mu_i l_a} \qquad (9\text{--}18)$$

Equation 9–18 is very instructive. It states that for a given NI product, the flux density in the iron with an air gap of length l_a is smaller than with zero air gap in the ratio $l_i/(l_i + \mu_i l_a)$. This states quantitatively what is shown in Fig. 9–6 — that at a given H (proportional to NI), B with an air gap is lower than B without the air gap.

This can also be stated another way; the air gap increases the magnetic path length by an amount $\mu_i l_a$. Thus, for permeability of 1,500 (average permeability of ferrite cores), adding on air gap of length l_a increases the effective magnetic path length by $1,500 l_a$.

In Eq. 9–18, the maximum flux density in iron, B_i, will occur at maximum I in the inductor. This maximum I is the maximum at the top of the current ramp in Fig. 9–2E, or it is the sum of $I_{\text{dc(load max)}} + \Delta I_L/2$, where ΔI_L is the peak-to-peak current ramp calculated in Eq. 9–4. In Eq. 9–18, B_i will be set (for a ferrite core inductor) to 2,000 G to prevent the core from rising on the slow knee of its hysteresis loop at maximum temperature (Fig. 8–4A).

Thus, as soon as the number of turns N and iron core length l_i are chosen, Eq. 9–18 permits selecting an air gap length. N and l_i are chosen as soon as a specific ungapped core is chosen. The selection of an air gap is described in the following section.

Core Geometry Selection to Avoid Saturation   The criterion for core selection is related to the product of the core winding area (A_c) and the area A_e of its magnetic path in much the same way as this product is the criterion of transformer core selection (Eq. 8–7).

For any inductor, the voltage across it may be defined either in terms of the rate of change of current in it or the rate of change of flux in its core. Or

$$E = L(di/dt) = N(d\phi/dt)10^{-8}$$

From which $L = N(d\phi/di)10^{-8} = NA_e(dB/di)10^{-8}$

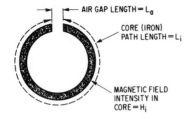

AIR GAP LENGTH = L_a

CORE (IRON)
PATH LENGTH = L_i

MAGNETIC FIELD
INTENSITY IN
CORE = H_i

Fig. 9–7. Adding an air gap flattens the core's hysteresis loop, as shown in Fig. 9–6. Flux density for a core of permeability μ_i, air gap length L_a, iron path length L_i is

$$B_i = 4\pi N I \mu_i/(l_i + \mu_i\, l_a).$$

where L is in henrys for N in turns, A_e is in square centimeters, dB in gauss, and di in amperes. Now, $dB = B_{max}$ for $di = I_{max}$.

Then
$$A_e = \frac{(LI_{max})10^{+8}}{NB_{max}} \tag{9–19}$$

But the core winding area (A_e) must be chosen to accommodate the required number of turns at the specified safe-current density and fraction of the total core winding area usable.

Thus, assume only 75% of the core winding area A_c is usable and assume N turns of wire, whose area per turn is A_t. Then

$$NA_t = 0.75A_c$$

or
$$A_c = NA_t/0.75 \tag{9–20}$$

with A_c and A_t in square centimeters. And multiplying Eqs. 9–19 and 9–20

$$A_eA_c = \frac{(LI_{max}NA_t)10^{+8}}{NB_{max}(0.75)} = \frac{1.33(LI_{max}A_t)10^{+8}}{B_{max}} \tag{9–21}$$

In Eq. 9–21, as soon as the wire area is specified (on the basis of safe operating current density), all terms on the right-hand side are specified and the product A_eA_c is fixed. A core with the required product is then selected from the vendor's data sheet. Once this core is selected, A_e is determined from the data sheet, and from Eq. 9–19, N is calculated, since all other parameters in it are already fixed.

With N calculated, Eq. 9–18 determines $l_i + \mu_i l_a$, since all other parameters in it are fixed. For a known core, l_i is given in the data sheets or is calculable from its geometry. Finally with $l_i + \mu_i l_a$, l_i, and μ_i fixed, l_a, the required air gap length, is determined.

Design Example: Core Selection and Turns and Air Gap Calculations
Step-by-step design decisions will now be made for the specification of the inductor selected in Sect. 9.1.7. That inductor, it will be recalled, had a dc load current of 2.71 A, a peak-to-peak ΔI_L of 1.09 A, and an inductance of 1.5 mH.

First, from Eq. 9–21, the required cores A_eA_c product will be calculated. The wire area A_t is chosen on the basis of a safe current density. As a first guess, a current density of 300 circular mils/ampere will be chosen. Resulting core temperature rise will later be calculated to verify this is a safe choice of current density. Total circular mil area of the wire is then calculated as

$$A(\text{circular mils}) = 2.71(300) = 813 \text{ circular mils}$$

From the wire table in Fig. 8–10, the wire having the closest circular mil area to this is No. 21 wire (812 circular mils). And from the wire table, the diameter of this wire is 0.031 in. Assuming wire area per turn is D^2 rather than $\pi D^2/4$, the wire area per turn is $(0.031)^2 = 0.00096$ sq in. $= 0.0062$ sq cm.

In Eq. 9–21, take $B_{max} = 2,000$ G, which is safely below saturation for ferrites. Then the required $A_e A_c$ product for the core is from Eq. 9–21:

$$A_e A_c = \frac{1.33(1.5 \times 10^{-3})(2.71 + 1.09/2)(0.0062)(10^{+8})}{2,000}$$

$$= 2.01 \text{ cm}^4$$

Looking through a ferrite core vendor's catalog,[2] a ferrite cup core Ferroxcube type 3622 (Fig. 8–3) is found to have about the required $A_e A_c$ product. Its A_e is quoted as 2.02 sq cm; its winding area (in the associated 3622-1D bobbin) is 0.748 sq cm. This gives an $A_e A_c$ product of 1.51 cm^4, which is close enough.

The number of required turns is calculated from Eq. 9–19:

$$N = \frac{(LI_{max})10^{+8}}{A_e B_{max}} = \frac{(1.5 \times 10^{-3})(3.26)(10^{+8})}{2.02(2 \times 10^{+3})} = 120 \text{ turns}$$

The 3622 bobbin has an area (Fig. 8–3) of 0.116 sq in. The area per turn of wire is then $0.116/120 = 9.67 \times 10^{-4}$ sq in. and its diameter is $(9.67 \times 10^{-4})^{1/2} = 31$ mils. But this is the diameter of the No. 21 wire selected in calculating the required $A_e A_c$ product for the core. The 3622 core can thus handle the required 120 turns of No. 21 wire at the specified current density of 300 circular mils/ampere.

Now the air gap must be specified from Eq. 9–18. In that equation, μi is the "average" permeability of the core material. Choose Ferroxcube 3B7 material, which has an average permeability of 1,900.[3] Then for a B_{max} of 2,000 G, $I_{max} = 2.71 + 1.09/2 = 3.26$ A, and N $= 120$ turns, from Eq. 9–18,

$$l_i + \mu_i l_a = \frac{0.4\pi N I \mu_i}{B_i} = \frac{0.4\pi(120)(3.26)(1,900)}{2,000} = 467 \text{ cm}$$

Since the 3622 core has a mean path length l_i of 5.3 cm,[4]

$$l_i + \mu_i l_a = 467$$

Or $$l_a = \frac{467 - 5.3}{1,900} = 0.24 \text{ cm}$$

The cup core comes in two halves. Thus, if a spacer is located between the two halves, the air gap is actually twice the spacer thickness, since this spacer is in series with both "legs" of the core. The spacer thickness must then be 0.24/2 or 0.12 cm.

This completes the magnetic design of the inductor, which will have an inductance of 1.5 mH at a dc current of 2.71 A and a peak-to-peak ac current of 1.09 A. It will not saturate at the peak input current, since the design set the

[2] Ferroxcube Corp., "Linear Ferrite Materials and Components."
[3] Ferroxcube Corp., Bulletin 330-B, p. 16
[4] Ferroxcube Corp., "Linear Ferrite Materials and Components," pp. 2–61.

maximum flux density at peak input current at 2,000 G. Even at 100°C, this core material only begins to saturate slowly at about 2,500–3,000 G (Fig. 8–7B). Ferrite type 3B7 is not much different in the shape of its hysteresis loop from the type 3C8 shown in the same figure.

Thermal Analysis of Gapped Inductor

It is of interest to estimate temperature rise of the coil and case of the inductor designed in the previous section. First, consider the inductor is heat sunk. Assume the core is encapsulated (as was the transformer of Sect. 4.3.3) in a thin-walled aluminum can and has a 0.1-in. thickness of RTV potting material between its outer wall and the inner wall of the aluminum can.

The can is then heat sunk by inserting it in a snug-fitting hole in the metal mass which comprises the heat sink. The heat-flow path to a close approximation is radially outward from the winding, through the outer lip of the ferrite toroid (Fig. 8–3), through the 0.1-in. thickness of the RTV potting material and the aluminum can, and to the inside surface of the hole in the heat sink.

Then, as in Sect. 4.3.3, the major thermal resistance in this heat-flow path is that of a cylinder of RTV of 0.1-in. thickness and height equal to that of the height of the windings (0.574 in. from Fig. 8–3). Since the heat-flow path is radially through the wall of this cylinder, its thermal resistance in °C/watt is from Eq. 4–4:

$$\Delta T/P = L/KA$$

where L is in centimeters, A in square centimeters, and K in cgs units ($= 0.0026$ for RTV from Fig. 4–5). Here $A = \pi DH$, and, from Fig. 8–3, $D = 1.42$ in. and $H = 0.574$ in. (dimension K of Fig. 8–3). Then

$$A = \pi(1.42)(0.574) = 2.56 \text{ sq in.} = 16.5 \text{ sq cm}$$

Then $\qquad \Delta T/P = 0.1(2.54)/(0.0026)(16.5) = 5.9°C/\text{watt}$

The bobbin for this core is specified as having a mean length of turn for the wire of 2.92 in. For 120 turns, this is $120(2.92) = 350$ in. or 29 ft. Number 21 wire is rated at 12.8 ohms/1,000 ft and, hence, the coil resistance will be only $12.8(29/1,000) = 0.37$ ohms. This gives an I^2R loss of $(2.71)^2(0.37) = 2.7$ W.

Thus, assuming the only significant thermal resistance is the 5.9°C/watt calculated above for the RTV cylinder, temperature rise between coil and heat sink is

$$\Delta T = (\Delta T/\Delta P)P = 2.7(5.9) = 15.9°C \cong 16°C$$

For a heat sink temperature of, say, 65°C, this is still only a $65 + 15.9 \cong 81°C$ temperature for the coil – easily safe enough for Formvar wire insulation and the bobbin, which are rated at 130°C.

If the inductor is not heat sunk, its thermal resistance to ambient air is calculable from its outer surface area. The 3622 pot core has an outer surface area from Fig. 8–3 of

$$2(\pi D^2/4) + \pi DH = 2[\pi(1.42)^2/4] + \pi(1.42)(0.88) = 7.1 \text{ sq in.}$$

Assume the aluminum can in which it is encapsulated raises the outer surface area to 8 sq in. Then, from Fig. 4.7, at this area, the thermal resistance to ambient

PERMEABILITY vs dc BIAS

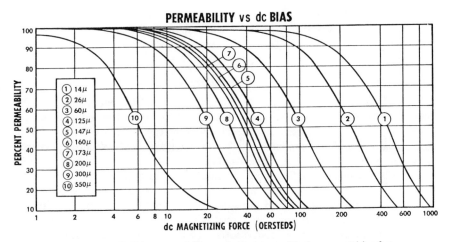

Fig. 9-8. Falloff in permeability or inductance with dc current bias for powdered iron (MPP) cores. Magnetizing force in oersteds $= 0.4\pi NI/L$, where L is the magnetic path length in centimeters, N is the number of turns, and I is dc bias in amperes. (*Courtesy* Magnetics, Inc.)

air is 18°C/watt at a 1-W power level. From Fig. 4–8, at a 2.7 power level, this reduces to 0.85(18) = 15°C/watt.

Thus, temperature rise of case above ambient air is 2.7(15) = 41°C. With a coil-to-outer case rise calculated above as 16°C, if no heat sink is provided, the coil would rise 16 + 41 = 57°C above the ambient air. At a 65°C ambient, this would make the coil temperature 65 + 57 = 122°C – quite close to the 130°C rating for the plastic bobbin and the Formvar insulation.

Because of the possibility of local hot spots within the inductor, the average temperature should be lowered 10–15°C. This could be done by fastening the inductor to the metal chassis to dissipate some of its heat by conduction or by increasing the radiating surface of the metal can by some type of elementary finned heat sink in good thermal contact with the inductor can.

Powdered Iron Cores for Preventing Magnetic Core Saturation

Molypermalloy powder (MPP) cores offer a useful alternative to conventional gapped cores for applications in which there is a direct current component tending to saturate the core.

The principal magnetic component in MPP cores is "molypermalloy," a magnetic alloy of 80% nickel and 20% iron. The magnetic alloy is formed into a brittle alloy and milled into a powder. The powder is then mixed with an insulating ceramic, which puts an effective "air gap" between particles of magnetic material. The insulated magnetic particles are then pressed into toroidal cores and annealed.

Such cores have an effective air gap uniformly distributed throughout the material and thus also have the "flattened" hysteresis loop of Fig. 9–6. They can stand large direct-current bias without saturating.

The advantage of the MPP cores is mainly in the savings of labor and assembly costs in not having to handle the two magnetic halves and the spacer

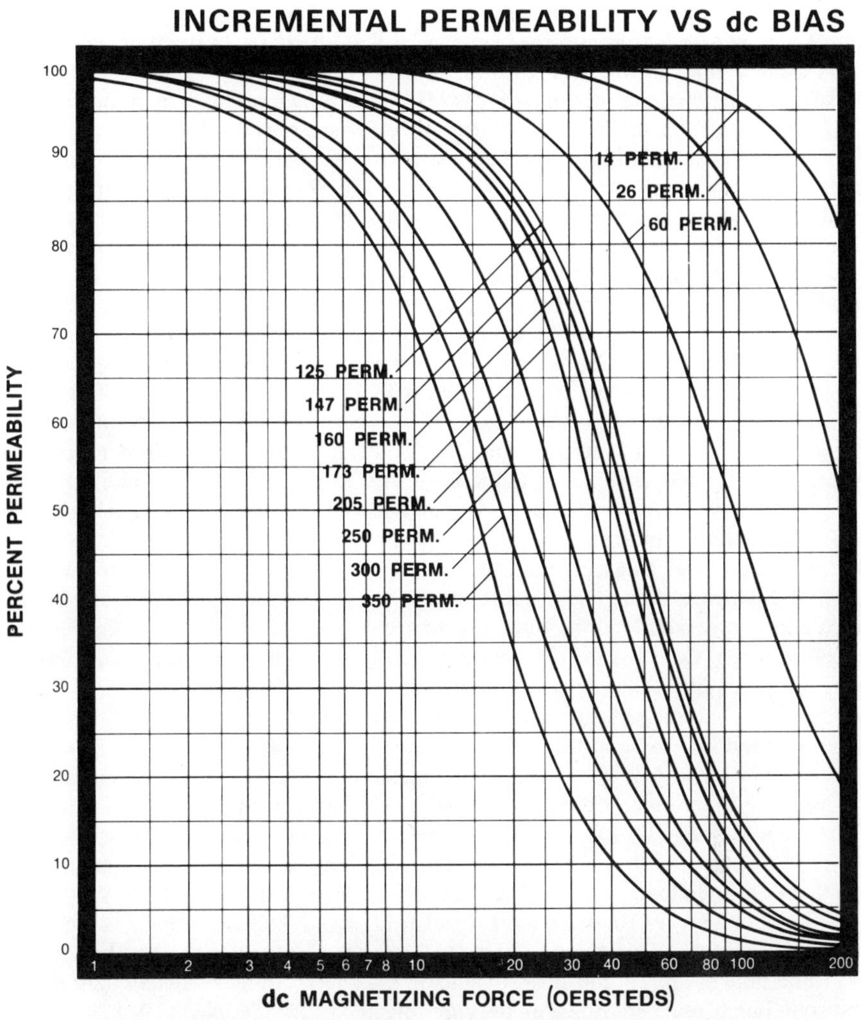

INCREMENTAL PERMEABILITY VS dc BIAS

Fig. 9–9. Falloff in permeability or inductance with dc current bias in inductor for molybdenum permalloy powder (MPP) cores. (*Courtesy* Arnold Engineering Co.)

of conventional gapped cores. The MPP core is particularly attractive for low inductances – under 500–1,500 μH.

There are two principal MPP core vendors: Arnold Engineering Co.[5] and Magnetics, Inc.[6] They offer a large selection of different toroidal core sizes with zero bias permeability ranging from about 14 to 500. The higher-permeability materials saturate at lower dc magnetization levels (Figs. 9–8 and 9–9).

---

[5] Arnold Engineering Co., Bulletin PC104E, "MPP" Cores.
[6] Magnetics, Inc., Catalog MPP3035, "Molypermalloy Powder Cores."

The selection of a specific core size and core material for a desired inductance at a given dc current bias can be done by a set of iterative calculations using vendor's curves (Fig. 9–8), showing percent permeability reduction versus dc magnetizing force in oersteds ($H = 0.4\pi NI/L$, where H is in oersteds for I in amperes, magnetic path length L in centimeters, and N in turns).

The problem in selecting a core size and permeability can be appreciated from the following. From a curve such as in Fig. 9–8, a certain percent permeability, P (or inductance), reduction is first assumed for material of the selected permeability. This fixes the magnetizing force H in oersteds, which must not be exceeded if the permeability reduction is as assumed. From this value of H, the required number of turns for the given dc bias is calculated from $H = 0.4\pi NI/L$, where L is the magnetic path length for the initially selected core.

For each core and material, the vendor supplies a proportionality factor K (Fig. 9–12), which is the inductance in millihenries per 1,000 turns. The inductance for any other number of turns N is then L (in henrys) $= KN^2 \times 10^{-9}$.

It must result that the value of N selected to give a certain percent P permeability reduction yields an inductance from $L = KN^2 \times 10^{-9}$ no more than P percent below the desired values. N can be increased P percent to achieve the desired inductance, but if the calculated value of L is more than P percent below the required value, a larger core size (larger outside diameter, OD) or lower permeability material must be selected and the calculation repeated. Such iterative calculations are rapidly done once the first core selection has shown in what direction to go. One vendor (Magnetics, Inc.) presents a core and permeability selection procedure that simplifies the choice of a core. Because selection of the core to avoid saturation is almost the most significant choice in the filter design, it is presented here by courtesy of the vendor.

Powdered Iron Core Selection Procedure   The selection procedure is described in the vendor's data sheet (Fig. 9–10) and makes use of the selector chart shown in Fig. 9–11. An inductor meeting the specification for the filter designed in Sect. 9.1.7 will be chosen. That inductor had a required inductance of 1.5 mH at a dc load current of 2.71 A and peak-to-peak ΔI_L of 1.09 A.

As in Fig. 9–10, calculate LI^2, where L is in millihenries and I is the dc current in amperes. This gives $LI^2 = 1.5(2.71)^2 = 11$. Now go to the chart in Fig. 9–11 and take LI^2 of 10, the closest value on the chart. Going vertically until the first solid line is reached, it is seen the core selected is the 55438 (Fig. 9–12). This core is available in the indicated geometry and permeability ranges shown in Fig. 9–12. In accordance with Fig. 9–10, it can be used at any permeability equal to or lower than that at the intersection of the coordinate and the first solid permeability line. Use it at a permeability of 60, since that requires a minimum number of turns.

Figure 9–12 shows that the 55439 core (same geometry as the 55438 but with a permeability of 60) has a K factor of 135 mH/1,000 turns. Thus, at zero dc bias, its required number of turns for 1.5 mH is $N = [(1.5 \times 10^{-3})/(135 \times 10^{-9})]^{1/2} = 105$ turns. Now the percent reduction in permeability for 2.71 A of dc bias must be checked. The magnetizing force for a magnetic path length of 10.74 cm (Fig. 9–12) is

$$H = \frac{0.4\pi NI}{L} = \frac{0.4\pi(105)(2.71)}{10.74} = 33 \text{ Oe}$$

SELECTION PROCEDURE

Only two parameters of the design application must be known:

Inductance required with dc bias

dc current

1. Compute the product of LI^2 where:

   L = inductance required with dc bias (millihenrys)
   I = dc current (amperes)

2. Locate the LI^2 value on the Core Selector Chart. Follow this coordinate to the intersection with the first core size that lies within the family of solid permeability lines. (Small core sizes are at bottom, large sizes at top). This core size is the smallest that can be used.

3. Any solid permeability line that passes through the intersection point of the LI^2 and core size coordinates or crosses the LI^2 coordinate below this intersection point may be used.

   The choice of permeability can be based on Q requirements at the operating frequency of the application. Use the Q curves for this selection.

   If Q is not a consideration, use the highest permeability indicated, as this choice will yield the lowest winding factor.

4. The design application may call for a Q requirement at a higher frequency than the core/permeability combinations indicated in Steps 2 and 3.

   By following the LI^2 coordinate to lower permeabilities and larger core sizes, an optimum choice for this type design may be made. For a given permeability, always use the core size just above the permeability line.

5. Inductance, core size, and permeability are now known.

   The nominal inductance (millihenrys per thousand turns) can be obtained from the Inductance Table . With this information, use a Core Calculator to calculate the number of turns needed to obtain the required inductance .

   Increase the number of turns obtained in this calculation by 10%.

6. Choose the correct wire size using the Wire Table.

7. The core chosen will have an inductance equal to or greater than that required, when biased with the specified dc current. The winding factor will be between 25% and 40%.

Fig. 9-10. Selection procedure for choosing a specific powdered iron core size and number of turns for a desired inductance at a specified dc current bias in the inductor. (*Courtesy* Magnetics, Inc.)

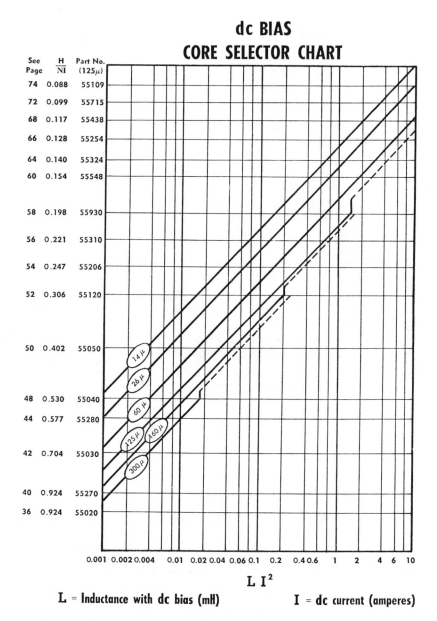

dc BIAS
CORE SELECTOR CHART

See Page	$\dfrac{H}{NI}$	Part No. (125μ)
74	0.088	55109
72	0.099	55715
68	0.117	55438
66	0.128	55254
64	0.140	55324
60	0.154	55548
58	0.198	55930
56	0.221	55310
54	0.247	55206
52	0.306	55120
50	0.402	55050
48	0.530	55040
44	0.577	55280
42	0.704	55030
40	0.924	55270
36	0.924	55020

$$L\,I^2$$

L = Inductance with dc bias (mH)   **I** = dc current (amperes)

Fig. 9–11. Selector chart for choosing core size and permeability from LI^2 in accordance with Fig. 9–10 for MPP cores. (*Courtesy* Magnetics, Inc.)

Now referring to Fig. 9–8, it is seen at 33 Oe the percent reduction in permeability and, hence, of inductance is about 8%. This can be recovered by increasing the number of turns by about 8%, which would increase inductance by

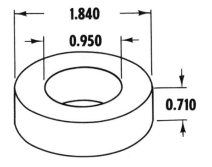

WINDOW AREA	842,700 cir. mils	
CROSS SECTION	0.308 sq in.	1.990 sq cm
PATH LENGTH	4.23 in.	10.74 cm
WEIGHT	6.4 oz	182. g

WINDING TURN LENGTH

WINDING FACTOR	LENGTH/TURN	
100% (UNITY)	0.284 ft	8.66 cm
60%	0.253 ft	7.71 cm
40%	0.222 ft	6.78 cm
20%	0.209 ft	6.37 cm
0%	0.204 ft	6.22 cm

CORE DIMENSIONS AFTER FINISH

OD(MAX)	1.875 in.	47.6 mm
ID (MIN)	0.918 in.	23.3 mm
HT (MAX)	0.745 in.	18.92 mm

WOUND COIL DIMENSIONS

UNITY WINDING FACTOR

| OD (MAX) | 2.51 in. | 63.8 mm |
| HT (MAX) | 1.525 in. | 38.7 mm |

MAGNETIC INFORMATION

PART NO.	PERM μ	INDUCTANCE @ 1000 TURNS MH±8%	NOMINAL DC RESISTANCE OHMS/MH**	FINISHES AND STABILIZATIONS*	GRADING STATUS 2% BANDS	B/NI GAUSS PER AMP. TURN
55441–	14	32	0.141	A2	*	1.64 (<1500 gauss)
55440–	26	59	0.0766	A2	*	3.04 (<1500 gauss)
55439–	60	135	0.0335	ALL†	YES	7.02 (<1500 gauss)
55438–	125	281	0.0161	ALL	YES	14.6 (<1500 gauss)
55437–	147	330	0.0137	ALL†	YES	17.2 (<1500 gauss)
55436–	160	360	0.0125	ALL†	YES	18.7 (<1500 gauss)
55432–	173	390	0.0116	ALL†	YES	20.2 (<1500 gauss)
55435–	200	450	0.0100	ALL†	YES	23.4 (<600 gauss)
55433–	300	674	0.0067	A2 and L6	YES	35.1 (<300 gauss)

Fig. 9–12. Data for a typical powdered iron (MPP) core inductance at zero dc current bias for N turns is: $L = (L_{1,000}) N^2 10^{-9}$, where $L_{1,000}$ is the inductance in millihenrys per 1,000 turns and L is the inductance in henrys. For inductance at other than zero bias, refer to Fig. 9–8. (*Courtesy* Magnetics, Inc.)

$(1.08)^2$. But since the larger number of turns increases core saturation and decreases permeability by roughly $(1/1.08)$, the net inductance gain is approximately 8%.

Thus, the complete design is the 55439 core with $(1.08)(105) = 113$ turns. This core has a winding area (Fig. 9–12) of $(0.95)^2/4$ or 0.71 sq in. Assuming 75% of the area is occupied by the wire, the wire area per turn is $0.71(0.75)/113 = 0.0047$ sq in. Assuming area per turn is D^2, the wire diameter is $(0.0047)^{1/2} = 0.068$ in., which corresponds to No. 14 wire. Figure 9–12 shows the mean length of turn at 60% winding factor to be about 0.26 ft. Thus, total wire resistance for 113 turns of No. 14 wire at 2.5 ohms/1,000 ft. (Fig. 8–10) is $113(0.26)(0.0025) = 0.07$ ohms. Power dissipation in the coil is $I^2R = (2.71)^2(0.07) = 0.51$ W, considerably less than the 2.7 W for the gapped core of Sect. 9.1.8. This is explained, of course, by the fact that the MPP design used a larger core, permitting larger wire size.

9.2   Circuit Considerations in Step-Down Switching Regulators

9.2.1 Pulse-Width-Modulator Circuit

Up to this point, this chapter has considered only the major power elements of the switching regulator of Fig. 9–1. That figure shows the essential elements needed to complete a regulator design. The first element is a dc difference amplifier or voltage comparator that samples a fraction of the output voltage to be regulated and compares it to a standard reference. The output is an error voltage proportional to the difference between the sampled fraction and the reference voltage.

The amplified dc error voltage then must be converted in a "width modulator" to a switch turn-on pulse whose width varies as the output voltage varies. Polarities are chosen such that an increase in output voltage causes a shorter output pulse. This pulse is then fed through a pulse amplifier to turn the switch on and off. Regulated output voltage in Fig. 9–1 is $V_o = V_{in}(T_{on}/T)$, and the T_{on}/T ratio is adjusted automatically by the negative-feedback network to make the sampled fraction of the output voltage equal to the reference voltage. Thus, in Fig. 9–1

$$V_o = \left(\frac{R1 + R2}{R2}\right)V_r = V_{in}\left(\frac{T_{on}}{T}\right)$$

The dc voltage comparator of Fig. 9–13 may be either the two-transistor difference amplifier of Sect. 6.5.1 or one of the many available operational amplifiers such as the 741 or the 723 series (using only the difference amplifier portion of it).

The pulse-width modulator is usually implemented as shown in Fig. 9–13. A triangle is generated by integrating the basic square wave of period T. This is usually available as an input to the power supply if the switching regulator is to be synchronous with the system clock frequency. If not available as an input, the power supply can generate this square wave either with a free-running multivibrator, a Jensen magnetic oscillator (Sect. 2.4.3), or an integrated circuit oscillator (SE 555), followed by an integrated circuit divide-by-two element.

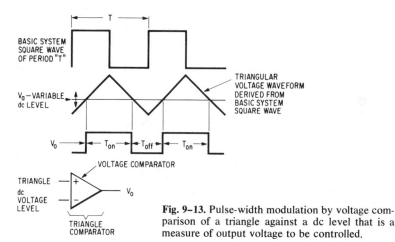

Fig. 9–13. Pulse-width modulation by voltage comparison of a triangle against a dc level that is a measure of output voltage to be controlled.

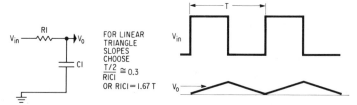

Fig. 9–14. Generating the triangle for the comparator of Fig. 9–13 by integrating the basic system square wave.

The width-modulated pulse whose duration is proportional to the amplified difference between the reference and a fraction of the output voltage is generated in a second comparator. Inputs to this comparator are the amplified dc error voltage and the triangle as seen in Fig. 9–13. With the triangle at the noninverting input to the comparator, whenever the triangle level is above the dc level input at the inverting terminal, the comparator output is high. Conversely, the comparator output is low whenever the triangle level is below the dc level input. This comparator too may be a two-transistor difference amplifier or preferably an integrated-circuit operational amplifier, for with the high-gain operational amplifier, the instant of crossing the triangle and level is marked more sharply and output pulse rise and fall times are faster.

It can be seen that with the triangle at a fixed dc voltage level, as the dc voltage at the comparator's inverting terminal moves upward, the duration of the positive-going output signal decreases. If the duration of this positive-going signal fixes the duration of the switch (Fig. 9–1) "on" time, and if the dc level input to the comparator is proportional to the difference between a fraction of the power supply output voltage and a reference voltage, the output voltage is controlled. An increase in output voltage causes a rise in the dc level input to the comparator, the duration of its positive-going output pulse decreases, and the switch "on" time and, hence, the power supply output voltage decreases as $V_o = V_{in}(T_{on}/T)$.

Triangle Generation by Integration of System Square Wave

Given the input square wave, the simplest means of generating a triangle is integrating the square wave with a time constant long compared to $T/2$ as shown in Fig. 9–14. For $(T/2)/R1C1 = 0.3$, the exponential capacitive rise is only 25% up to the top of the input square wave and triangle slopes are sufficiently linear. Thus, the integrator is chosen so that $R1C1 = 1.67\ T$.

If a shorter time constant is used, the "triangle" becomes more exponential at its ends. Then, if very long or very short "on" times are required, the exponential crosses the dc level at a more shallow slope, and the instant of crossing is not marked so sharply.

This can result in jitter at the leading or trailing edge of the switch output waveform. The jitter in turnon and turnoff translates as width modulation into ripple output voltage. Also, the shallow crossing of the exponential against the level makes the circuit sensitive to noise at the instant of crossing. Such noise can result in multiple crossings of the dc level and thus false turnons and turnoffs.

Triangle Generation by Constant-Current Charging and Charge Dumping a Capacitor

An alternative method of generating the width-modulating triangle is shown in Fig. 9–15. This scheme generates a triangle with constant slope, and, hence, the instant when it crosses the dc level is as sharp whether it crosses the level near the top or the bottom of the triangle. The circuit is often used in radar systems for generating linear CRT deflection waveforms.

The circuit works as follows. A constant-current source is formed by Q1 and the diode D1, zener Z1 in its base and resistor R1 in its emitter. Diode D1 compensates for the base-emitter voltage variation with temperature of Q1. The current generated by Q1 is then $V_z/R1$. This current flows out of its collector into the capacitor C1. Thus, with a constant current, C1 charges linearly at a rate $\Delta V/\Delta t = I/C = V_z/R1C1$.

Now at the end of each period T, a narrow pulse (short compared to T) turns Q2 on and shorts it to ground. This dumps the accumulated charge on C1. After the trigger pulse goes away, Q2 opens up and the constant current from Q1 starts another linear ramp.

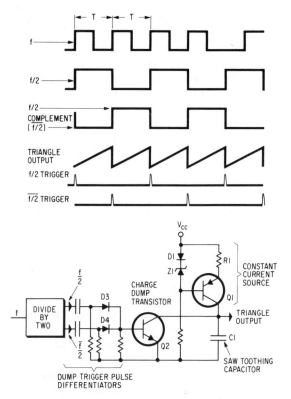

Fig. 9–15. An alternative scheme for generating the width-modulating triangle.

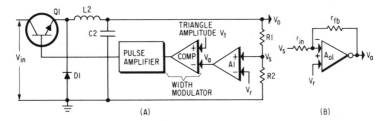

Fig. 9–16. (A) Complete switching regulator. For a given percent input voltage change, $\Delta V_{in}/V_{in}$, the percent output change is given by $\Delta V_o/V_o \cong (\Delta V_n/V_{in})/\{(A1)(V_{in}/V_t)[R2/(R1 + R2)]\}$. (B) Controlling gain of the amplifier of Fig. 9–16A to avoid excessive open-loop gain, which can cause loop oscillation. With the feedback network shown, $\Delta V_a/\Delta V_s = r_{fb}/r_{in}$.

The trigger pulses are usually easily available or are easily generated as in Fig. 9–15. If the basic square wave available has a frequency f, there is usually a divide-by-two circuit in the system. Pulses at a period of T are required. These can be obtained by differentiating the leading edges of the $f/2$ and $\overline{f/2}$ waveforms, selecting the positive-going differentiated pulses only (by D3, D4) and "oring" them into the base of Q1.

Alternatively, the f waveform itself can be used without the divide by two. By differentiating the f waveform and selecting only the positive-going pulse, pulses at a period of T are obtained at each positive-going transition of the f square wave.

9.2.2 Voltage Gain through Switch and Width Modulator

In the width modulator of Fig. 9–13, it is not clear initially what determines the selection of peak-to-peak triangle amplitude. It actually affects the voltage gain through the switch and width modulator as can be seen from Fig. 9–16 and the following. From Eq. 9–1, $V_o = V_{in}T_{on}/T$. Then,

$$\frac{\Delta V_o}{\Delta T_{on}} = \frac{V_{in}}{T}$$

Considering the triangle in the width modulator of Fig. 9–13, it is seen that, when the variable dc voltage level is at the top of the triangle, T_{on} is zero; when the level is at the bottom of the triangle, T_{on} is equal to T.

Then, in Fig. 9–16, for a peak-to-peak triangle voltage, V_t,

$$\frac{\Delta T_{on}}{\Delta V_a} = \frac{T}{V_t}$$

and

$$\frac{\Delta V_o}{\Delta V_a} = \left(\frac{\Delta V_o}{\Delta T_{on}}\right)\left(\frac{\Delta T_{on}}{\Delta V_a}\right)$$

Or the voltage gain through the switch and width modulator is

$$\frac{\Delta V_o}{\cdot \Delta V_a} = \left(\frac{V_{in}}{T}\right)\left(\frac{T}{V_t}\right) = \frac{V_{in}}{V_t} \tag{9-22}$$

9.2.3 Total Open-Loop dc Voltage Gain and Line Voltage Regulation

Referring to Fig. 9–16, for an open-loop gain $A1$ in the reference voltage – sampled output comparator – the total power supply open-loop gain [excluding the $R2/(R1 + R2)$ network] is

$$A_t = A1(V_{in}/V_t) \qquad (9\text{–}23)$$

Now, from Eq. 9–1, in the absence of feedback

$$V_o = V_{in}(T_{on}/T)$$

or

$$\Delta V_o = \Delta V_{in}(T_{on}/T)$$

But with feedback, assume a line change causing a change at the input to the switch of V_{in}. Then from Fig. 9–16

$$\Delta V_o = \left(\frac{T_{on}}{T}\right)\Delta V_{in} - \Delta V_o\left(\frac{R2}{R1 + R2}\right)\left(\frac{V_{in}}{V_t}\right)A1$$

$$\Delta V_o = \frac{\Delta V_{in}(T_{on}/T)}{1 - A1(V_{in}/V_t)[R2/(R1 + R2)]}$$

Dividing both sides of the above by $V_o = V_{in}(T_{on}/T)$ results in

$$\frac{\Delta V_o}{V_o} = \frac{\Delta V_{in}/V_{in}}{1 - A1(V_{in}/V_t)[R2/(R1 + R2)]} \qquad (9\text{–}24)$$

which states that the percentage change in output voltage is equal to the percentage change in input voltage divided by $1 - A1(V_{in}/V_t)[R2/(R1 + R2)]$.

Since

$$|\, A1(V_{in}/V_t)[R2/(R1 + R2)]\, |\, >> 1$$

then

$$\frac{\Delta V_o}{V_o} = \frac{\Delta V_{in}/V_{in}}{A1(V_{in}/V_t)[R2/(R1 + R2)]} \qquad (9\text{–}25)$$

For $\pm10\%$ change in input voltage, if the output voltage change is to be 0.1%, the product $A1(V_i/V_t)[R2/(R1 + R2)]$ must equal 100.

Line Voltage Regulation for Switching Regulator of Sect. 9.1.7

It is instructive to consider the required gain $A1$ for the step-down switching regulator of Sect. 9.1.7. In that regulator, V_{in} was nominally $+157$ V and V_o was 110 V. Then for a reference voltage at the $A1$ difference amplifier of Fig. 9–16A of 6.2 V

$$R2/(R1 + R2) = 6.2/110 = 0.056$$

And for a peak-to-peak triangle input voltage to the width-modulating comparator of $V_t = 3$ V, $V_{in}/V_t = 157/3 = 52$. Then, for a 0.1% output change with a 10% input change, from Eq. 9–25

$$A1(V_{in}/V_t)[R2/(R1 + R2)] = A1(52)(0.056) = 100 \qquad (9\text{–}25\text{A})$$

or $A1 = 34$. This is a relatively modest gain – far less than is achievable from an integrated-circuit operational amplifier-operated open loop.

To avoid the possibility of loop oscillations, the operational amplifier open-loop gain A_{OL} can be reduced to any desired value by the resistor feedback network shown in Fig. 9–16B. The gain with the resistors is the well-known gain of an operational amplifier with feedback resistors

$$A_{fb} = -R_{fb}/R1$$

9.2.4 Switch Base Drive Circuits

Heretofore, the means of coupling the variable pulse-width signal to the base of the switch transistor has not been considered. The means by which this is done can spell success or failure for the supply, for, if this is done in a way that results in long storage and fall times, there will be a long overlap of high current and voltage during turnoff and consequently high power dissipation — especially at high switching frequencies — 20 kHz and above. It also can result in second breakdown (Sect. 2.1.9).

The optimum means of driving the base of the switch transistor is to provide a large forward overdrive ($I_c/I_{bf} = 10$) to achieve fast turnon, and also to provide a large reverse-base current at turnoff to minimize turnoff and especially storage delay.

High forward overdrives are always easy to achieve, but the simplest dc base-drive schemes have no negative potential with respect to the instantaneous switch base voltage to provide a reverse-base current. Establishing such a negative potential is somewhat expensive in components and space as the emitter of the switch (for an emitter-loaded switch) moves from ground to $+V_{in}$. For off-the-ac-line switching regulators, the switch emitter moves about 150 V (for 120 V_{ac} inputs) or 300 V (for 230V_{ac} inputs). Thus, to provide a substantial source of substantial reverse-base drive requires a small floating voltage source that moves up and down with the switch transistor emitter. Such a supply is often used, but the simplest base drive scheme having no such reverse drive will be considered first.

DC-Coupled Switch Base Drive

The simplest base-drive scheme for the case in which the load is driven from the emitter is shown in Fig. 9–17A. It is the same circuit used in Fig. 6–17A to drive the base of an emitter-loaded npn series-pass transistor.

The base of the switch itself (Q1) or the npn Darlington driver must have a current source fed from a voltage higher than $+V_{in}$, but, since there is no potential higher than $+V_{in}$, the simplest driver is a pnp device that can supply substantial current even at $V_{ce(sat)}$ of about 0.4 V.

Thus, pnp driver Q3 supplies the current for the npn Darlington Q2, and the controlling amplifier is an npn driver Q4 whose base remains fixed with respect to ground and is simply a current switch supplying or removing current from the base of Q3. Base potential of Q4 moves only from ground to $+V_{be}$ or to about +0.8 V.

This chain of dc-coupled transistors is very inexpensive and is frequently used as is, but, at turnoff, turn-off delays of Q4, Q3, Q2, and Q1 are in series and can add up to a substantial amount. Q1 does not saturate because the Darlington driver Q2 prevents it (Sect. 2.1.9). Similarly, Q2 does not saturate, since the collector-emitter voltage of Q3 prevents that. Thus, Q1 and Q2 have no storage — only turn-off delays. These can be minimized by making their base-emitter resistors small — generally between 20 and 50 ohms. But Q3 and Q4 do saturate

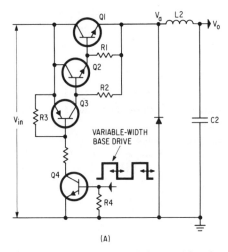

Fig. 9–17. (A) Completely dc-coupled switch base-drive. Stored charges in Q3 and Q4 slow up turn-off and storage times. Difficulty of supplying reverse-base drive slows these times considerably.

and contribute long storage and turn-off times. These should be minimized to improve efficiency and avoid the possibility of second breakdown.

Baker Clamps to Minimize Storage Delay in dc-Coupled Base-Drive Circuits

Saturation and consequent long storage time in Q3 and Q4 of Fig. 9–17A can be largely eliminated by Baker clamp diodes as in Fig. 9–17B. These diodes D1, D2, and D3 for Q3 and D4, D5, and D6 for Q4 operate to prevent the collector-base junction from taking on a forward bias—the condition for saturation. Their behavior is detailed in Sect. 2.1.9. With Baker clamps and low base-emitter resistors (R3 and R4), the total turn-off plus storage delay in the entire chain Q1–Q4 can be kept under 2 μsec—even for slow power transistors at Q1 and Q2.

If necessary, turn-off delay in Q4 can be reduced ₋till further by traditional means. Thus, the Q4 base can be driven by a resistor shunted by a speed-up capacitor that will pull reverse-base current at the sharp negative-going edge of the input voltage waveform. An emitter resistor shunted by a capacitor will also help speed up Q4 turn-off time.

Reverse-Base Drive for Minimizing Storage Delay

There are innumerable ways a reverse-base drive can be supplied to the bases of the switch transistor and its Darlington driver. Unfortunately, most of these schemes require a small auxiliary negative bias power supply floating on the emitter of the switch and riding up and down with it.

A frequently used possibility—varied by different designers in some minor ways—is shown in Fig. 9–17C. Here, a small transformer with floating secondary generates two voltages, $+V1$ and $-V1$. The secondary center tap is tied to the emitter of Q1. And thus, the two voltages float up and down with the emitter of Q1. At turnoff of the switch Q1 and its driver Q2, Q6 and Q7 are

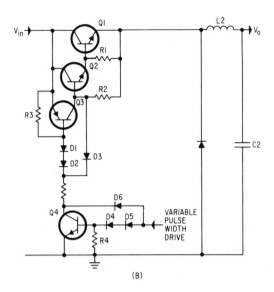

(B)

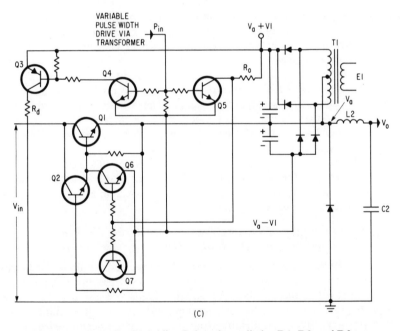

(C)

Fig. 9–17. (*Cont'd.*) (B) Adding Baker clamp diodes D1, D2, and D3 to Q3 and D4, D5, and D6 to Q4 prevents them from saturating and speeds up storage and turn-off time. (C) Switch base drive, which permits reverse-base current to Q1 and Q2 for fast turnoff, requires floating power supplies, $\pm$V1, which move up and down with V_a.

turned on and present a short from Q1 and Q2 bases to a potential $-V1$ volts below the emitters. With a reverse potential of about -4 V, Q1 and Q2 will turn off rapidly. To avoid reverse-bias second breakdown (Sect. 2.1.9) resistors can be placed in the collectors of Q6 and Q7 to limit the reverse-base current to the switch transistors. Q6 and Q7 are small TO5 transistors having low storage time. They are normally off, except when Q1 and Q2 are to be turned off.

The forward-base drive for the Darlington driver does not come from a pnp driver as in Fig. 9–17A but rather from the positive floating voltage source $V_a + V1$. Transistors Q4 and Q5 are normally off and make up a switch to turn on drive current to the base of Q2. When point P_{in} in Fig. 9–17C goes positive, Q4 turns on. This saturates Q3 and applies drive to base Q2 of magnitude

$$I(Q2) = \frac{V1 - (V_{be(Q1)} + V_{be(Q2)})}{R_d}$$

Simultaneously, when Q4 is turned on, Q5 is turned on and diverts current from R_o into the collector of Q5. This removes the base drive to Q6 and Q7 and they are off, thus permitting Q1 and Q2 to turn on.

When the switch is to be turned off, point P_{in} goes low, Q5 turns off, current from R_o turns on bases of Q6 and Q7. This shorts the bases of Q1 and Q2 to $(V_a - V1)$. With this reverse voltage at their bases, Q1 and Q2 turn off fast. Simultaneously low input at P_{in} turns off Q4 which turns off Q3 and thus removes forward drive to the base of Q2. With the removal of forward drive and application of reverse drive to the base of Q1 and its driver Q3, the switch opens in considerably under 1 μsec.

Transformer T1 is a small ferrite transformer fed from some available high-frequency source in the system — usually a low-power, square-wave amplifier driven from the input-synchronizing signal. The variable pulse-width drive generated by the triangle comparator (Sect. 9.2.1) is coupled into P_{in} by transformer coupling. In such transformer coupling, care must be taken that transformer does not saturate when T_{on} is more than 50% of T.

Although such a complex reverse-base drive circuit is often used, it is questionable whether the added parts and complexity result in a significant advantage over a carefully designed dc-coupled circuit like in Fig. 9–17B with its Baker clamps to reduce storage times.

Stored Energy in Coupling Transformer during On Time for Minimizing Turn-Off Storage Delay

A relatively simple means of providing reverse-base drive for turning the switch transistor off rapidly is shown in Fig. 9–18. Here, the coupling transformer is made with a sufficiently low magnetizing inductance so that the core absorbs adequate energy from the driving source during the "on" time. With a clamped primary drive from a source that can supply the desired base current plus the desired build-up in magnetizing current, the secondary voltage will not droop during the "on" time.

The build-up in magnetizing current during the "on" time is a ramp of peak amplitude $I = ET_{on}/L_m$, where E is the applied primary voltage and L_m is the magnetizing inductance. By making L_m small enough, a large increment of energy is taken from the primary source. When the primary source opens up,

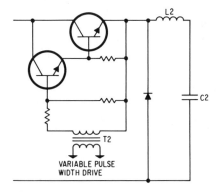

Fig. 9–18. Storing energy in the transformer magnetizing inductance during the "on" time and using it during the "off" time to provide reverse-base drive for fast turnoff.

voltage across primary and secondary reverse in polarity and the energy $\frac{1}{2}L_m(\Delta I)^2$, stored during the "on" time, is available as reverse-base drive to turn off the switch driver.

9.2.5 Emitter- Versus Collector-Loaded Switches

All switching regulator schematics presented thus far have their loads at the emitter (Figs. 9–1 and 9–17). This presents something of a problem if a power supply as shown in Fig. 9–17C is used to provide reverse-base drive, for such a power supply moves up and down an amount V_{in} volts, and the switch must supply the current needed to move its capacitance to chassis through a large voltage swing with fast rise and fall times.

Some designers prefer putting the load at the collector and using the switch transistor in the negative leg of the supply source. This is shown in Fig. 9–19A. This configuration does have many advantages, since no circuitry is attached to the collector, which moves through the large voltage swing of V_{in} volts. The base drive to Q2 is to a point that has only a dc voltage difference between itself and the negative output terminal. This voltage difference is $(V_{in} - V_o)$. Now the positive terminals of input and output are common rather than the negative terminals as in emitter-loaded regulators.

The dc-coupled control scheme for coupling between pulse-width drive from the triangle comparator to the base of the power switch is shown in Fig. 9–19A. It utilizes an npn driver (Q4) at $-V_o$ controlling a pnp level-changing amplifier at $+V_{in}$. This latter reaches down and acts as a current source to the base of the Darlington driver.

This circuit of Fig. 9–19A is the analog of the emitter-loaded scheme of Fig. 9–17A. It is shown with Baker clamp diodes D1, D2, and D3 to reduce storage delay in the pnp driver Q3 and with diodes D4, D5, and D6 for reducing storage delay in Darlington driver Q2.

If there are no floating supplies to be used (as in Fig. 9–17C), and Baker clamp diodes of Fig. 9–17B suffice to reduce storage delay, collector loading appears to have little advantage over emitter loading. If auxiliary power supplies are needed to provide reverse bias for fast turnoff of Q1, Q2, and Q3 in Fig. 9–21, such supplies are at fixed dc potentials at $+V$ and $-V$. Since they do not swing through large voltages at switching rates, their capacity to chassis is unimportant. Transformers for such supplies can be small, inexpensive line-frequency types, and all the control circuitry at the output of such supplies does not have to move with the collector through large voltage swings at high switching rates. In this case, collector loading has clear advantages over emitter loading.

With collector loading of Fig. 9–19, there are also numerous other simple ways of providing reverse bias for fast switch turnoff. Thus, in Fig. 9–19B the variable-width base turn-on pulse is coupled via R1–C1 in parallel, to the base of the Darlington driver. It can be easily arranged that the control voltage at the input end of R1–C1 moves between emitter potential of Q1 (for Q2 and Q1 off)

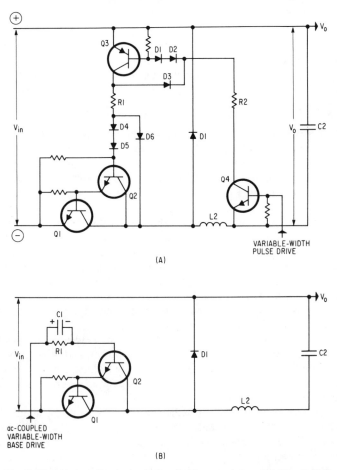

Fig. 9–19. (A) A collector-loaded switching regulator. (B) Simple RC speed-up technique provides reverse drive to Q2 to reduce its storage delay in the collector-loaded switch circuit. This is not as easily possible with emitter-loaded switches.

and, say, 4 V above the Q1 emitter (for Q2 and Q1 on). The Q2 base drive is thus the conventional resistance coupled drive with capacitive speed-up. When the input goes high, there is additional capacitive overdrive via C1 to speed up turn-on time. When the input goes low, since C1 has accumulated a 4-V charge in the polarity indicated, Q2 is subjected to a 4-V reverse bias and turns off rapidly. Since the Darlington connection keeps Q1 from saturating, its storage delay is low and total turn-off time is fast.

9.2.6 Optoelectronic Couplers

An invaluable component in the design of switching power supplies is the "optoelectronic coupler." This device, on a silicon integrated circuit chip, is used to transmit signals between points at different dc voltage levels or, indeed, between points having large and varying ac voltages between each other. There is no electrical connection across the interface between transmitting and receiving points, and, hence, these points are unrestricted in their relative voltage level.

The "optocoupler" consists of an infrared-light-emitting diode serving as a transmitter. Its light output is modulated by the dc or ac control current applied to the diode input terminals. The "receiver" is a single or Darlington transistor whose output current is proportional to diode light output.

Its characteristic curve, essential for most designs is shown in Fig. 9–20A. This curve shows "transistor current versus collector-to-emitter voltage" for various diode input currents. An important characteristic—equivalent to β in a normal transistor—is the "transfer gain." This is either defined as the dynamic gain $\Delta I_{(transistor)}/\Delta I_{(diode)}$ or the static transfer gain, which is the ratio of dc transistor current/dc diode current at a fixed collector voltage, which is usually taken at 5 V. DC transfer gain for a typical optocoupler, the 4N22, ranges between 0.25 and 0.4 for a diode input current of 10 mA.

Designs can be done and operating points in transistor collector-emitter voltage and current can be predicted exactly as with conventional transistors by drawing collector resistance load lines on the characteristic curves of Fig. 9–20A. Thus, Fig. 9–20B shows a 1,000-ohm load line drawn from a supply voltage of 15 V. At 24 mA of diode current, transistor operating point is at P1 with the transistor in saturation at V_{ce} of about 1.0 V. At zero diode current, operating point is at P2 with V_{ce} at 15 V and I_c at the "dark current" level, specified as 100 nA.

The optocoupler has many applications.[7] It can be operated in a switching mode with square waves of diode current at one dc voltage level modulating transistor currents and producing square waves of voltage across a collector load resistor at any arbitrarily different dc voltage level. In a square-wave switching mode, the optocoupler is not as fast as switching transistors. Turn-on and turn-off speeds for most types are in the range of 2–15 μsec, but this can be improved by overdriving with diode input current.

The optocoupler can also be used in an on–off control mode in which switching speeds under 1 μsec are not essential. In such a mode, a voltage to be sensed at one voltage level can be made to control operations, such as lighting

---

[7] Texas Instruments, Inc., "The Opto Electronics Data Book for Design Engineers."

fault lights and energizing relays at other dc voltage levels. Under- or overvoltage sensing of power supply output voltages can thus be monitored as shown in Fig. 9–21A.

There a fraction of the output to be sensed is compared against a reference voltage in a voltage comparator. For $[R2/(R1 + R2)]V_o < V_r$, the voltage comparator removes diode current from the opto and reduces opto transistor current to zero. The supply current from R1 is diverted to the base of Q1, turning it on so that it can light fault lights, open relays, etc. The dc level at the emitter of Q1 can be at any potential with respect to the potential at the

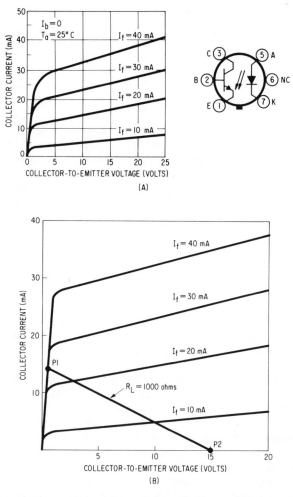

Fig. 9–20. (A) An optoelectronic coupler and its symbol. Current in the diode element at one dc voltage level controls transistor current at an arbitrarily different voltage level. (B) A 1,000-ohm load line from a supply voltage of 15 V. Modulating diode current between 0 and 30 mA switches transistor collector potential between P1 and P2.

bottom end of V. Obviously, a large variety of sensing functions using a voltage comparator in an inverting or noninverting mode is possible. Although such voltage comparator–switch transistor-enabling functions can be implemented without the optocoupler, the feature that the opto can operate at different dc levels for the control signal and the output response makes it such a valuable device.

Figure 9–21B shows the use of an optocoupler in a linear mode. It level shifts a dc voltage that is the amplified dc difference between a reference voltage and a fraction of the supply output voltage. The level shifting is from ground or frame reference at the output of the power supply to a point referenced to the negative end of the ac line-operated bridge rectifier. As noted above, such a point has a high ac voltage with respect to ground, and, without the dc isolation provided by the optocoupler, such a level translation would not be possible. The amplified error signal is fed to the input of a triangle comparator (Fig. 9–13),

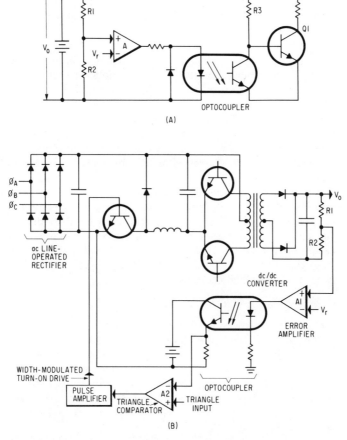

Fig. 9–21. (A) On–off control applications using an optocoupler. (B) Using an optocoupler in a linear mode to translate an amplified error signal to a triangle comparator at a different dc voltage level.

which generates the variable-width switch turn-on pulse as discussed in Sect. 9.2.1. With the polarities shown in Fig. 9–21B, an increase in output voltage results in a decreased width turn-on pulse and consequently a decreased or corrected output voltage.

9.2.7 Gain, Phase Margin, and Loop Stability in Step-Down Switching Regulators

Having negative feedback, the regulator has an odd number of phase reversals or $-180°$ phase shift at dc. But phase shifts at various points in the loop — particularly through the LC filter — increase with frequency. At some frequency, where the sum of all the accumulated phase shifts adds up to another $-180°$, the total open-loop gain must have dropped to less than unity (less than zero decibels) or the circuit will have positive rather than negative feedback and will oscillate.

The design of a feedback loop is thus not complete until the total open-loop gain and phase shift around the loop have been calculated. And it has been verified that at the frequency where the phase shift is $-180°$ (aside from the $-180°$ contributed by the odd number of phase reversals), the total loop gain has fallen to less than zero decibels.

The procedure to check this is to separately examine each element in the loop contributing to phase shift. For each element, phase shift versus frequency is plotted on semilog paper. From these plots, at each frequency, the phase shift in degrees is read for each element and the individual phase shifts added algebraically. At the frequency where the sum is $-180°$, the gain in decibels must be less than zero decibels.

Now the gain in decibels versus frequency for each element in the loop is plotted separately. Then, at each frequency, the gain in decibels is read for each element and the gains in decibels added algebraically to give the total open-loop gain versus frequency.

At the frequency where the total phase shift was $-180°$, the total gain must have fallen below zero decibels. If it has not, open-loop gain must be reduced at the frequency where the phase shift has reached $-180°$. But gain should not be reduced at dc, since presumably dc gain has been selected to achieve the desired line voltage regulation.

How gain at the $-180°$ phase shift frequency can be reduced without affecting dc gain will be taken up below.

Gain and Phase Shift of LC Filter

The above sequence of steps can easily be done if a simple means of calculating gain for each element of the loop is available. The elements whose gain must be considered are seen in Fig. 9–16A. They consist of the LC filter, the switching gain from V_a through the width modulator and switch, the sampling network $[R2/(R1 + R2)]$, and the comparator $A1$. If there is another voltage amplifier after $A1$ this must also be considered. Gain and phase shifts of these elements can be considered separately, since they produce no loading effect on one another.

Gain and phase shift of the LC filter network is of most importance because it contributes most of the phase shift in the loop. Oscillations, if they are possible, will occur somewhere near the resonant frequency of L2–C2. Phase shift and gain of L2–C2 can be read from the normalizing curves of Figs. 9–22 and 9–23, which have been obtained by computer calculation. The filter is a series L, shunt C filter loaded by a resistance $R_o = V_o/I_o$. The fact that it is involved in a switching operation and input is actually the width-modulated square wave of amplitude V_{in} (Fig. 9–2B) is irrelevant.

Phase shift versus frequency is shown in the normalized curve of Fig. 9–22. Phase shift is strongly dependent on the ratio $R/(L/C)^{1/2}$. High values of $R/(L/C)^{1/2}$ represent the strongly underdamped case in which phase shift is close to $-180°$ for this element alone at frequencies near the self-resonant frequency.

In most switching regulators, the filter is strongly underdamped. Thus, in the filter designed in Sect. 9.1.7 values were $L = 1.5 \times 10^{-3}$ H, $C = 125 \times 10^{-6}$ F, and $I_o = 2.71$ A at $V_o = 110$ V. This gives $(L/C)^{1/2} = (1.5 \times 10^{-3}/125 \times 10^{-6})^{1/2} = 3.5$ ohms. And $R_o = 110/2.71 = 40$ ohms. Then $R = 11.4 (L/C)^{1/2}$. By interpolation in Fig. 9–22, it is seen that at this value the filter itself yields $-165°$ of phase shift at a frequency of $f = 1.2f_o = 1.2/2\pi(LC)^{1/2}$ or at 441 Hz. Thus, if any other elements yield only an additional $-15°$ of phase shift at 441 Hz, oscillations will result if gain is greater than zero decibels at that point.

Gain versus frequency for the LC filter is read from Fig. 9–23, in which there is a considerable positive bump in gain for underdamped cases. Thus, at $R_o = 11(L/C)^{1/2}$, there is a resonant bump in gain of about $+20$ dB at $f_o = 1/2\pi(LC)^{1/2}$. Thus, from Figs. 9–22 and 9–23, phase shift and gain for values of LC can be read directly after calculating the damping constant $R_o/\sqrt{L/C}$.

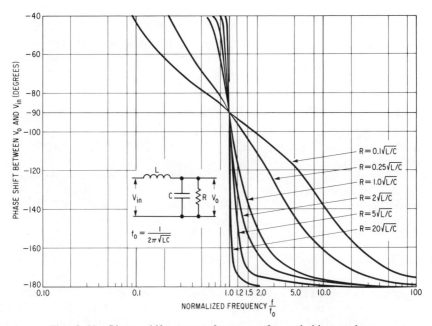

Fig. 9–22. Phase shift versus frequency for switching-regulator LC filter.

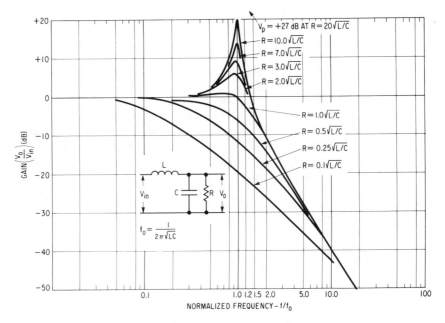

Fig. 9–23. Gain versus frequency for switching-regulator LC filter.

Gain and Phase Shift of Width Modulator–Switch Combination

This has been calculated in Sect. 9.2.2. It is shown that there the gain is V_{in}/V_t, where V_t is the peak-to-peak triangle voltage. In the frequency range of interest (around the LC filter resonant frequency), this contributes no phase shift. Its gain is then 20 log (V_{in}/V_t) in decibels at all frequencies.

Gain and Phase Shift of Sampling Network

Figure 9–16A shows no capacitors around R1 or R2. Thus, their gain is independent of frequency and is 20 log [R2/(R1 + R2)] in decibels at all frequencies. If the total loop phase shift reaches $-180°$ at a point where total gain is greater than zero decibels, a phase lead or advance is easily possible by adding a capacitor across R1. But this increases the gain at high frequencies where the impedance of the capacitor is comparable or less than R1. If such a capacitor is added, gain and phase must be calculated for the network. This is discussed fully later in this section.

Gain and Phase Shift of Difference Amplifier

The difference amplifier may be either an operational amplifier operated open loop or with an input and feedback resistor as in Fig. 9–16B. Alternatively, it may be a two-transistor difference amplifier as in Sect. 6.5.2 (gain = $10I_oR_a$ from Eq. 6–26). Neither the open-loop operational amplifier or the two-transistor difference amplifier have significant phase shift near the self-resonant frequency of the LC filter and, hence, only their gain is important. The open-loop operational

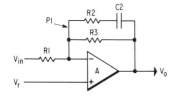

Fig. 9–24. An amplifier having a gain of R3/R1 at dc and R2/R1 at higher frequencies where $X_{C2} \ll R2$.

amplifier gain is given in vendors' data sheets. For the two-transistor difference amplifier gain from Eq. 6–26 in decibels is 20 log $(I_o R_a)$.

Operational Amplifiers with RC Feedback Networks

The difference amplifier of Fig. 9–16A can be operated open loop, in which case its gain is very high and may cause oscillations.

A simple means of providing it with a known lower and stabilized gain with tailorable gain and phase shift versus frequency characteristics is shown in Fig. 9–24. It is a very useful device, for it permits high gain at dc where it may be needed to attain the required dc line regulation. By permitting its gain to drop off at higher frequencies, the possibility of oscillation at frequencies near the self-resonant frequency of the LC filter is avoided.

Qualitatively, it can be understood as follows. It is an operational amplifier and with high enough open-loop gain, $A1$, its closed-loop gain is $Z_{fb}/R1$, where Z_{fb} is the impedance between V_o and P1. Now at dc, $X_{C2} \gg R2$ and also $X_{C2} \gg R3$. Hence, the feedback circuit "does not know" R3 is shunted by anything—i.e., $Z_{fb} \cong R3$ and at dc, gain is R3/R1. At a higher frequency where $X_{C2} \ll R2$ and R2 < R3, $Z_{fb} \cong R2$ and closed-loop gain is R2/R1.

At high frequencies and dc, the circuit is purely resistive and yields these gains without phase shift, but, at intermediate frequencies, these gains are intermediate and a phase shift is introduced.

Gain Calculation for Operational Amplifier with RC Feedback Network

The exact gain and phase shift versus frequency of an operational amplifier with RC feedback as in Fig. 9–24 may be calculated as follows. Gain of an operational amplifier is

$$V_o/V_{in} = -Z_{fb}/Z_{in}$$

Now in terms of the p operator ($p = j\omega$), Z_{fb} for the circuit in Fig. 9–22 is the parallel impedance of R3 and R2, C2 in series. Thus

$$Z_{fb} = \frac{R3(R2 + 1/pC2)}{R3 + R2 + 1/pC2} = \frac{R2R3 + R3/pC2}{R2 + R3 + 1/pC2} = \frac{R3(1 + pR2C2)}{1 + p(R2 + R3)C2}$$

And gain is

$$G = \frac{-Z_{fb}}{Z1} = \frac{-R3(1 + pR2C2)}{R1[1 + p(R2 + R3)C2]} \tag{9–26}$$

Gain versus frequency can easily be plotted from this as follows: At dc, $p = j\omega = 0$ and gain is R3/R1, as stated above. The transfer function of Eq. 9–26 has in the theory of complex variable terms a "pole" in the denominator at a frequency of $f_p = 1/2\pi(R2 + R3)C2$ and a "zero" in the numerator at a frequency of $f_z = 1/2\pi R2C2$. The ratio $f_z/f_p = (R2 + R3)/R2$. Now Eq. 9–26 can be rewritten as

$$G = \frac{-Z_{fb}}{Z1} = \left(\frac{-R3}{R1}\right)\left(\frac{1 + jf/f_z}{1 + jf/f_p}\right)$$

$$= \left(\frac{R3}{R1}\right)\left(\frac{1 + j(f/f_p)[R2/(R2 + R3)]}{1 + j(f/f_p)}\right) \qquad (9\text{–}26A)$$

And for $f/f_p > 10$

$$G \cong -\left(\frac{R3}{R1}\right)\left(\frac{R2}{R2 + R3}\right)$$

And for $(R2 + R3) = kR2$

$$G = \frac{-Z_{fb}}{Z1} = -\left(\frac{R3}{R1}\right)\left(\frac{1}{k}\right)$$

And gain in decibels is $G = 20 \log (R3/R1) - 20 \log k$.

Thus, if gain is plotted on semilog paper as in Fig. 9–25, with gain in decibels vertically and frequency in hertz horizontally, the gain at dc and low frequency is a horizontal line at a decibel level of $20 \log (R3/R1)$. And at high frequency where $f \cong 1/2\pi R2C2$, gain is $20 \log k$ below that as shown in Fig. 9–25. The gain at intermediate frequencies can be drawn in quite accurately in the following manner. It is well known that immediately beyond a pole at the so-called "corner frequency" of $f_p = 1/2\pi(R2 + R3)C2$, gain commences, falling off at the rate of 6 dB/octave. Thus, gain at intermediate frequencies can be drawn onto Fig. 9–25 by going to the frequency $f_p = 1/2\pi(R2 + R3)C2$ on the horizontal

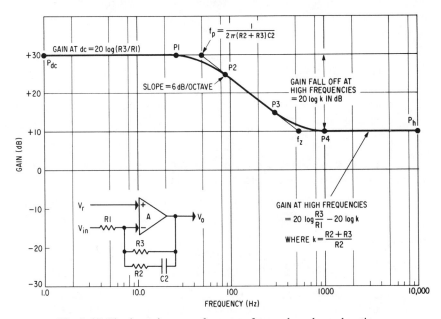

Fig. 9–25. Plotting gain versus frequency from pole and zero locations.

dc gain line $[G = 20 \log (R3/R1)]$ and drawing a line with slope of 6 dB/octave. This intersects the high-frequency gain line at f_z. Now gain around the f_p, and f_z points can be estimated quite accurately by drawing in smooth asymptotic curves between the 6-dB/octave sloped line and the two horizontal lines. Thus, the complete gain versus frequency curve is $P_{dc} \to P1 \to P2 \to P3 \to P4 \to P_h$.

Thus, in any special case of a feedback amplifier such as in Fig. 9–24 where R1, R2, R3, and C2 are known, the gain-versus-frequency characteristic can be calculated as above. But to make the technique more universal and permit synthesizing a circuit with desired gain and frequency characteristics, the normalized curves of Fig. 9–26 are presented.

The curves of Fig. 9–26 give the gain falloff versus normalized frequency for a number of different values of drop in decibels from the dc gain. These are valuable because it is often desired to drop the gain at high frequency from its dc value by various amounts of decibels. The frequency is normalized in terms of the pole frequency; i.e., the horizontal coordinate is f/f_p, where f_p is the pole frequency $1/2\pi(R2 + R3)C2$. From Fig. 9–26, a feedback network can easily be synthesized to have any desired dc gain and gain falloff at high frequency, and the components can be selected to have desired gain and frequency characteristics. This can be seen in the following design example.

Design Example: Selection of a Feedback Network for Desired dc Gain, High-Frequency Gain Falloff, and Calculation of Its Gain Frequency Characteristics Consider an operational amplifier for the switching regulator of Sect. 9.2.3. Assume it had a dc gain of 40 (= +32 dB). Further, assume that analy-

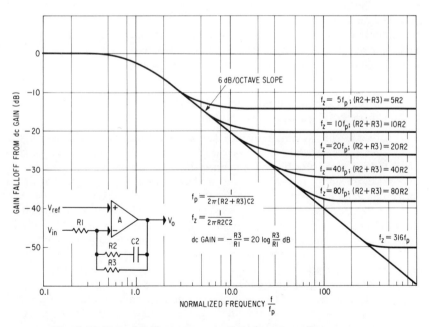

Fig. 9–26. Gain falloff versus normalized frequency (frequency normalized to frequency of pole f_p) for an operational amplifier with RC feedback network as above.

sis showed that, because of the phase shift due to the LC filter in the switching regulator, the system was close to oscillation at some point near the resonant frequency of the LC filter, which is assumed to be 450 Hz. Then, to prevent the oscillation, it is desired to drop the gain from its +32-dB value at dc to −6 dB at 450 Hz. It is desired to select the feedback network of Fig. 9–24 to achieve this.

The gain dropoff is $32 + 6 = 38$ dB. Then, from Fig. 9–26, for a gain dropoff of −38 dB, it is seen $R2 + R3 = 80\ R2$. It was assumed its dc gain was 40, then $R3/R1 = 40$. Then, in Fig. 9–26, it is seen the earliest frequency at which the 38-dB drop in gain is achieved is at about a normalized frequency of $f/f_p = 103$. If this gain dropoff is to occur at 450 Hz, the pole frequency, f_p, is equal to

$$f_p = f/103 = 450/103 = 4.37\ \text{Hz} = 1/2\pi(R2 + R3)C2$$

We thus have three equations:

(1) $R2 + R3 = 80\ R2$

(2) $R3 = 40\ R1$

(3) $4.37 = 1/2\pi(R2 + R3)C2$

But we have four unknowns in R1, R2, R3, and C2, and we are thus at liberty to choose one arbitrarily. Select $R1 = 1,000$ ohms. Then

From (2), $R3 = 40\ R1 = 40,000$ ohms

From (1), $R2 + 40,000 = 80\ R2$ or $R2 = 506$ ohms

From (3), $C2 = 1/2\pi(R2 + R3)\ (4.37) = 0.90\ \mu F$

This network does achieve the desired gain dropoff, but it also does introduce a phase shift, and care must be exercised that this added phase shift plus that contributed by the LC filter does not add up to a total of −180° at any frequency at which the total loop gain is greater than zero decibels.

Thus, the phase characteristics of the RC feedback network must be calculable. This is done as follows.

Phase Calculation for Operational Amplifier with RC Feedback Network

Phase shift versus frequency can be calculated from Eq. 9–26 for specific values of the variables. It is a laborious task that can be done quite easily by computer, but it can also be drawn in normalized fashion with sufficient accuracy by some fairly simple procedures. This is shown in Fig. 9–27, in which again the horizontal coordinate is not frequency but frequency normalized to the frequency of the "pole," f_p. The phase shift curves are drawn as follows. It is known that the phase shift due to a "pole" is −45° at the "pole" frequency $f_p = 1/2\pi(R1 + R2)C2$. To a close approximation, the slope of the phase–frequency curve is −45°/decade as it passes through the −45° point at P_o (where $f/f_p = 1$). Thus, a line P1–P2 is drawn through the point $f/f_p = 1$, $\theta = -45°$ with a slope of −45°/decade.

At some very high frequency where $X_{C2} \ll R2$, the feedback is purely resistive. That is, gain is R2/R1 and there is no phase shift (note that the −180° phase reversal due to the fact that the amplifier is an inverting type is ignored in Fig. 9–27). Thus, all phase characteristics in Fig. 9–27 must asymptotically approach zero at high frequency.

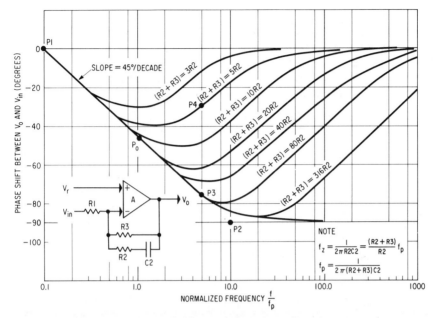

Fig. 9–27. Phase shift versus normalized frequency for operational amplifier shown.

Phase shift at any intermediate point is drawn as follows: It is known that, as the frequency of the "zero" is reached, it provides a +45° phase shift above that resulting from the phase lag due to the "pole" by itself. Thus, any phase curve for a "zero" at a frequency of $f_z = kf_p$ is obtained by moving down the P1–P2 line (lag due to the "pole" by itself) to a normalized frequency $f_z/f_p = k$. This point (say as P3 for $f_z = 5f_p$) identifies the "zero" coming in with its +45° phase advance. Now move up vertically from P3 an amount 45° to P4. Through P4 draw a straight line of positive slope +45°/decade.

At the bottom apex of the −45°/decade slope from the "pole" and the +45°/decade slope from the "zero," draw a smooth curve asymptotically joining both straight lines. Then, at the upper end of the +45°/decade slope, draw a smooth curve asymptotically joining the zero phase shift axis and the +45°/decade upward sloping line. This represents the −90° lag introduced by the pole being canceled and brought back to zero by the phase advance due to the pole as it asymptotically approaches +90° in an inverse tangent fashion.

Although this may seem an inaccurate, empirical procedure, better done by calculating gain and phase from Eq. 9–26A by computer, it does give a better physical insight into the problem and highlights the significance of the "pole" and "zero" frequencies and it does yield phase-versus-frequency curves with errors of no more than about 5° and is adequate for its intended use. Figure 9–27 gives phase–frequency characteristics for "zero" frequencies at 3, 5, 10, 20, 40, 80, and 316 times as great as the "pole" frequency. The curves are plotted in terms of the frequency normalized to the "pole" frequency.

From the gain and phase curves in Figs. 9–26 and 9–27 of the LC filter network and the gain–phase characteristics of other elements in the loop, the entire loop gain–phase characteristic can be plotted. Further, by setting the "pole" and "zero" frequency of the amplifier of Fig. 9–24 at the proper points along the frequency axis, gain and phase dips may be so located relative to the LC filter gain and phase curves that at no point where the total loop phase shift is −180° is the gain greater than unity.

Design Example: Tailoring Gain and Phase Frequency Characteristic to Achieve Overall Loop Stability

Consider a series-switch step-down switching regulator as in Fig. 9–16. Equation 9–25 shows that the percentage change in output voltage is the percentage change in input divided by the total open-loop gain: $A1(V_{in}/V_t)$ [$R_b/(R_a + R_b)$]. For a 10% input change to result in only a 0.1% output change, this total gain must equal 100 or +40 dB. As in Sect. 9.2.3, for $V_{in}/V_t = 157/3 = 52$ and $R_b/(R_a + R_b) = 6.2/110 = 0.056$, the difference amplifier gain at dc must be $A1 = 100/(52)(0.056) = 34$ or 31 dB.

Now consider whether the loop will be stable if nothing is done to tailor the gain and phase characteristics (such as by the addition of R2–C2 in Fig. 9–29) of any element in the loop. In the frequency of interest, around the self-resonant frequency of the LC filter, the only significant gain and phase changes are then those of the filter itself, since it is only at that frequency that the possibility of oscillation exists. Beyond that, the LC filter gain falls at 12 dB/octave and the total gain has dropped to zero decibels long before phase shifts due to the transistor and its stray capacitances arise.

Thus, with $A1$ designed to give a dc gain of +31 dB for a total open-loop dc gain of +40 dB, the gain–frequency characteristic of the entire loop (assuming R2 and C2 are not yet in the circuit) is plotted in Fig. 9–29. It has a constant gain out to the frequency where the LC filter approaches resonance. The effect of the filter can be read from Fig. 9–23, which shows "gain change" from its unity value (zero decibels) at dc. In the particular circuit of Fig. 9–29, $(L/C)^{1/2} = ((1.5 \times 10^{-3})/(125 \times 10^{-6}))^{1/2} = 3.5$ ohms. The effective load resistance is $V_o/I_o = 110/2.7 = 41$ ohms. Thus, $R/(L/C)^{1/2} = 41/3.5 = 11.6$. The closest curve of Fig. 9–23 to this is the one for $R/(L/C)^{1/2} = 10$. Take gain from this characteristic. Normalized frequency in Fig. 9–23 is f/f_o, where $f_o = 1/2\pi(LC)^{1/2} = 1/2\pi(1.5 \times 10^{-3})$ $(125 \times 10^{-6})^{1/2} = 367$ Hz. Now Fig. 9–23 can be entered at any frequency to read the gain change from its zero decibels value at dc. This change is added or subtracted to +40 dB to obtain the absolute value of total open-loop gain, which is plotted in Fig. 9–29. That curve is seen to have the resonant bump up to +60 dB at the filter-resonant frequency.

In a similar fashion, the phase characteristic of Fig. 9–22 is read from the $R/(L/C)^{1/2} = 10$ curve at the appropriate normalized frequency. This phase shift is also plotted in Fig. 9–29 and represents total open-loop phase shift versus frequency, since thus far no other elements in the loop are contributing phase shift.

It is now seen in Fig. 9–29 at 367 Hz that the loop phase shift is −90° and gain is +60 dB, but because of the highly underdamped LC filter, at 410 Hz, the phase shift is up to −160° and loop gain is still up at +50 dB. Another 20° of phase shift due to parasitic elements would cause oscillation. Although 20° stray phase shift is somewhat difficult to obtain, at a frequency of 480 Hz, phase

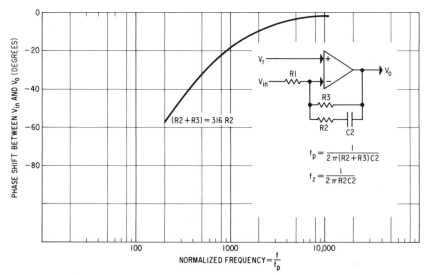

Fig. 9–28. Phase shift versus normalized frequency (tail of same curve in Fig. 9–27).

shift is −174° and gain is still about +40 dB. Now another 6°, which is not difficult to pick up, will result in oscillations.

The circuit is thus very prone to oscillate somewhere in the region of 410–480 Hz. This can be avoided by introducing a phase lead or dropping the open-loop gain by about −50 dB. Generally, negative-feedback loops are designed with margin so that, at the frequency at which total loop phase shift is 180°, loop gain is at most −10 dB. Thus, dropping gain off its present value by −50 dB at all points beyond, say, 400 Hz will ensure the circuit will not oscillate if the method chosen introduces no phase shift.

The required gain dropoff can be obtained by adding elements R2 and C2 across R3 as shown in Fig. 9–29. From Fig. 9–26, it is seen to obtain a gain falloff of −50 dB, and R2 must be selected so that (R2 + R3) = 316 R2. With C in series with R2, this puts in a "zero" at a frequency of $1/2\pi$R2C2, which is at a frequency 316 times as high as the "pole" at a frequency $1/2\pi$(R2 + R3)C2.

There is one more degree of freedom left: the absolute value of the zero or pole frequency fixed by the selection of C2. If the −50 dB gain is to be obtained from 410 Hz on outward, Fig. 9–26 shows we can locate it at $f/f_p = 400$ when $f = 410$ Hz. Beyond $f/f_p = 400$, we have achieved the −50 dB gain dropoff.

Figure 9–27 shows phase shift versus normalized frequency for various values of f_z/f_p. Figure 9–28 is the tail end of the $f_z/f_p = 316$ curve of Fig. 9–27. It carries phase shift down toward zero at high values of f/f_p. At the tail, this curve is accurately drawn as an inverse tangent curve displaced along the f/f_p axis. This can be seen as follows: At high frequencies, R3 $\gg$ R2 + X_{C2}, and the transfer ratio (Eq. 9–26) is $Z_{fb}/Z_{in} = (R2 + X_{C2})/R1$. The phase shift due to this transfer function is

$$\tan \theta = \frac{X_{C2}}{R2} = \frac{1}{2\pi f C2 R2} = \frac{f_z}{f} = \frac{316 f_p}{f} = \frac{316}{f/f_p}$$

or
$$\theta = \tan^{-1}\left(\frac{316}{f/f_p}\right)$$

Thus, the phase shift curve is drawn as an inverse tangent curve passing through $-45°$ at $f/f_p = 316$.

If we did select R2 + R3 = 316 R2, to give $f_z = 316 f_p$, but set the pole at $f/f_p = 400$ for $f = 410$ Hz to achieve the -50-dB gain falloff from Fig. 9–26, then Fig. 9–28 shows we would pick up another $-40°$ of phase shift at 410 Hz, and the circuit would oscillate just below 410, where the full -50-dB gain dropoff is not yet achieved and the LC phase shift is high.

Thus, the -50 dB gain dropoff must be picked up at a point where Fig. 9–28 shows very little additional phase shift with the addition of R2 and C2. In Fig. 9–28 on the $f_z = 316 f_p$ curve, at $f/f_p = 4,000$, there is only an additional $-5°$ phase shift picked up. Thus, if we set $f/f_p = 4,000$ for $f = 410$ Hz, where Fig. 9–29 shows an additional $-5°$ phase shift can be tolerated, then

$$f_p = f/4,000 = 410/4,000 = 0.1 \text{ Hz}$$

and
$$f_p = 1/2\pi(R2 + R3)C2 = 0.1 \text{ Hz}$$

It has been shown above that the required dc gain was 34 or R3/R1 = 34, and, for the dc gain dropoff of -50 dB, (R2 + R3) = 316 R2. Thus, with four variables and three conditions, we are at liberty to choose one variable. Arbitrarily set R1 = 5,000 ohms. Then

$$\text{R3} = 34(5,000) = 170,000 \text{ ohms}$$

and
$$\text{R2} = \text{R3}/315 = 170,000/315 = 540 \text{ ohms}$$

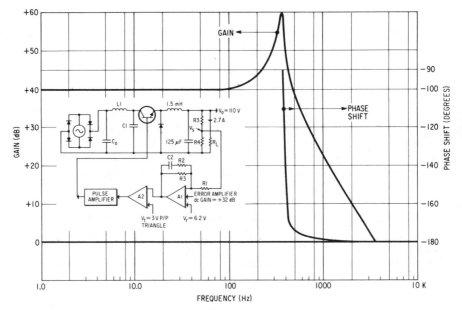

Fig. 9–29. Total open-loop gain and phase shift versus frequency for LC filter and operational amplifer in series.

Finally $C2 = 1/2\pi(170,540)(0.1) = 0.9 \ \mu F$

The loop is now stabilized. Gain characteristics can be drawn onto Fig. 9–29 by moving each point on the gain curve down −50 dB at all frequencies after 410 Hz. Phase characteristics can be drawn onto Fig. 9–29 by adding the phase shift of Fig. 9–28 to that of Fig. 9–29.

It should be noted that, although the loop is stable, by being forced down to a low value of f_p (0.1 Hz), loop response will be slowed down as the operational amplifier gain starts falling at 6 dB/octave at 0.1 Hz.

Higher bandwidth is obtainable by using two operational amplifiers each providing half the desired total dc gain of +31 dB. Each can be operated with its feedback network set to give a gain dropoff of −26 dB [(R2 + R3) = 20 R2 in Fig. 9–26]. This yields the desired −52 dB gain dropoff, but, from Fig. 9–27, each can be set to give its gain dropoff at $f/f_p = 400$ at $f = 400$ Hz. This adds only 2° of phase shift at 410 Hz for each amplifier. Now the pole frequency is $f_p = 400/400$ or 1 Hz rather than 0.1 Hz, and the loop frequency response will be higher.

Another alternative is to reduce the LC filter phase shift by adding a small resistor (R_s) in series with the ground end of the filter capacitor. Referring to Fig. 9–22, at frequencies where $X_c < R_s$, the shunt impedance to ground at the output node is now a resistor rather than a capacitor, and the output–input phase lag is that of a series L–shunt R rather than series L–shunt C. Maximum filter phase lag is thus 90° rather than 180°. The value of R_s should be minimized to avoid increasing switching frequency ripple voltage. The equivalent series resistance (ESR) of the filter capacitor itself helps in this respect, but it is an uncontrolled parameter and varies widely from unit to unit.

Input Ripple Attenuation and Feedback Loop Stability

Equation 9–25 states that the percentage change in regulator output voltage is equal to its input change (collector of the switch transistor in Fig. 9–29) divided by the feedback amplifier's open-loop gain.

This open-loop gain was set at 100 at dc so that an input change of ±10% (due to ±10% ac line changes) results in a 0.1% regulator output change. But if the feedback network is to provide ripple attenuation of the same factor (output ripple percentage is equal to 1/100 of the input ripple) open-loop gain at the fundamental ripple frequency (120 Hz in a single-phase bridge or 360 Hz in a three-phase, full-wave bridge) must still be 100.

However, in the section just completed, loop stability was achieved by dropping open-loop gain at the filter's self-resonant frequency of 380 Hz as much as −50 dB. This dropped gain at the fundamental ripple frequency (360 Hz in the three-phase or 120 Hz in single-phase systems) by the same amount.

Thus, the feedback network, although providing dc output changes of 1/100 of the dc input changes, does not provide any attenuation at all of the ripple from input to output.

Hence, if such a switching regulator is driven from a source having ripple superimposed on its average dc voltage level, some other tool must be available to reduce output ripple other than the brute-force means of dropping gain off drastically. The ripple frequencies are too close to the usual LC-filter self-resonant frequencies and reducing gain at the LC-filter frequency also reduces it about the same amount at the ripple frequency.

Three-Phase Rectifier Output Filter for Reducing Ripple Input to a Switching Regulator The simplest tool for reducing switching regulator output ripple is not to do it at all with the feedback amplifier but to do it with an LC filter between the output of the rectifier and the input to the collector of the switching transistor as shown in Fig. 9–29.

For three-phase, full-wave rectifiers, the filter components are relatively small, since the fundamental ripple frequency is 360 Hz. An appreciation of the size of the LC filter following a three-phase, full-wave bridge can be obtained from the following. Assume a choke input filter following a three-phase, full-wave bridge rectifier as in Fig. 5–1:

$$V_{\text{ripple(rms)}} = 0.057\, V_{\text{rms(ac input)}}$$

$$V_{\text{dc(output)}} = 1.35\, V_{\text{rms(ac input)}}$$

$$V_{\text{ripple(rms)}} = \left(\frac{0.057}{1.35}\right) V_{\text{dc(output)}} = 0.042\, V_{\text{dc(output)}}$$

$$V_{\text{ripple(p/p)}} = (2.82)(0.042)\, V_{\text{dc(output)}} = 0.12\, V_{\text{dc}}$$

Or the peak-to-peak ripple at the input to a single-stage LC filter following the bridge rectifier output is 12% of the dc output voltage. If the filter is to reduce the ripple by a factor of, say, 10 to 1%, which is tolerable, then

$$X_C \cong 0.1\, X_L \qquad \text{and} \qquad 1/\omega C = 0.1 \omega L$$

or
$$LC = \frac{10}{\omega^2} = \frac{10}{(2\pi 360)^2} = 1.93 \times 10^{-6}$$

and for reasonable value for C of, say, 300 μF,

$$L = \frac{1.95 \times 10^{-6}}{300 \times 10^{-6}} = 6.5 \text{ mH}$$

Single-Phase Rectifier Output Filter for Reducing Ripple Input to a Switching Regulator With single-phase power, the filter after the usual bridge rectifier must be a capacitive input π type as shown in Fig. 9–29. The input capacitor C_o is relatively large and is chosen to yield a reasonably small peak-to-peak triangular ripple voltage. This ripple is then further attenuated by the L1-C1 filter. Magnitude of filter components may be estimated as follows:

C_o is chosen from Fig. 5–5 to be proportional to output load current. From Fig. 5–5 it is seen that at 60 Hz, choosing a capacitor whose magnitude is 1,000 μF/load ampere yields a peak-to-peak ripple voltage of 8.3 V. Then the percentage output ripple at the top of C_o is

$$\Delta V_o/V_o = 8/V_o$$

For the usual 115 V_{rms} input voltage, dc output is $\cong$ 150 V. Thus,

$$\Delta V_o/V_o = 8/150 = 0.053 \qquad \text{or } 5.3\%$$

Assume the L1–C1 filter is to reduce this by one-fifth to 1% at the input to the switching regulator. Then

$$X_{C1} \cong \left(\frac{1}{5}\right) X_{L1} \qquad \text{and} \qquad 1/\omega C1 = \omega L1/5$$

or
$$L1C1 = 5/\omega^2 = 88 \times 10^{-6} \qquad \text{for } f = 120 \text{ Hz}$$

And in the usual supply having single-phase 115-V ac input, output power from the rectifier is no more than about 150 W. Above that output power, a three-phase power source is generally made available. Then for 150 W, dc output current is 1 A and with C_o chosen as above at 1,000 μF/ampere, its magnitude is just 1,000 μF. Then the size of the filter inductance L1 is

$$L1 = \frac{88 \times 10^{-6}}{1,000 \times 10^{-6}} = 88 \text{ mH}$$

It can be seen that an LC filter for ripple reduction to the switching regulator in a single-phase power system leads to quite large filter components and makes it more essential that the ripple attenuation be done in the feedback amplifier itself.

Phase Lead Networks for Feedback Loop Stabilization   Earlier in this section, the problem of the gain being greater than unity at the frequency when the loop phase shift was $-180°$ was solved by dropping the gain at that frequency, but that also dropped gain at the usual input ripple frequencies and made the feedback network incapable of providing adequate ripple attenuation.

As shown above with three-phase input power, an LC filter ahead of the switching regulator can provide adequate ripple attenuation with acceptably small components, but for single-phase power with a fundamental ripple frequency of 120 Hz, the necessary filter components are rather large and ripple attenuation is preferably done in the feedback amplifiers.

This can be done without dropping off gain at the ripple frequency by a capacitor C3 across the sampling resistor R3 (Fig. 9–29). This provides a positive phase shift rather than the negative one exhibited by the amplifier of Fig. 9–27. Thus, in Fig. 9–29, in which the total phase shift around the loop is rapidly approaching $-180°$ close to the resonant frequency of the LC filter, the total phase shift will be boosted back upward from $-180°$ at that frequency. It will only come back down to $-180°$ again further on beyond the filter self-resonant frequency. But at that point the LC filter gain, which is falling at -12 dB/octave will have brought the total loop gain down below zero decibels and the loop will be stable.

Gain and phase shift between output and input of a lead network such as in Fig. 9–30 may be calculated from its transfer function. Thus

$$\frac{V_s}{V_o} = \frac{R4}{R4 + \dfrac{R3(1/pC3)}{R3 + 1/pC3}} = \frac{R4(R3 + 1/pC3)}{R4(R3 + 1/pC3) + R3/pC3}$$

$$= \frac{R4 + p(R4)(R3)(C3)}{R3 + R4 + p(R4)(R3)(C3)} = \frac{\left(\dfrac{R4}{R3 + R4}\right)(1 + pR3C3)}{1 + p\left(\dfrac{R4R3}{R3 + R4}\right)C3}$$

and for $p = j\omega = j2\pi f$

$$\frac{V_s}{V_o} = \frac{\left(\dfrac{R4}{R3 + R4}\right)(1 + j2\pi f R3C3)}{1 + j2\pi f\left(\dfrac{R4R3}{R3 + R4}\right)C3}$$

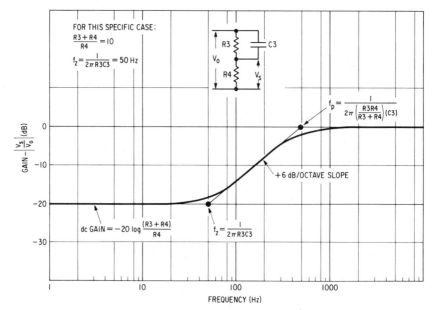

Fig. 9–30. Gain (V_s/V_o) versus frequency for a phase lead network.

And for f_z and f_p defined by

$$f_z = 1/2\pi R3C3$$

$$f_p = \frac{1}{2\pi\left(\dfrac{R4R3}{R4+R3}\right)C3} = \left(\frac{R4+R3}{R4}\right)f_z = kf_z$$

Then

$$\frac{V_s}{V_o} = \frac{\left(\dfrac{R4}{R3+R4}\right)[1 + j(f/f_z)]}{1 + j(f/f_p)} \qquad (9\text{–}27)$$

or

$$\frac{V_s}{V_o} = \left(\frac{R4}{R3+R4}\right)\frac{[1 + j(f/f_z)]}{[1 + j(f/kf_z)]} \qquad (9\text{–}28)$$

This transfer function is in a way the "mirror image" of that of the feedback amplifier of Eq. 9–26A. Its gain–phase characteristics can be obtained from Figs. 9–26 and 9–27 by a simple interchange of signs and redesignating the horizontal axis as f/f_z. This can be seen from the following.

At dc, $f = 0$ and, from Eq. 9–27, the transfer function or $V_s/V_o = R4/(R3 + R4)$. This is, of course, what is expected: At dc it is a simple resistive voltage divider whose output is $R4/(R3 + R4)$ times as large as its input.

And in complex variable terms it has a "zero" in the numerator at a frequency of $f_z = 1/2\pi R3C3$ and a "pole" in the denominator at a frequency

$$f_p = \frac{1}{2\pi\left(\dfrac{R4R3}{R4+R3}\right)C3} = \frac{k}{2\pi R3C3}$$

But now in contrast to the feedback amplifier of Eq. 9–26A, the "pole" is at a higher frequency than the zero. For values of $k > 1$ and low values of f/f_z, Eq. 9–28 simplifies to

$$\frac{V_s}{V_o} = \left(\frac{R4}{R3 + R4}\right)[1 + j(f/f_z)]$$

The absolute magnitude of this is a gain, which at $f/f_z = 1$ is +3 dB greater than the dc gain of R4/(R3 + R4). Thereafter it increases at +6 dB/octave, but at higher frequencies where f/f_z and $f/kf_z \gg 1$, Eq. 9–28 simplifies to

$$\left(\frac{R4}{R3 + R4}\right)\left(\frac{jf/f_z}{jf/kf_z}\right) = \left(\frac{R4}{R3 + R4}\right)\left(\frac{R3 + R4}{R4}\right) = 1$$

Gain rises to unity, which is what is to be expected, since at high frequencies $X_{C3} \ll R3$. This can be drawn on semilog paper as in Fig. 9–30. There, gain in decibels is plotted vertically and frequency is plotted horizontally. Its gain at dc is $-20 \log [(R3 + R4)/R4] = -20 \log k$. It remains constant at this value out to the "zero" frequency where it starts rising at +6 dB/octave until it hits the zero decibels gain line. The actual gains at the apex of the 6 dB/octave sloping line and the two horizontal gain lines can be drawn in as smooth curves asymtotically joining the sides of those apexes.

Now a set of universal gain curves can be drawn (Fig. 9–31) with the horizontal coordinate being the normalized frequency, normalized now to the frequency of the zero. The gain starts rising at the "zero" frequency at 6 dB/octave.

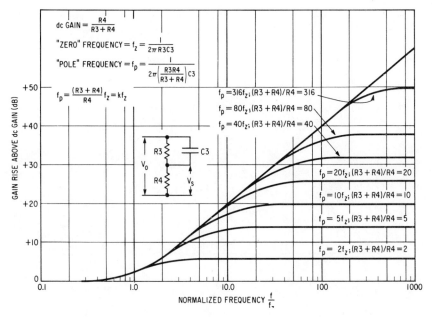

.**Fig. 9–31.** Gain rise above dc gain versus normalized frequency for phase lead network.

This is in contrast to the feedback amplifier (Fig. 9–26), in which gain started falling at 6 dB/octave at the frequency of the "pole." The vertical coordinate in Fig. 9–31 is the gain rise above its value at dc.

It can be seen that the normalized gain curve for the "lead network" of Fig. 9–31 is the mirror image of that for the feedback amplifier of Fig. 9–26. Thus, if the curves for the feedback amplifier are rotated about the zero decibels axis (or the sign of the vertical coordinates designated "+" rather than "–") and if the horizontal axis is labeled f/f_z rather than f/f_p, the gain curves for the "lead" network result.

From Fig. 9–31, gain for any combination of R3, R4, and C3 at any frequency can be determined. In a similar way, the phase shift between output and input for the lead network is the mirror image of that for the feedback amplifier (Fig. 9–27). The phase shift for the lead network of Fig. 9–31 can be read directly from Fig. 9–27 by changing the sign of the phase shift from minus to plus and designating the horizontal axis coordinate as f/f_z rather than f/f_p. This is shown in Fig. 9–32.

Design Example: Loop Stabilization by Introduction of a Phase Lead to Permit Adequate Gain for Ripple Attenuation The gain and phase shift curves of Figs. 9–31 and 9–32 can be used to stabilize the loop discussed earlier in this section without the drastic gain dropoff that left the feedback amplifier unable to attenuate input ripple.

Figure 9–29 shows gain and phase characteristics of the entire loop before addition of R2, C2 across R3. It is seen in the vicinity of 450 Hz, the loop phase shift is $-170°$, and gain is still up at $+45$ dB. Another $-10°$ phase shift will result in oscillations.

Add a capacitor across R3 to provide a positive phase boost from the appropriate curve of Fig. 9–32. Since in Fig. 9–29 $V_o = 110$ V and $V_s = 6.2$ V,

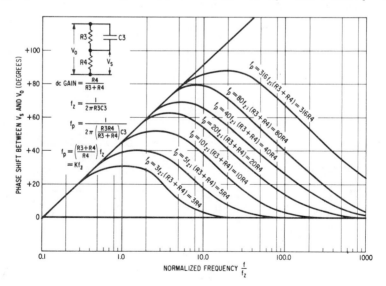

Fig. 9–32. Phase shift versus normalized frequency for phase lead network.

(R3 + R4)/R4 is determined as $110/6.2 = 18$. Use the curve of Fig. 9–32 closest to this: $(R3 + R4)/R4 = 20$.

This gives $f_p = 20 f_z$ and, from Fig. 9–31, at high frequencies, coming along with boost in phase there will be a $+26$ dB boost in gain. It must then be true that with the gain added to that of Fig. 9–29, the total loop gain is less than zero dB at the frequency where the boosted-up phase has fallen back down to zero at the tail end of the curve of Fig. 9–32.

The point where the boosted phase has fallen back down to zero is determined by where on the frequency axis the "zero" is located. Thus, without the phase boost, we are at $-170°$ phase shift at 450 Hz (Fig. 9–29). Put the point just below the broad peak of the $f_p = 20 f_z$ curve of Fig. 9–32 at 450 Hz. Thus, choose $f/f_z = 2$ at $f = 450$ Hz. This gives a boost of $+58°$ at 450 Hz and its net phase shift there is the $-170°$ from Fig. 9–29 plus the $+58°$ from Fig. 9–32 for a total of $-170 + 58 = -113°$. It is now safe against oscillation at that frequency. For $f/f_z = 2$ at 450 Hz, $f_z = 225$ Hz.

Now check at what frequency the gain has fallen back to zero. With $f_p = 20 f_z$, Fig. 9–31 shows gain has been boosted at high frequencies by $+26$ dB. Figure 9–29 shows that, before the boost was added, total loop gain had fallen to zero at 3,500 Hz. With the boost capacitor in, it is $+26$ dB at that frequency and falls with the LC filter slope at -12 dB/octave. Thus, draw a line through $+26$ dB at 3,500 Hz with a slope of -12 dB/octave. This hits zero decibels again at 10 kHz, and with $f_z = 225$ Hz, at 10 kHz, $f/f_z = 10,000/225 = 44$.

From Fig. 9–32, at $f/f_z = 44$, $f_p = 20 f_z$, phase shift is still boosted $+25°$. This is $25°$ above the $-180°$ contributed by the filter. The circuit is thus stable; at the point where the total loop gain has already fallen to zero, the total loop phase shift is still $25°$ short of $-180°$.

Now gain at the ripple frequency of 120 Hz is still high enough to provide adequate ripple attenuation. Thus, from Fig. 9–29 at 120 Hz, the gain before the boost capacitor was added was $+40$ dB. From Fig. 9–31, at 120 Hz, with $f_z = 225$, $f/f_z = 120/225 = 0.53$, the boost capacitor adds another $+1$ dB gain to this. With a total loop gain of $+41$ dB (gain $= 112$), the output ripple is $\frac{1}{112}$ of the input ripple. Specific values for R3, R4, and C3 can now be chosen. There are two conditions

(1) $(R3 + R4)/R4 = 110/6.2$ (from Fig. 9–29)

(2) $f_z = 225$ Hz $= 1/2\pi R3 C3$

And with three variables—R3, R4, and C3—and two conditions, we are at liberty to arbitrarily choose one. Generally, R4 would be chosen low enough so that the impedance looking back into the R3–R4 junction is low compared to the input impedance of the error amplifier of Fig. 9–29.

Thus, arbitrarily select the current down through the sampling resistor chain to be 5 mA. (This will yield low enough impedances.) Then

$$R4 = 6.2/0.005 = 1,240 \text{ ohms}$$
$$R3 = (110 - 6.2)/0.005 = 20,760 \text{ ohms}$$
$$C3 = 1/2\pi f_z R3 = 1/2\pi(225)(20,760) = 0.034 \ \mu\text{F}$$

Optimizing Phase Lead Bump Location along the Frequency Axis A good physical insight into where to locate the phase "leads" or "bumps" along the frequency axis can be obtained by transferring the curve of Fig. 9–32 to a transparency. Align the zero phase shift axis of this transparency vertically with that of a curve showing phase versus frequency of the rest of the loop (Fig. 9–29). Then, by moving the transparency horizontally along the frequency axis, it is easy to see where to locate the $f/f_z = 1$ point in absolute frequency so as to spread out the positive phase bump over the points in frequency where oscillation is most likely before the addition of the phase lead. It is also easy to read the sum of the phase bump introduced by the lead network and that of the rest of the feedback loop at any frequency.

9.3   Turn-On and Turn-Off Problems in Switching Regulators

Switching regulators, especially when operated from off-the-ac-line rectifiers, are prone to second-breakdown problems at either turnon or turnoff.

The problem at turnon is due to the fact that the feedback loop, seeing low output voltage, turns fully on to 100% duty cycle in an attempt to bring the output up. The switching inductor (L2 of Fig. 9–1), however, is designed to give a ΔI of about 40% of the maximum dc current in about 60–80% of the switching period, which is only about 30–40 μsec at 20 kHz switching rate.

Now if at turnon the width modulation circuitry produces full 100% duty cycle, current in the switching inductor rises to the point where its iron is saturated, and the switching transistor now sees a capacitive load rather than an inductive, current-limiting one. If the line rectifier output rises fast and the inductor saturates early, before the output filter capacitor charges up, the resultant current spike in the switch transistor can exceed forward-biased second-breakdown limits of the device and destroy it. The problem is more serious in off-the-line switching regulators operating off a rectified 300 V (from a three-phase bridge and a 208-V line-to-line input). Generally, with rectified 160 V (three-phase 120-V line-to-neutral rectifier or single-phase 120-V bridge output), there is no problem for most of the available high-voltage switching transistors.

A usual remedy for such a problem is a "soft-start" circuit. This uses a capacitor located (such as at the reference input to the error amplifier) so as to force a minimum duty cycle at initial turnon. As the capacitor charges up, transistor switch "on" time duty cycle increases slowly, the switching inductor cannot saturate, and high-transistor current spikes are prevented.

But care must be exercised in such soft-start circuits because now, if the supply is turned off and rapidly turned on, the capacitor may not have time to discharge. At the fast re-turnon, if the capacitor has not fully discharged, turnon is now certain to start with 100% duty cycle and remain there long enough to saturate the core in the switching inductor. The consequent high transistor pulse can cause it to fail in second-breakdown mode. There are many circuit tricks to get around this; they usually involve sensing for turnoff and rapidly discharging the slow start capacitor.

Similar problems can occur at turnoff. As the supply is shut down, the main error amplifier senses low output and commands 100% duty cycle. Now, if the output filter capacitance discharges rapidly but the input line rectifier slowly, a problem can arise. With 100% duty cycle, the switching inductor can saturate and with a large voltage across the switching transistor, which now is on 100% of the time, destructive current spikes can occur before the input line rectifier has fully lost its charge.

Such problems are unique to the circuit details, and, although no solutions are offered here, it can only be suggested that such transient current spikes be looked for by oscilloscope probing of breadboards. Generally, switching the supply on and off and observing transistor switch currents with an oscilloscope current probe on a slow free-running oscilloscope time base (1–2 sec/cm) can spot such spikes.

9.4   Width-Modulated dc/dc Converters

The series-switch step-down switching regulator is an efficient way of deriving a lower voltage from a higher one. However, the output has one terminal common to the input. If the input is the ac-rectified line, there is no dc isolation from the ac line — this is unacceptable in most cases.

There are a number of alternatives if dc isolation is required. A dc/dc converter can be built and fed from the rectified ac line voltage. After secondary rectification, which gives isolation from the ac line, a step-down switching regulator can be used to derive the desired voltage.

Alternatively, a step-down switching regulator can be built to be fed from the rectified ac line. This preregulated output would feed no external loads, but would be used to drive a dc/dc converter whose rectified secondary output could be used directly (output would be constant against line changes as the dc input to the converter is regulated). If desired, outputs could be step-down "switch" or "series-pass" regulated to give regulation against load changes also. Such block-diagram combinations of pre- and postregulators are fully discussed in Chap. 3.

But most of these schemes involve handling the total power twice: once in a step-down preregulator and again in the dc/dc converter. Also if dc/dc conversion comes ahead of the step-down switching regulator, the main power is still handled twice.

A simple way out of handling the power twice is to width modulate the duration of each half cycle in a dc/dc converter. The free-wheeling diode and LC filter, now located in the secondaries, perform the same function of taking a width-modulated square wave and generating ripple-free dc voltage. The width-modulated inverter, then, combines in one building block the function of width-modulated regulation and dc/dc conversion.

This half-cycle, width-modulated inverter is discussed in detail in Sect. 2.5, and its basic circuit configuration is shown in Figs. 2-21, 2-22, and 2-24.

It is unnecessary to go into details of its design here since they have already been covered. All aspects of the dc/dc converter portion — transformer design, core selection, turns calculation, transistor selection criteria, and thermal calculations — are handled exactly as in a conventional unmodulated dc/dc converter as discussed in Chap. 8. The LC filter design at the secondary is handled just as in the step-down switching regulator calculations of Sect. 9.1.5. Finally the width modulation techniques are exactly as discussed in Sect. 9.2.1. They gate a triangle against a dc level proportional to the difference between a reference voltage and a fraction of the output voltage. This gating generates a pulse whose width fixes the "on" time of each inverter in its half cycle so as to keep the output constant.

Merits of the half-cycle, width-modulated inverter are discussed fully in Sect. 2.5.2. Various building block combinations of the width-modulated inverter are discussed in Chap. 3. An overview of their potential applications in power supply systems can be had in a study of Figs. 3–5, 3–6, 3–9, and 3–12.

9.5   Width-Modulated Step-Up Switching Converters

This regulator is discussed in broad outline in Sect. 1.3, and its basic circuit diagram is shown in Fig. 1–6.

The regulator finds application, of course, wherever a higher voltage is required and the only source available is a lower-voltage one. There is no dc isolation from the negative terminal of the input source; hence, if the stepped-up output is to be used external to the power supply, the negative terminal of the input source must already be dc isolated from the ac line.

The step-up regulator finds its most frequent application as a step-up preregulator operating directly off the rectified ac line. Most often, such an ac line preregulator is a series-switch step-down regulator as described throughout this chapter (Fig. 9–1). But one undesirable aspect of the step-down preregulator is that it draws large amplitude and fast rise and fall time current steps from the input source (see Fig. 9–2C).

These chopped current steps are troublesome. Drawn through inductance of the wiring to the input source, they cause inductive voltage and current spikes that cross talk into other sensitive wires in the system. Even if local rfi filtering is used, the wiring from the series switch itself to the rfi filter can cause cross-talk problems. These chopped current pulses also impose a difficult ripple current rating on the rfi filter capacitor.

In contrast, the current drawn from the input source in the step-up switching regulator does not come in steps with sharp rise and fall times. Rather, it is a dc current that never drops to zero but has a slow triangular ripple component superimposed on it (Fig. 9–33D). This gives far less rfi and internal cross-talk problems and is one of the chief advantages of the step-up regulator.

A detailed description of step-up regulator current and voltage waveforms will clarify its operation and simplify making the various design decisions.

9.5.1 Critical Waveforms in Step-Up Switching Converters

The major elements of the converter and its critical waveforms are shown in Fig. 9–33. The major design decisions are selection of the output capacitor output inductor L and switch transistor Q. Since the inductor carries a dc component, it must be designed so as not to saturate at maximum load current. Also, maximum voltage to which the transistor switch is subjected must be calculated to verify that it operates within its ratings.

The basic operation of the converter is considered in Sect. 1.3. There it is pointed out that when Q1 is on (Fig. 9–33), diode D1 is reverse biased and C_o must supply the full output load current by itself. The switch is closed for a time T_c and is open for a time T_o. Output voltage is (from Eq. 1–4): $V_o = V_{in} (1 + T_c/T_o)$.

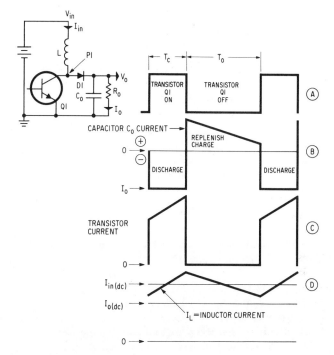

Fig. 9–33. Critical waveforms in step-up switching regulator for T_c/T_o $= 0.5; V_o = 1.5 V_{in}$; and $I_{in} \cong 1.5 I_o$.

9.5.2 Selection of Output Filter Capacitor

Now if C_o must supply the full load current for a time T_c and if its voltage droop at the end of T_c is to be no more than ΔV_o, C_o is given by $C_o = I_o(T_c/\Delta V_o)$.

But $T_o + T_c = T = 1/f$, where T is the switching period and f is its frequency. Then

$$T_c = T - T_b$$

but $$V_o = [(T_c + T_o)/T_o]V_{in} = (T/T_o)V_{in}$$

and $$T_c = T - T_o = T - (V_{in}/V_o)T = T[(V_o - V_{in})/V_o];$$

then $$C_o = I_o T_c/\Delta V_o = I_o(V_o - V_{in})/fV_o\Delta V_o \qquad (9\text{–}27)$$

This fixes the value of C_o for a desired output voltage V_o, minimum ripple ΔV_o, switching frequency f, output voltage and current V_o and I_o, and nominal input voltage V_{in}.

9.5.3 Selection of Energy Storage Inductor

Figure 9–33 shows current supplied by C_o during T_c to be $-I_o$ (current out of the top of C_o is taken to be negative). Now, during T_o, Q1 opens and the inductive kick at the bottom end of L drives point P1 positive until diode D1 connects. Now L supplies load current to R_o at a voltage V_o and must also supply current to replenish the charge C_o lost when it alone was feeding the load. The charge C_o lost during T_c is $I_o T_c / C$. Thus, during T_o, the volt second area of the current flowing into C_o must equal $I_o T_c$ or

$$\int_0^{T_o} I_c dt = I_o T_c$$

The actual current flowing into C_o during T_o is the difference between the load current and the inductor current.

But the inductor current has a dc or average value plus a ramp component. This average is determined as follows: Assuming no internal losses for the moment, $V_{in} I_{in} = V_o I_o$. Now, I_{in} is the average current taken from V_{in} or the average current flowing into the inductor I_L. Since $V_o = V_{in} (1 + T_c/T_o)$ (from Eq. 1–4),

$$I_{in(dc)} = I_o \left(\frac{V_o}{V_{in}}\right) = \frac{I_o V_{in} (1 + T_c/T_o)}{V_{in}} = I_o \left(\frac{T_c + T_o}{T_o}\right)$$

The ripple component of current is a ramp, for during T_c there is a constant voltage of V_{in} across L and after a time T_c current increases in it by an amount $+\Delta I_L = V_{in} T_c / L$. When Q1 is open for a time T_o, the voltage across L reverses polarity and the current in it ramps down by $-\Delta I_L = (V_o - V_{in})/L$. And in the steady state $+\Delta I_L$ during T_c is equal to $-\Delta I_L$ during T_o.

The magnitude of ΔI_L is selected just as in the series-switch inductor (Sect. 9.1.5, Eq. 9–14) so that the peak inductor current $(= I_{in(dc)} + \Delta I_L/2)$ is no more than 20% greater than the maximum average dc current. This makes it easier to keep the inductor from saturating. It also minimizes the peak current in Q1 and reduces dissipation and stress in it. It also makes lower in value the minimum load at which it is possible to operate. The current in the inductor at the bottom of the ripple triangle in Fig. 9–30 must not be permitted to fall to zero before the end of T_o.

Hence, ΔI_L is chosen as 1.4 $I_{in(dc, nom)}$ and the inductor is calculated from:

$$L = \frac{V_{in(nom)} T_c}{\Delta I_L} = \frac{V_{in(nom)} T_c}{1.4 I_{in(dc, nom)}}$$

But, from above, $T_c = (V_o - V_{in})/f V_o$. And assuming negligible losses,

$$V_o I_o = V_{in(nom)} I_{in(dc, nom)}$$

or $I_{in(dc, nom)} = V_o I_o / V_{in(nom)}$

Then $$L = \frac{V_{in(nom)} T_c}{1.4 I_{in(dc, nom)}} = \frac{(V_{in(nom)})^2 (V_o - V_{in(nom)})}{1.4 f V_o^2 I_o} \qquad (9\text{–}28)$$

This gives the required value in terms of output voltages, current, nominal input voltage, and switching frequency — all of which are known.

The current in C_o during T_o can now be seen in Fig. 9–33B. It is the difference between the output load current I_o and the inductor current during T_o. That last current is the sum of the dc input current plus the downward-going ramp $-\Delta I_L$ calculated above. It can be seen that the volt second area of the current waveform into C_o during T_o is equal to the volt second area of the current taken out of C_o during T_c.

9.5.4 Transistor Voltage and Current and Power Stresses

The maximum voltage stress on transistor Q1 is, of course, V_o, which is an input design parameter and is $V_{in}(1 + T_c/T_o)$. Thus, unlike dc/dc converter circuits, the transistor can be stressed to more than twice the dc input.

The current step in the transistor Q1 can be approximated for power dissipation purposes by a square step of amplitude $I_p = I_o(V_o/V_{in})$. This lasts for a time T_c and the resultant dc dissipation in the transistor is $I_o(V_o/V_{in})(V_{ce(sat)})$ (T_c/T). To a close approximation, it can be assumed the high-voltage–high-current overlap losses during turnon and turnoff (Sect. 2.1.3) will equal these losses.

9.5.5 Avoiding Switching Inductor Saturation

The inductor carries a dc current $I_o(V_o/V_{in})$ and has a peak-to-peak ripple component of 40% of that value (Sect. 9.1.4). The inductor should be designed to avoid saturation either by use of a gapped core or a powdered iron core as discussed in Sect. 9.1.8.

9.5.6 Width-Modulated, Step-Up Regulator

All that is required to make a step-up regulator out of the converter is the same set of elements shown in Fig. 9–1 for the step-down regulator. These are a negative-feedback loop consisting of an output voltage sampling resistor chain, a difference amplifier, and triangle voltage level to pulse width converter to control the switch duty cycle. These have all been discussed in connection with the step-down regulator and need not be considered here.

The width modulator, which is the heart of the feedback chain, can be the same triangle-level comparator. Often, if fixed frequency operation is not necessary, the closed-switch time is kept constant and the period varied by the voltage at the output of the main dc error amplifier. This is currently best done with a number of available integrated dircuit voltage-controlled oscillators that generate a fixed pulse width at a frequency determined by a dc input control voltage.

9.6   Integrated-Circuit Building Blocks for Control Circuitry in Pulse-Width-Modulated dc/dc Converters

Integrated circuit modules such as binary counters, multiple NAND gates in one package, and timers that can be used either as monostable multivibrators ("one shots") or astable multivibrators (square-wave oscillators) offer a simple and inexpensive way to implement pulse-width control circuitry. At the time of this writing such building blocks can be bought for less than 50 cents (100 + quantity). All the circuitry required to generate the usual two 180° out-of-phase variable-width drive pulses can be assembled from three to five integrated circuit building blocks, three resistors, and two capacitors. In the usual case, the width-modulated output pulses must control bases of power transistors whose emitters are referenced to input ground. This, in off-the-ac-line rectifiers, may be 150–300 V away from output ground, which is the reference for the variable-width control pulses. Thus, to provide the dc isolation between the generator of the variable-width pulses and the power inverter bases, two additional low-power transistors and two pulse transformers may be required.

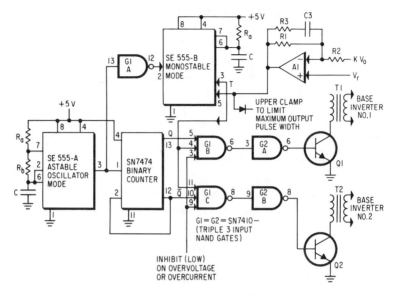

Fig. 9–34. Pulse-width control circuitry using integrated-circuit building blocks.

A large variety of logic configurations and building blocks may be used to generate the two 180° out-of-phase width-modulated control signals. Generally, the scheme is to route a variable-width pulse alternately through two NAND gates on alternate half cycles under control of a binary counter, which is triggered at the leading edge of the variable-width pulse. A typical example of such a logic configuration is shown in Fig. 9–34.

Figure 9–34 makes use of two triple three-input NAND gate modules (SN 7410) and a dual D type flip-flop (SN7474 of which only one is used) operated as a binary counter by connecting its $\overline{Q}$ output to its data input and two SE555[8] timers. The SE555 is a useful timer in that it can be operated as a free-running square-wave oscillator (astable mode) and also as a monostable multivibrator ("one shot").

As a one shot, the SE555 emits a positive-going output pulse at its output (pin 3) when triggered by a negative-going pulse at the "trigger input" (pin 2). The duration of the positive output pulse (with control pin 5 connected to ground via a capacitor) is given by $T_o = 1.1 R_a C$. The pulse-width sensitivity to supply voltage variation is 0.02%/volt, to temperature variation (assuming constant R_a and C) is 0.01%/°C. The output pulse width may be controlled by varying the dc voltage at the "control" input (pin 5). Variation of this voltage from 0.2 to $0.6 V_{cc}$ varies the pulse width from $0.22 R_a C$ to $1.1 R_a C$. Since the dc output voltage of the converter is proportional to the "on" time pulse width, output voltage may be kept constant by driving pin 5 of the "one shot" by an error voltage that is proportional to the difference between a reference voltage and a fraction of the output dc voltage.

---

[8] Signetics Co. Data Sheet.

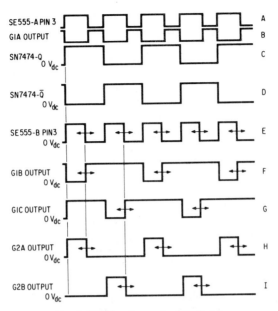

Fig. 9–35. Waveforms for Fig. 9–34.

The SE555 can also be used as a free-running square-wave oscillator if connected as shown in Fig. 9–34(SE555A). In this mode, the duration of the positive portion of the square wave at pin 3 is given by $T_p = 0.685(R_a + R_b)C$; the duration of the negative portion by $T_n = 0.685R_bC$. The period of the square-wave oscillator is then

$$T = T_p + T_n = 0.685(R_a + 2R_bC)$$

and its frequency is

$$f = \frac{1}{T} = \frac{1.46}{R_a + 2R_bC}$$

The operation of the logic block diagram of Fig. 9–34 can be understood from the waveforms in Fig. 9–35.

Figure 9–35A shows the output at SE555A, pin 3. Frequency of this astable multivibrator is chosen to be twice the desired square-wave frequency of the converter. Relative duration of the positive and negative portions of the waveform are not important. The SN7474 connected as shown operates as a binary counter and changes state at every positive-going transition of the "clock" signal at pin 1. Out-of-phase outputs from the binary counter are shown as Q, $\bar{Q}$ in Figs. 9–35C and 9–35 D.

Monostable SE555B requires a negative-going transistor at trigger pin 2 to generate its output pulse. The third NAND gate of G1 (G1A) is used as a single input inverter to generate the negative-going transition (Fig. 9–35B) at each change of state of the binary counter.

G1A also serves the valuable purpose of providing a slight delay in the leading edge of the SE555B positive-going output signal beyond the binary counter output voltage transition. This prevents false narrow negative-going output spikes from positive NAND gates G1B and G1C. Such false narrow outputs occur if there is a momentary overlap of high voltage as one input falls while the other input rises. Such false narrow output pulses can destroy the power inverters by causing false turnons, increasing their power dissipation or causing simultaneous inverter conduction.

Postive logic NAND gates G1B and G1C serve to route the pulse from SE555B through to their respective outputs on alternate half cycles as negative-going pulses (Figs. 9–35C and 9–35F). NAND gates G2A and G2B are used as single-input inverters to give positive-going output pulses on alternate half cycles (Figs. 9–35H and 9–35I). Transistors Q1 and Q2 are pulse amplifiers and the pulse transformers T1 and T2 permit delivering the output pulses to the power inverter bases at any arbitrary dc level.

The negative-feedback loop is closed through error amplifier A1 — an operational amplifier whose dc gain is R1/R2. Its gain phase shift-versus-frequency characteristic is tailored by R3 and C3. As the output voltage tends to rise, KV_o moves upward and A1 output moves downward. Now the lower voltage at SE555B pin 5 reduces its output pulse width and also that of the positive-going pulses at the outputs of G2A and G2B. This reduces the power-inverter-on times and decreases the dc output voltage of the filter in the secondary of the main power transformer.

An upper clamp is provided at pin 5 to limit the maximum output pulse width to less than about 90% of the half period of the binary counter output.

The logic of Fig. 9–34 is a general illustration of what can be done. It can be simplified in various ways. Gate G1A may be eliminated by narrowing the negative portion of the SE555A output and using the negative transition to trigger SE555B, the positive-going transition (perhaps 1 to 2 μsec later) to drive the binary counter. This permits using a single Quad-2 (four two-input NAND gates in one package) for what is now in two packages (G1B, C, G2A, B). The 555 timers are presently available as two timers in one package (556). The package count is thus now down to three (not counting error amplifier A1) as compared to five in Fig. 9–34.

Just recently, integrated circuit modules that perform all of the functions of Fig. 9–34 in one single package have become available.[9] Although presently they are more expensive, the decreased package count may make them more economical when assembly and logistic costs are considered.

9.6.1 Motorola MC3420 Switching-Regulator Control Circuit Module[10]

The usual switching-regulator control circuit consists of two variable-width rectangular pulses which occur symmetrically within alternate half cycles of the fundamental switching frequency and are capable of being width modulated by the dc control voltage. This dc control voltage is the amplified difference between the voltage to be regulated and a reference voltage.

The circuit in Fig. 9–35 generates such pulses using four to five conventional integrated circuits (timers, NAND gates), each in its own dual-in-line

---

[9] Motorola MC 3420, Silicon General SC1524.
[10] Data and information courtesy of Motorola, Inc.

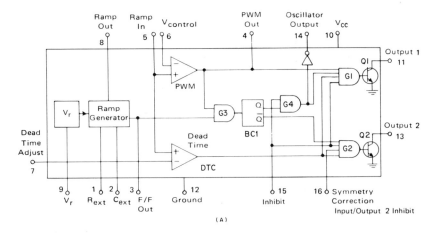

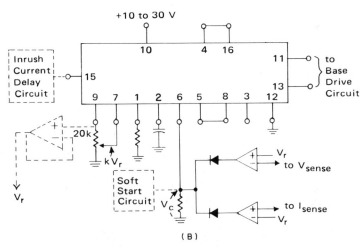

Fig. 9-36. Motorola MC3420 IC switching regulator control circuit. (A) Block diagram. (B) Typical application. (*Courtesy* Motorola, Inc.)

(DIP) package. The Motorola MC3420 (Fig. 9–36) performs all and somewhat more of the functions of the circuit in Fig. 9–35 in a single integrated circuit in one DIP package. Complete details can be obtained from the manufacturer's data sheet, but briefly its operation is as follows:

The ramp generator in Fig. 9–36A contains a flip-flop. When the circuit is connected as in Fig. 9–36B, the "ramp generator" is a free-running triangle oscillator whose frequency is fixed by the values of the external resistor (R_{ext}) and external capacitor (C_{ext}), as shown in Fig. 9–36D. Because of internal circuit details, when the flip-flop signal at pin 3 is high, the triangle ramps downward; when the flip-flop signal at pin 3 is low, the triangle ramps upward. The triangle ramps between +2 and +6 V.

The triangle is compared (pin 8 connected to pin 5) against a dc voltage level in triangle comparator PWM. Whenever the triangle voltage at pin 5 is

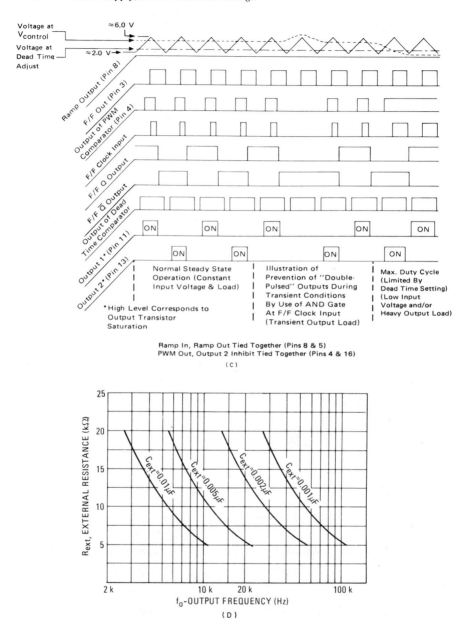

Fig. 9–36. (*Cont'd.*) Motorola MC3420 IC switching regulator control circuit. (C) Critical waveforms. (D) Frequency determination. (*Courtesy* Motorola, Inc.)

above the control voltage at pin 6, the output of the PWM is high; when the triangle is below the control voltage, the PWM output is low. Thus, by varying the amplitude of the control voltage between +2 and +6 V, the PWM output signal at pin 4 varies in width. The control voltage at pin 6 is the amplified error signal — the amplified difference between the reference voltage and the dc voltage being regulated. The width-modulated signal at PWM sits symmetrically on either side of the positive peak of each triangle and decreases in width as the voltage at pin 6 moves toward the top of the triangle.

With pin 4 connected to pin 16, the variable-width PWM pulses are steered on alternate half cycles through paths G1–Q1 and G2–Q2 by the action of binary counter BC1. The clock pulse used to trigger BC1 is obtained by "adding" the PWM and flip-flop (pin 3) outputs. This ensures that under transient conditions, the pulse is steered through alternate outputs. Counter BC1 is triggered on the negative-going edge of the signal from G3, which occurs on the trailing edge (negative-going edge) of the PWM pulses at pin 4. Because of the slight delay in G3, BC1, and G4, all of the trailing edge of the PWM pulse gets through G1 or G2 before that same trailing edge changes the state of BC1.

Input at pin 15 to gate G4 is normally high, thereby enabling the gate. Under various system conditions (overvoltage, overcurrent, or inrush current limiting) when it is desired to inhibit both outputs, pin 15 can be brought to logic zero or less than 0.7 V.

To avoid the problem of simultaneous conduction and possible destruction of power inverter transistors (Sect. 8.7.1), it is desirable to have a minimum "dead time" or gap between the end of one pulse and the start of the next at the output points, pins 11 and 13. This is done with the dead-time comparator (DTC) which compares the PWM triangle with a constant reference voltage (derived from the reference source at pin 9). For the entire time that the triangle is below the voltage at pin 7, both outputs at pins 11 and 13 are inhibited (outputs both high). Thus, raising the voltage at pin 7 higher than the triangle trough of 2.0 V increases dead time.

The "on" time of output 2 can vary independently of pin 1. This is sometimes desirable to avoid the problem of a power transformer core "walking" up or down its hysteresis loop (Sect. 8.7.6). Operation of the transformer core can be kept centered on its hysteresis loop by a feedback loop which alters the relative "on" time of two transistors in a push–pull dc/dc inverter.

Symmetry correction can be achieved by opening the pin 4–pin 16 connection and driving pin 16 separately, or by varying the slope of the rise time at pin 16 while leaving undisturbed the rise time at the corresponding input to gate G1. The exact circuit details of such a symmetry correction must be examined carefully. Especially under turn-on or transient conditions, if Q1 and Q2 "on" times become significantly unequal (about 15% may be enough), the power transformer core can move after only a few cycles into saturation and destroy the power transistor.

9.6.2 Silicon General SG1524 Switching-Regulator Control Circuit[11] Module

This module, also in one integrated circuit DIP package, contains all the circuitry to generate the adjustable-frequency, width-modulated, 180° out-of-phase control pulses required to drive inputs of power transistors of switching

---

[11] Data and information courtesy of Silicon General Inc., from R. Mammono, "Simplifying Converter Design with an Integrated Regulating Pulse Width Modulator," Silicon General, Inc.

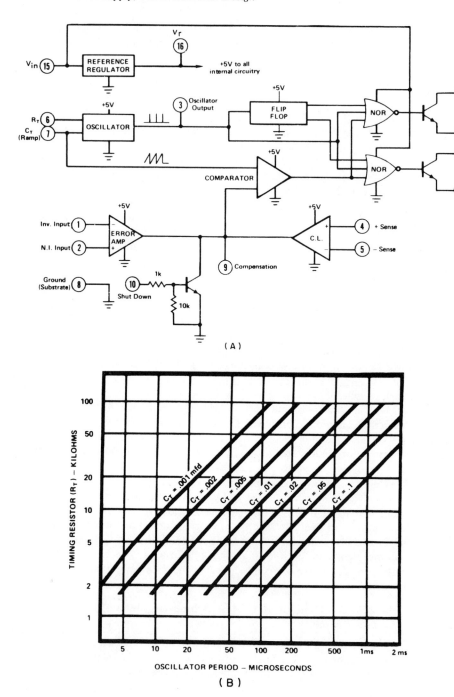

Fig. 9–37. Silicon General switching regulator control module SG1524. (A) Block diagram. (B) Oscillator period as a function of $R_T C_T$. (*Courtesy* Silicon General, Inc.)

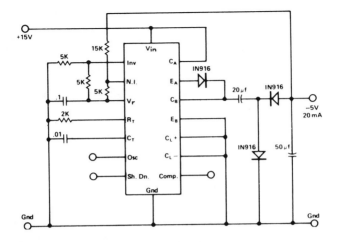

PART 1. The capacitor-diode output circuit is used here as a polarity converter to generate a −5 volt supply from +15 volts. This circuit is useful for an output current of up to 20 mA with no additional boost transistors required. Since the output transistors are current limited, no additional protection is necessary. Also, the lack of an inductor allows the circuit to be stabilized with only the output capacitor.

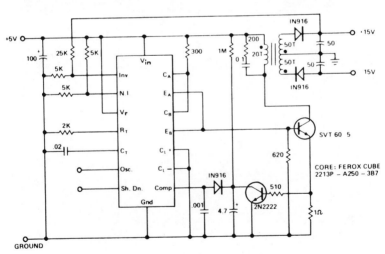

PART 2. Another low-current supply is the flyback converter used here to generate ±15 volts at 20 mA from a +5 volt regulated line: The reference generator in the SG1524 is unused with the input voltage providing the reference. Current limiting in a flyback converter is difficult and is accomplished here by sensing current in the primary line and resetting a soft-start circuit.

Fig. 9–38. Typical applications of the Silicon General switching regulator control module SG1524. (*Courtesy* Silicon General, Inc.)

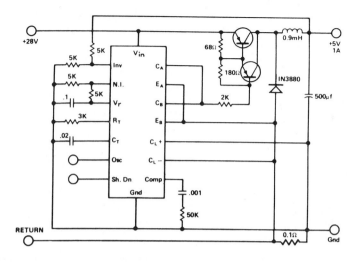

PART 3. *In this conventional single-ended regulator circuit, the two outputs of the SG1524 are connected in parallel for effective 0 - 90% duty-cycle modulation.   The use of an output inductor requires an R-C phase compensation network for loop stability.*

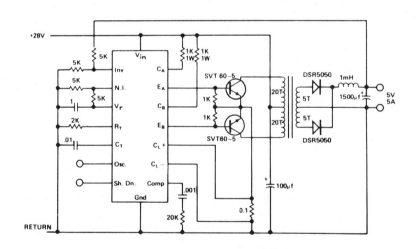

PART 4. *Push-pull outputs are used in this transformer-coupled DC-DC regulating converter. Note that the oscillator must be set at twice the desired output frequency as the SG1524's internal flip-flop divides the frequency by 2 as it switches the P.W.M. signal from one output to the other. Current limiting is done here in the primary so that the pulse width will be reduced should transformer saturation occur.*

Fig. 9–38. (*Cont'd.*) Typical applications of the Silicon General switching regulator control module SG1524. (*Courtesy* Silicon General, Inc.)

regulators. Its basic block diagram is shown in Fig. 9–37A, and complete details on its operation and applications are given in the manufacturer's data sheets. Briefly, the circuit operation is as follows:

The module outputs are two width-modulated, 180° out-of-phase control "switches." These switches are two npn transistors that are alternately on and off for alternate half cycles of the fundamental frequency. Both emitters and collectors are brought out, thereby permitting the driving of either npn or pnp transistors. The "on" times are controlled by the dc voltage at the input of the triangle comparator shown in Fig. 9–37A. This control voltage is normally the output of the main error amplifier and is the amplified difference between the reference voltage (generated internally) and a fraction of the voltage to be regulated. The triangle comparator generates at its output a negative-going rectangular pulse whose duration corresponds to the length of time the triangle amplitude is less than the error amplifier input to the comparator. This negative-going pulse is steered alternately by the binary counting flip-flop through the two positive logic NOR gates (any one input "high" yields a "low" output, or all inputs "low" yield a "high" output).

The third input to the positive logic NOR or negative logic NAND gates is a narrow positive pulse corresponding in time to the negative-going edge of the triangle (sawtooth). It thus corresponds in time to the leading edge of the negative-going output pulse from the triangle comparator, and it ensures that there is a minimum "dead time" between the end of a positive pulse at the base of one output transistor and the start of the next positive pulse at the base of the second output transistor. As discussed in Sect. 8.7.1, this is done to avoid simultaneous conduction in the driven power transistors and their possible failure at maximum duty cycle.

A current-limiting comparator is also included in the module and is used for overcurrent sensing. Whenever pin 4 in the module is higher than pin 5, the triangle comparator input from the current limiter is low and comparator output is high. This causes the NOR gate outputs to go low and turns off both output transistors. Pins 4 and 5 of the current-limiting comparator are bridged across a small current-sensing resistor in series with the current to be limited. A bias voltage at either pin 4 or 5 is used to set the threshold at which limiting occurs. If the bias source is derived from the output voltage being regulated, foldback current limiting is possible.

The basic operating frequency of the module is determined by an external resistor (R_T) and capacitor (C_T) which control the frequency of the internal sawtooth oscillator. Frequency dependence on R_T and C_T is shown in Fig. 9–37B. The sawtooth output is compared in the triangle comparator to the amplified error signal to derive the width-modulated control signal. Some typical applications of the module are shown in Fig. 9–38.

PROBLEMS

9.1 In a step-down switching regulator operating at a 40 kHz rate from a supply voltage that has a nominal input of 30 V with ±10% tolerance, what are the maximum, nominal, and minimum switch-on-time duty cycles for a constant output of 21 V? What are the maximum, nominal, and minimum on and off times?

9.2 In a single-phase, off-the-line bridge rectifier, with a nominal input of 120 V_{ac}, the peak output voltage at the top of the ripple triangle is $+167$ V.

   a. With 20 V of peak-to-peak ripple and line voltage tolerance of $\pm 12\%$, what is the maximum output voltage at the top of the ripple triangle and the minimum output voltage at the bottom of the ripple triangle?

   b. Using a switching regulator to convert this rectifier output to a constant $+105$ V, what are the maximum and minimum switch-on-time duty cycles?

   c. For a switching frequency of 30 kHz, what are the maximum and minimum switch-on and switch-off times?

9.3 In the switching regulator of Prob. 9.1, assuming nominal voltage input and an output power of 200 W, what is the magnitude of the switching inductor limiting the peak output current to 20% above the nominal value?

9.4 From Prob. 9.3:

   a. What is the average current drawn from the input source at nominal input voltage?

   b. Assuming a 1-V drop across the switch transistor in the closed position and ac switching losses equal to dc switch transistor losses, what are ac and dc losses in the transistor?

   c. What are dc losses in the free-wheeling diode?

   d. Assuming 5 W control circuit and switch transistor drive power losses, what are the total internal losses in the supply, its input power, and efficiency?

9.5 In Prob. 9.2, what is the size of the required switching inductance so that at nominal input voltage, at a power output of 500 W, at a switching frequency of 30 kHz, the peak inductor current is limited to a maximum of 20% above the dc output current?

9.6 In Prob. 9.1, select the size of the filter capacitance to achieve an output ripple of 100 mV peak to peak.

9.7 In Prob. 9.5, what is the size of the filter capacitor required for a peak-to-peak output ripple of 0.1%?

9.8 Assume the inductor of a switching regulator has a required inductance of 1.5 mH and carries an average current of 3 A and a peak current of 3.6 A.

   a. At a current density of 400 circular mils/ampere, what size wire is appropriate for this?

   b. What is the area per turn in square centimeters?

   c. At a peak magnetic flux density of 2,000 G, what is the required product of core winding area A_c and core "iron" area required for such an inductance?

   d. Which of the cores in Figs. 8–2 to 8–6 can be used for this inductor?

   e. What is the required number of turns for 1.5 mH?

   f. What is the required core winding area and does the selected core have at least that area?

   g. Assuming 3B7 core material and the selected core, what is the required total magnetic path length and the required air gap to avoid saturation?

9.9 In a block-diagram scheme such as in Fig. 9–21B, consider the output of the bridge rectifier is 270 V $\pm 10\%$. Assume the switching regulator chops this down to 180 V at the input to the dc/dc converter whose output is to be 5 V. Assume the amplitude of the triangle input to the triangle comparator is 5 V peak to peak.

    a. What is the gain at nominal ac line input from the output of the bridge rectifier to the output of the chopped down +180 V?

    b. What is the gain from output of the dc/dc converter to its 180-V input?

    c. For a ±10% input ac line change to result in only a ±5 mV change at the 5-V output, what is the required total open-loop gain?

    d. To achieve the 0.1% output change for a 10% input change, what is the required gain from input to the error amplifier to input to the triangle comparator with an error amplifier reference voltage of 5.00 V?

    e. For an optocoupler gain of 0.2, what is the required gain in the error amplifier?

9.10 Derive an expression for the self-resonant frequency of the LC filter in terms of input, output voltage, switching frequency, and percentage output ripple.

9.11 In Probs. 9.2 and 9.5, with the calculated values of L, C, and R, what damping factor curves $(R/\sqrt{L/C})$ are to be used in calculating gain and phase shift from Figs. 9–23 and 9–22?

9.12 In Probs. 9.2 and 9.5, what is the self-resonant frequency of the LC filter?

9.13 In Probs. 9.2 and 9.5, what gain and phase shift are provided by the LC filter at a point 20% above its self-resonant frequency?

9.14 In an operational amplifier as in Fig. 9–24, for an input resistor R1 of 3,000 ohms, what are the values R3 for a dc gain of +46 dB and what is the value of R2 for a high-frequency gain of 2?

9.15 What is the value of C in series with R2 of Prob. 9.14 that gives only a 6° phase shift at 600 Hz?

Index